The Norse Myths

The Norse Myths

Heilan Yvette Grimes

Hollow Earth Publishing

The Norse Myths

ISBN-10: 1879196-02-6   ISBN-13: 978-1-879196-02-5

First Paperback Edition, February 24, 2010.

10   9   8   7   6   5   4   3   2   1

Hollow Earth Publishing
PO Box 51480
Boston, MA 002205-1480

hollowearthpublishing@gmail.com

Colophon: The Cover, Half Title, Title, Section/Chapter Openings are all set in Fertigo Pro. The text is set in 10/12 Bembo × 30.

Francesco Griffo (1450-1518 A.D.) was a typeface designer working for Aldus Manutius. One of his innovations was the italic font, which he designed around 1502.

Griffo's is a sad story. It was the custom in this era that towns, royalty, or central governments controlled the printing concession for an area. The Venetian government gave Aldus Manutius the printing concession for the city Venice and environs. After many years, and designing some of the most successful typefaces of the era, Griffo decided to go out on his own, taking all the matrices and punches he had cut for his typefaces with him so he could create sets of typefaces to sell to other printers. However, Manutius claimed all rights to Griffo's lifetime of work and the Venetian government backed him up. Since Manutius was the only printer in the area, Griffo had no hope of employment. He couldn't create sets of fonts from the typefaces he had designed because he didn't have the matrices or punches. He couldn't create new faces because he didn't have the tools, or a concession to give him the legal right to do so. In 1516 Griffo returned to his hometown of Bologna, a broken man. Sometime thereafter he was accused of beating his son-in-law to death with an iron bar. Nothing further is known of him.

Bembo is a typeface designed by Griffo around 1495 for Petro Bembo, the humanist poet, later a Cardinal and private secretary to Pope Leo X. The typeface was designed specifically for Bembo's 60-page book *Petri Bembi de Ætna Angelum Chalabrilem liber,* about his trip to Mount Aetna, published in February 1496.

The version of Bembo used in this book was designed in 1929 by Stanley Morison for the Monotype Corporation based on Griffo's original font. Special characters and accented characters were created by the author, Heilan Yvette Grimes, using Fontographer.

The cover Yggdrasyll image is from Viking Club Translation Series–Vol. II, *The Elder or Poetic Edda, Commonly Known as Sæmund's Edda, Part I.–The Mythological Poems.* Edited and Translated with Introducton and Notes by Olive Bray, illustrated by W.G. Collingwood, Printed for the Viking Club, King's Weighhouse Rooms, London, 1908. Chapter opening serpent, and header swords, are all taken from *The Viking Age, Vols. I & II* by Paul B. Du Chaillu, Charles Scribner's Sons, 1889.

for
Lin and Sage

Contents

Part Three: The Ending of All Things

Glossary

Norse Genealogy

Preface

This book is a fairly straightforward redaction of the Norse Myths, and I hope the most complete and accurate available in English. I have tried to be as true to the original sagas as possible, and only have taken literary license in a few instances when I felt the story being told would be more cohesive with my additions. I have tried to make the order of events follow a logical form. My placement of certain events differs from other authors. But I have tried to make certain that an event occurs before it is mentioned as historical by other characters, and have made certain that swords or other magical implements are actually owned by the characters before they are used.

The sagas were formed and passed from generation to generation over a period of several hundred years. Because they were told in many different regions, and over such a long period of time, there are several versions of some of the sagas. I have tried to take the best of each version and combine them to form a complete, cohesive story.

In many instances the Northern languages (Swedish, Danish, Norwegian, Icelandic, Old Norse, German) use different accent marks and spellings for the same word. I have left these accents out of the main text to aid in readability, and have settled on the spellings used in the main text out of personal preference. The Glossary contains various spellings, as well as different accented versions of the characters, places and things used in this book. In many instances these spellings and accents were incorrectly used in English language books about the sagas. I have not indicated the misused versions in this book, since that is not the purpose of this book. The Glossary listings in parenthesis after the word that was used in the main text merely indicate that these were versions of the word used by other writers in other versions of the sagas.

I hope you enjoy this book. I would certainly welcome your comments and suggestions, both critical and praiseworthy after you have finished reading it.

Heilan Yvette Grimes
yvettegr@hotmail.com

Acknowledgements

As much as some authors hate to admit it, no book is born by itself. There are many others who contribute, sometimes not even realizing they've done so.

First and foremost thanks goes to Lin Haire-Sargeant and Sage Green, for encouraging me to keep writing. Lin, especially gets multiple thanks for her sainted reading and editing of this book in more permutations than friendship requires; and without once complaining when I presented her with a yet another manuscript saying there were just a few more changes I'd like her to look at and tell me what she thought. Her suggestions were always insightful and spot on. This book contains a lot fewer "that's" and a lot more commas than it would have had without her help.

Thank you to my father, James Grimes, and grandfather, Ernest "Tony" Gullett. They always believed I could do amazing things, even when circumstances seemed to indicate otherwise. They never faltered in their belief in me. Other writers should be so lucky to have that kind of support.

I was captured by the Northern Thing quite early on. My first interest in Norse Mythology came from a simplified version of Thor and the story of Skrymir's glove in an elementary school reader. Next, I had to do a report in fifth grade about Jack and Jill. Instead of just reciting it, I did some research and found out it came from the story of Hjiuki and Bil from the Norse myths.

Next, in sixth grade my friend Debby Wood taught me to draw an arcane linking chain symbol. When I asked what it meant, she wouldn't tell me then, but said when we grew up she would tell me. As a hint she told me it was very mysterious and all powerful. It was important for me never to forget it. In the meantime while waiting to grow up I scoured libraries trying to find out what the symbol meant. The closest I came were some Nordic linked chains. I figured it meant I was supposed to learn what I could about Norse Mythology and Scandinavian Sagas. So, I proceeded to do so. Many many years later at a school reunion I ran into Debby and said now that we were grown up, could she tell me the secret mystery to the linking chain symbol. I'd been waiting all these decades to find out what it meant. I had started studying Norse Mythology

and Scandinavian Sagas because I thought that's what it meant. I drew the symbol on a napkin, exactly as she had taught me. I asked if it had anything to do with Norse Mythology or Sagas, which I had spent years studying? Debby looked puzzled, and said she had no idea what I was talking about. Didn't remember any of it. Probably something her brother drew one evening and she just passed it on to me. The mysterious knowledge saved for adulthood was probably her brother's joke. So, in a way, this book is the result of Debby Wood's older brother's joke. Be careful what you base your life on.

Of course, I had to do research when I was a kid. I began with the Lane Public Library in Hamilton, Ohio, and soon exhausted their resources. I started frequent trips to the Cincinnati Public Library, which because of the German influence, was a treasure trove of information. Even though I lived in a different town, they gave me a library card and let me take out books. And, I hope I don't get anyone in trouble at this late date, but even non-circulating books from the 19th century. Several books seemed to never have been read. I found one from the mid-1800's with uncut pages. But, I eventually exhausted their resources, too.

On a whim I wrote to King Frederick IX of Denmark telling him I was rewriting The Norse Myths and all the Sagas in English, but was having difficulty finding sources. Could he suggest anything? Every day I check the mail. Nothing happened. Weeks turned to months. Nothing. So I continued organizing everything I had. Typing out stories and sagas, filling notebooks, searching for any new bits of information. I had begun going to old bookstores and buying whatever old books on Norse Mythology and Scandinavian Sagas I could find.

Then one day when I got home from school my Grandmother told me there was a huge box in the living room for me. It was from the National Museum of Denmark (Nationalmuseet) in Copenhagen. Inside were photocopies of all the Sagas. Hundreds of years of sagas. Apparently the King had asked them to photocopy from their collection or any others in Denmark. I was awed. I didn't need other sources. I had copies of the originals. So a huge thank you to King Frederick IX and the National Museum of Denmark. I can truly say that this book (and future volumes of Sagas) would not have been possible without you.

As I started pulling out manuscripts I came to the realization that they were not in English. They were in Old Iceland and Old Norse. So, my next thank you goes to The News Depot in Hamilton, Ohio. I frequently used them to order books. I requested that they find out what was available and order any Old Norse or Old Icelandic dictionaries, which they did.

Now my thanks take a short jump across the ocean to England. Thank you to the legendary Foyle's Bookstore (W & G Foyle Ltd.) in London. The greatest bookstore in the world, exasperating as it was. On my first trip to London one of the first places I visited was Foyle's and bought a copy of every book they had about Norse Mythology and Scandinavian Sagas, including every dictionary, or grammar book we could find at that time. Find is the operative word. Enormous thanks to the sales staff because I browsed the shelves and couldn't find anything. I climbed ladders, got down on my hands and knees for bottom shelves, looked in boxes, moved piles of books. Nothing made any sense. And I was getting tired because there are 30 miles of shelves in the store. I spoke to Miss Foyle herself who explained the books were sorted and shelved

by publisher as if that were obviously the best way to do it. Well, that explained why nothing made any sense. And it added to the problem because I had no idea what I wanted, or whom had published anything. My foolish plan had been to go to Foyle's, find the Norse and Scandinavian Saga section, and buy things. I mentioned this to Miss Foyle but she didn't seem to grasp the concept of "by author" or "by topic". Seemed rather disdainful, in fact. Miss Foyle did order her staff to help me find what they could while I was there. They couldn't find a lot, though they all assured me they had seen lots of books on the topic, but they didn't know just where they had seen them. The solution was that they'd keep my name and address on a list. Every time they came across a Norse/Scandinavian Saga book, while looking for someone else's book, they'd pull it out and put it in a box with my name on it. If something new (actually quite old) came in, they'd hold it for me and not even put it on the shelves. After they'd accumulated several books they started "the correspondence ritual". I had told them just send me a bill, and I'd buy everything I didn't already have. They had a list of what I had so they could just compare everything to that list. But, there was a process they insisted they had to go through. I asked if we could streamline the process so I could buy books in a few weeks rather than half a year. But, they doggedly stuck to their procedure. They'd send a polite note to me in the United States inquiring whether or not I wanted the books on an enclosed list. If not, they'd release them into the store. I would then write back saying I wanted the books, and they could assume I'd want every book they ever acquired on Norse Mythology and Scandinavian Sagas that I didn't already have (I kept their list of my books updated). In response to this they'd send me an invoice. But, I wasn't to pay it immediately. Before they'd accept payment, I had to confirm the invoice was correct and I was willing to pay the amounts on the invoice. I'd write back assuring them I agreed to the amounts on the invoice and that they were fair and acceptable. Then, they sent me the invoice again with instructions to pay it. I'd pay it. Next came a confirming receipt saying I had paid and my check had cleared. Did I still want the books or would I prefer a refund? I'd send back that confirming receipt writing that everything appeared to be in order and that I indeed still wanted the books and there was no need to cancel the order or issue a refund. Then I'd receive another letter asking if I wanted the books shipped by air or by boat with prices for each. And, they always pointed out that shipping by boat was cheaper, though it took longer, and many times the package never arrived at all. In view of the fact we were already at the half-year mark and I would be extremely upset if the package were lost at sea, I always opted to have everything shipped by air and would respond with those instruction and another check for shipping costs. It was at this point they'd finally ship the books to me. This was the procedure for every book I ever ordered from Foyle's, bless their hearts. I loved their eccentricity. I once told someone about my experiences with Foyle's and they didn't seem surprised. They told me a famous quote about Foyle's which, after my experience, seemed all too true: "Imagine Kafka had gone into the book trade." Apparently, I'm not the only one who has had to navigate the labyrinthine world of Foyle's. I can only hope and dream that somewhere, (and who knows where?), there's a copy of this book lost forever on one of their shelves.

    This also brings me to the British Library which was always kind and helpful with the research I did there, sometimes, letting me go back into the bowels of the

library and just search amongst the stacks. I hope no one ever got in trouble for that. I was always respectful of the books.

Back to this side of the ocean and I'd like to continue my thanks by mentioning Marvel Comics and Thor Comic books and The Tales of Asgard and the fun I always had reading them. I've always defended Marvel for being inspired by the Norse Myths. Some of that defense can be read in Thor Comics #183 and #189.

Apologies to the student at UMASS/Boston who once handed in a paper about Norse Mythology, citing many books as references. How was he to know that his professor was best friends with someone who had more than a passing acquaintance with the Norse myths and who recognized immediately that his entire paper was based on Thor Comic Books (which he hadn't referenced)? Note to this student: Volstagg was not an original Norse God. Marvel made him up. Sorry about the failing grade.

I would also like to gratefully thank reader Elizabeth Gouldstone for taking the time to send me a list of errors and typos she found in the book. The corrections she suggested have been made. If anyone else finds any errors, please do not hesitate to contact me.

Thank you to writer/editor Lin Carter. When he was an editor at Ballantine Books I sent him a copy of the latest version of my in progress manuscript asking for suggestions. He wrote back with lots of cogent suggestions which showed he had actually read it. I took many of his ideas to heart and made changes. He also suggested I just use "The Norse Myths" as a title rather than my title, Â Mâtt Sínn (In Their Own Might). He was right. No one would know what the book was about with that title.

Finally, thank you to Hermann Pálsson, Professor of Icelandic Studies at Edinburgh University. When I was a kid and started struggling through those Icelandic Sagas in the original Icelandic I was filled with questions. I noticed the Penguin Books paperback Njal's Saga I had, had been edited by Magnus Magnusson and Hermann Pálsson. Indeed, Mr. Pálsson seemed to have written all of Penguin Book's Norse and Saga books I had in my library. I wrote to him care of Penguin Books with pages and pages of questions about Old Icelandic. They forwarded my letter to him. He wrote back an equally long letter answering all my questions in detail, and inviting me to send any further questions I might have directly to him at Edinburgh University. Thus began years of correspondence and an education in Norse Mythology and Scandianavian Sagas that I am blessed to have received. Thank you dear Hermann.

If anyone reading this book has any comments, questions, answers, and would like to contact me, don't hesitate to do so. I'm rather friendly, and don't bite.

Heilan Yvette Grimes
February 20, 2010
yvettegr@hotmail.com

Part One

In the Beginning

Chapter I

The Creation

In ageless time before the creation there was the Yawning Gulf called Ginnungagap. It was nothing; neither light nor dark, neither sound nor silence, neither inhabited nor inhabitable. Undisturbed with nothing to disturb it, it was calm as windless air. But there did dwell the Alfadir, a guiding spirit which existed by and in the nothing it had created. Time, or rather lack of time, passed. Perhaps an eternity or perhaps just a second passed, but a moment did come when the Alfadir created anew.

South of Ginnungagap the Alfadir created Muspelheimr, a blazing inferno with red-hot firebrands for the wind, and white-hot lava for the clouds. Above these clouds was the red-golden flickering hall of the fire jotun, Surtr. Clad in his coal-black armor with his uplifted right arm holding aloft a fiery sword called med sviga lævi, he was ever ready to strike down those who opposed him and any who sought to destroy Muspelheimr. His figure cast a long, ominous shadow over Muspelheimr; a ready reminder to his fiery demon subjects, the Mighty Sons of Muspel, also known as Muspel's Lytir, that he was indeed the Liege of Muspelheimr and they would do well not to forget it.

North of Ginnungagap the Alfadir created Niflheimr, a land as cold as cold could be. A blinding white land of eternal winter, composed in its awesome majesty of one mælstrom of haze and cold after another. The whirling eddies engulfed the region. These violent whirlpools were bane to all who dared inhabit this wasteland, making it known in time to come as the land of death.

Hvergelmir Well lay towards the center of Niflheimr. At one unknown moment the violent poisonous waters which churned in Hvergelmir Well broke and formed the great Elivagar River, which became the source from whence all rivers flow. It branched off into eleven other mighty rivers called Svoll, Gunthra, Fjorm, Fimbulthul, Slidr, Hridr, Sylgr, Ylgr, Vidr, Leiptr, and Gjoll.

In time the Elivagar River began flowing faster and faster making it impossible for its eleven branches to keep up with the rushing current. The tumescent rivers welled up from their banks, overflowed, and sent a poisonous scum into Ginnungagap. There it hung suspended, eventually congealing into rime and hoarfrost, growing and spreading

throughout the land. The fast breaking river caught up the sediment and formed them into great boulders which rolled over massive waterfalls, thundering into the nothing that was Ginnungagap. Sediment and boulders crushed and packed together to form land and mountains. This land from nothing was born of violence and became a harbinger of evil.

Ymir and His Creations

Sparks and molten lava flowed out of Muspelheimr, falling into Ginnungagap. Thus the searing heat of Muspelheimr and the unnatural cold of Niflheimr met. The rime and hoarfrost hanging motionless in Ginnungagap slowly melted, quickening the droplets into a creature of absolute evil, who was called Ymir. The giant race, known as jotuns, would call him by many names including Aurgelmir, Brimir, Blainn, Alvaldi, Thrigeitr, Thirvald, Neri, and Fornjotr.

The day after his creation Ymir went walking, exploring Ginnungagap. Suddenly he found himself very tired, so he laid down to rest, eventually falling asleep. As it happened he had fallen asleep near Muspelheimr and the heat caused him to sweat. The moisture from under his left arm formed two jotuns, one male and the other female. His left foot then begat a son upon his right foot. This son had six heads and he called him Thrudgelmir. Thrudgelmir in turn had a son whom he called Bergelmir.

The rime in Ginnungagap was Ymir's sole source of nourishment. There was nothing else he could eat to survive. After awhile he became bored with this diet and decided to find additional nourishment. But, there was nothing else. Deciding to make something for nourishment, he took rime and hoarfrost, fashioned a statue in the form of a cow, and called his creation Audhumla. It's lifeless state did him no good. Yet, as the heat from Muspelheimr had given him life, he surmised it would also give life to Audhumla. He carried this lifeless statue across Ginnungagap to the edge of Muspelheimr. Dull though he was, in this instance he was right. The intense heat from the inferno that was Muspelheimr, sparked life in the statue. At first she mooed, then ran away up the side of a hill. Ymir followed. Soon Audhumla's mooing took on a note of painful urgency as her udder filled with milk. Ymir didn't know what to do to help her. The task of thinking was hard enough for him. But he tried. In the meantime four rivers of milk burst from Audhumla's teats. Surprised at first, Ymir realized this liquid might be something he could drink. He cupped his hands and caught up some of the white liquid. Others would have found the milk tasted extremely bitter, but it was to Ymir's liking. And from then on he derived his nourishment only from Audhumla's milk. And he thrived on it, growing larger and larger each day.

Audhumla and Her Creations

For her nourishment, Audhumla licked the salty rimestones which could be found all over Niflheimr. One of the rimestones she had been licking began taking on the rocky form of a jotun. Curious as to what was happening, she licked at it all day and by evening hair appeared on the rimestone. On the second day at evening the full head was evident. Encouraged she licked even more furiously. The jotun stood upright at the end of the third day, lived, and was called Buri. Buri immediately had a son whom he named Bor.

Ymir was furious when he found out Audhumla had created a being. In his mind he was the only one who should create life. He stalked to Niflheimr searching for Buri determined to end this sort of thing and show Audhumla what would happen to any creatures she created. The mountains trembled at each step Ymir took. At first he couldn't find Buri. So, climbing to the top of a cliff, he surveyed the land and saw Buri in a valley below, fashioning his own statues.

"This must stop," thought Ymir. His creations' creation, must not also be allowed to create. Ymir, filled with rage, seized a nearby mountain and heaved it onto Buri, who was killed instantly, and his statues shattered around him, and along with them the generations which were never born. Ymir knew nothing of Bor's existence, or he would have sought him out to kill, also. From that time forth the descendants of Buri and Ymir hated and battled each other.

Bolthorn, another of Thrudgelmir's sons, had two children, one, a son named Mimir and the other, a daughter named Bestla. Bestla was exceedingly tall with a noble bearing. There weren't many others around, so it wasn't surprising when she and Bor met and married. A marriage at first out of convenience, but eventually they were very happy together and over time their family grew to include three sons, Odin, Vili, and Ve. Odin was the eldest, followed by Vili, and then Ve. They were the first of the Æsir and grew to maturity hidden from Ymir. Odin was the most powerful looking of the three. Although he had reached middle-age, his hair was still jet black, but his long beard was grey with age.

All the while Ymir continued to grow. And the larger he grew the more powerful he became and the more he used his power for evil. Odin, Vili, and Ve observed his growth and realized he had to be killed before he destroyed everything. They also knew if he became much more powerful destroying him would be an impossible task. So, they held a council, called a Thing, to decide what to do.

Odin, being the eldest, spoke first. "Soon Ymir will learn about us and try to destroy us as he destroyed our grandfather, Buri. So, we must destroy him first. If we wait much longer we'll be unable to best him, for he is growing more powerful even as I speak.

Vili and Ve nodded in agreement as Odin continued speaking, "I have a plan. Most of his time is spent sleeping, for he is a lazy oaf. While he is dreaming his evil dreams we shall come upon him unawares, even as he did to Buri, and slit his throat. Thus shall his death come to pass."

Vili and Ve shook their fists in agreement to the plan. It was simple, but effective.

With no time to waste the three immediately started on the long journey to the other side of Niflheimr in search of Ymir. They had to cross mountains of ice so high that from them they could see clear across Ginnungagap into the fires of Muspelheimr. And when they dared look into that raging furnace they saw Surtr taunting them with his fiery sword, med sviga lævi, beckoning them to come and do battle. But they knew they were not yet strong enough for that challenge, and it would be folly to try. But there would come a time when they would challenge him.

Some of the mountains they trekked across were shapeless, while others had strange forms. Some reminded the three Æsir of jotuns. As they scrambled over these mountains it almost seemed to them the mountains were trembling and trying to move. But throughout their journey they met no one in that desolate land.

They sought Ymir long before they found him. Finally, as they neared the edge of Niflheimr they saw him in the distance looking in their direction. Thinking he had seen them they quickly bent down low behind an ice-covered boulder. When they ventured to look up they found he was still staring in their direction. But rather than looking at them, his attention had been captured by something behind them that seemed to be worrying him. They took advantage of this opportunity and silently crept closer. Soon they were so close they could see the snarl on his face and the hollows between his craggy teeth. Next they stopped and waited for him to go to sleep, as was his wont. But on this particular day he showed no signs of being tires. He wandered back and forth, occasionally stepping away from Niflheimr into Ginnungagap whence he had been spawned. Then he'd retreat into Niflheimr and again pace back and forth. Something was worrying him. The three Æsir weren't concerned with Ymir's troubles. They had their own concerns.

His restlessness began to worry the three Æsir. For they were the ones who were beginning to tire. They now saw how large he was and how much larger he was growing even as they watched. It wouldn't be too long before destroying him would be impossible. But still he tirelessly remained awake. They quietly considered this unexpected problem amongst themselves.

Ve murmured, "We must do something quickly. Even now he grows more monstrous."

"I shall creep up and hit him upon the head with a stone," Vili whispered as he hurled an imaginary stone to the ground.

Forgetting his younger brothers had spoken before him, Odin said, "Then I shall run up and attack him."

So, they now had a plan. On the surface it didn't seem to be a very brilliant plan. But, it was something.

Vili moved cautiously around to the other side of the jotun, picked up a huge rimestone and hurled it at him. The stone caught Ymir in the middle of his forehead, staggering him. As he tottered backwards he tripped over a mountain and fell crashing to the ground, stunned. All of Niflheimr shook. Odin quickly climbed upon Ymir's chest and plunged his sword to the hilt into the jotun's throat. He wrenched the sword sideways causing a great gash to open across Ymir's neck. Blood spurted forth copiously, causing a great flood which washed Odin, Vili and Ve away in its tide. The three struggled for their lives against the rushing, pulsating current, and survived only by catching hold of the tips of some trees as the torrent of blood washed them passed the branches.

The profusely flowing blood engulfed all of Niflheimr in a red fast-breaking tide. The current caught Audhumla the cow by the legs as she was licking at a stone and pulled her under. She rose to the surface just once before being drowned. The head of the stone she had been licking gasped for air, but instead gulped down blood and was soon covered over and drowned.

All but two of the hrymthursar were drowned. As all around them were being swept away, Bergelmir and his wife scrambled into a hollowed-out tree called Lutr. Eventually they floated to a mill called Ludr, and were saved. After the flood they continued the race of hrymthursar.

Bor and Bestla also perished in the flood caused by their sons, Odin, Vili and Ve. They were on a high mountain when they saw the great crimson wave approaching. The two had just enough time to plant a seed under a rock before being engulfed by Ymir's blood. This seed was nourished by the strange tide and grew rapidly into the world tree Yggdrasyll.

The Construction of Midgardr

The Creation of the Dvergues

Almost as quickly as the blood had engulfed Niflheimr, it subsided. The three Æsir began constructing Midgardr from Ymir's remains. First the three sons of Bor and Bestla dragged Ymir's misshapen body from Niflheimr and set it in the midst of Ginnungagap where it floated in its own blood, undulating with the waves. Ymir's body had already begun to decompose. As it did so, it hardened and became Midgardr.

Odin's attention was caught by some maggots crawling in and out amongst Ymir's flesh, eating away at his carcass. Odin picked a maggot out of the corner of Ymir's mouth, gave it form and extraordinary intelligence, and named it Modsognir, who became the first of a race known as dvergues or dvergues. Sometimes they were also called dokkalfar, or dark alfs.

Odin commanded Modsognir, "Go and create a race of dvergues from the maggots in Ymir's body. Because you and your race are so repulsive and your appearance so frightful to the eyes, you will dwell underground in the land called Svartalfheimr and will not be permitted to come forth during daylight under penalty of uppr dagr. If you do you will be dayed-up and turned to stone."

Modsognir did as Odin commanded. He created Durinn and Dvalin. Durinn in turn created all the other dvergues.

One group of rock dvergues he created paid particular attention to his leadership and were known as either Durinn's Kin or Durinn's Folk. They included Bildur, Fragr, Buri, Gloinn, Bruni, Billing, Frar, Jari, Hlævangr, Skafidr, Grer, Haur, Sviarr, Lofar, Loni, Berling, and Alfrig. Nyi, Hefti, Nori, An, Hanar, Fundinn, Anar, Oinn, Veigr, Thror, Vinndalf, and Thrainn.

Dvalin also had a group devoted to him, known as Dvalin's Hosts. They lived in Juravale's Marsh. Their group included Draupnir, Haugspori, Dori, Skirfir, Ai who rode Hrafn, Frosti, Dolgthrasir, Hlevangur, Ori, Dufur, Virvir, Yngvi, Finnr, Harr, Alf, Gloi, Andvari, Skafidur, Eikinskajaldi, and Ginnarr. Dvalin rode to visit them on Modnir, his horse.

Other rock dvergues included Fjalarr, Galarr, Alviss, Sindri, Brokkr, Hugstari, Duf, Fidr, Dolgthvari, Hornbori, Falr, Hanar, Ingi, Horr, Vili, and Hledjolf. Earth dvergues included Thorinn, Dain, Althjofr, Sudri, Austri, Nordri, Vestri, Litr, Bafurr, Mjodvitnir, Bifurr, Nain, Bomburr, Fili, Nali, Bumburr, Nar, Gandalf, Midvitnir, Nyr, Kili, Nidi, Regin, Nyradr, Ori, Thekkr, Rekkr, Throk, Viggr, and Vitr. Other dvergues included Thjodreyrir, Dolgthoari, Duer, Fornbogi, Thrar, Frœgr, Heri, Vali, Haugstari, Nipingr, Hlidolfr, Nipung, Vegdrasil, Noinn, Sviorr, Vindalfr, Hugo, and Sviur.

They were homely looking creatures, black-complexioned with oversized heads and undersized stout legs. Crows feet set off their strange green eyes. The many lands in

Midgardr called them by various names. But whether they were called trolls, goblins, pucks, brownies, gremlins, Huldra folk, or kobolds, they still looked to Modsognir, Durinn, and Dvalin for leadership.

After their creation they immediately went forth to inhabit the caves and passages beneath Midgardr. Their nights were spent stealing the wealth of Midgardr by collecting all the precious stones, gold, silver and other valuable metals, and storing them in hiding places deep within Midgardr. They guarded their hoards and drew on them to fashion precious and magical objects. One such object was a red-pointed cap called a tarnkappe. Very few existed and those which did were greatly prized and well-guarded by their owners. A tarnkappe made its wearer invisible, which meant the sun's rays couldn't find him or her. The wearer could go about on Midgardr during the day playing tricks and taking advantage of his or her invisibility. These tricks could be simple jests such as turning over a milk pail filled with fresh goat's milk; or they could be hurtful and malicious, such as stealing young babies so they might be raised as their own, and later married to the tallest dvergues, hoping eventually such relations would make their race taller and no longer susceptible to uppr dagr.

Their regular tasks also included forging iron and making useful implements. Once populated, those on Midgardr purchased golden plates, jeweled necklaces, and magical swords from the dvergues, no matter how dear the price. But frequently these objects were misplaced or lost, or so the owners thought. But the dvergues were greedy and never liked to let go of their handiwork and quietly stole it back at night. The dvergues were also masters of runes and magic songs and possessed great wisdom. But they also were mischievous, and hoping to create confusion on Midgardr they repeated the sounds they heard over and over again. Thus were echoes called dvergues' voices.

The Creation of the Ljosalfar

Odin created a second group of beings, also from the maggots who were eating away at Ymir. He called them the ljosalfar, or light alfs. They were friends to the Æsir and in time would be given a land called Alfheimr, situated between Asgardr, the future home of the Æsir, and Midgardr. This convenient location allowed them to divide their time equally between the Æsir and those on Midgardr and attend to their duties which included helping to cultivate flowers and gardens as well as playing with butterflies and birds. They were pleasant to look at, and did not need to hide from the sun. They were helpful to those of Midgardr, though their shyness made them frequently flee before their presence was known, unless caught by surprise, which scared them even more. They left signs as to where they had been on Midgardr. They loved holding hands and dancing in large circles. The grass in these circles grew greener and thicker than the grass surrounding them. Such circles were called fairy rings. If a person on Midgardr stood in the exact center of a fairy ring he or she would either be blessed with seeing the fairies or cursed with immediate death. Sometimes both.

Ivaldi was the leader of the ljosalfar, and as such they were sometimes known as Ivaldi's Sons. Other alfs included Iri, Finnr, Bari, Lidskjalfr, Uni, Uri, and Var.

Next Odin, Vili, and Ve took Ymir's skull and positioned it high over Midgardr to form the sky. Odin took four dvergues, named Austri, Vestri, Nordri, and Sudri, and placed one at each corner to help hold the great skull steady on their shoulders.

But, mysteriously, to the south and above Ymir's skull was another sky called Andlang. And above it stretched a wide blue sky called Vidblain. The palace Gimle was situated there, and sometimes could be seen glinting golden through the clouds. No one knew who had built it, or how precisely to reach it. They could only see it's beauty and aspire to it. And sometimes they could catch a glimpse of white elves who were pure and good. The pure would live in Gimle beyond the end of time.

The three Æsir flung Ymir's brains high into the sky to make up the billowy clouds. What was left of Ymir's blood and sweat became the streams, rivers, lakes, and oceans of Midgardr. His bones were fashioned into craggy mountains; stones and pebbles were formed from what was left of his toes, splintered bones and double teeth. Flowers, grass, and moss were formed from his eyebrows; while his curly hair was used to make the trees. Odin took Ymir's eyelashes and hedged them round Midgardr to form a bulwark of protection against potential invaders, like the jotuns.

Odin, Vili, and Ve reached into Muspelheimr and took handfuls of burning cinders and flung them glowing into the skies over Midgardr and where the other eight Worlds of the Yggdrasyll were to be. Odin tossed one stream of sparks into the heavens forming a milk-white band across the sky which was ever after known as Odin's Way. But still theses celestial objects did not give off enough light, so Odin reached back into Muspelheimr and grabbed yet another handful of brands and threw them up to the skies. The three Æsir ordered the movements of these sparks. Some were fixed, some moved regularly, others irregularly. Some pulsed irregularly, some gave off strange sounds, while others seemingly weren't there at all.

Then the three sons of Bor created the animals of the sea and of the air. And as they walked in Midgardr the three created the beasts that were to inhabit the land.

Askr and Embla

While roaming about Midgardr surveying their handiwork, Odin, Vili, and Ve came to a seashore and found two pieces of driftwood on the beach. Vili picked up one piece and called it Askr. Ve picked up another piece and called it Embla. Both set to whittling their pieces into shapes. Ve's took the form of a woman, while Vili's took the form of a man.

Each of the three Æsir gave Askr and Embla gifts of being. Odin gave them each a soul and ond, the breath of life. Vili gave them odr, vit ok hrœring, thought, sense and understanding, as well as wit and movement. Ve gave them their faculties, malit, sjon, and heyrn, speech, sight and hearing. He also gave them litu goda, a good countenance and a fair complexion, as well as la ok litr, blood and a healthy hue. And lastly he gave them clothing.

Odin, Vili, and Ve were so pleased with Askr and Embla they gave them Midgardr to populate and rule over.

Askr and Embla roamed the land giving names to everything, and taming what animals they could. After much journeying they came to a house which was already built and waiting for them. And there they settled.

Askr and Embla were perfect, as were all their children for several generations. But after awhile the jotuns and other creatures of evil took on the form of human beings and intermarried with those of Midgardr and brought evil into their character.

The Separation of Light from Darkness

The next task facing Odin, Vili and Ve was the separation of light from darkness. For this they called upon the jotun Nott and her son Dagr to ride through the skies in their chariots, one after the other.

Nott was the daughter of Narfi, the first jotun who settled in Jotunheimr after the flood. Nott had been born in the dales beneath the ash Yggdrasyll and took after her jotun ancestry. She was dark with a shadow of long flowing black hair engulfing her figure.

Narfi arranged a marriage between Nott and Naglifar. Soon after they had a son and named him Audr. But, Narfi and Nott were not happy together and parted shortly after Audr's birth.

Next Nott married Anar and had a daughter whom they named Jordr. But this marriage, too, ended in failure.

Lastly she married Dellingr, the king of the dawn. He was related to the Æsir and was fair of mien, with golden red hair. The two were quite a contrast, he was as light as she was dark. But this marriage worked out. They had a son whom they named Dagr. He took after Dellingr's side of the family, being light-complexioned with glowing blond hair.

Dellingr lived in the eastern border of the lower world. And it was from here Nott began her journey. The dawn was a reflection of Midgardr's eastern horizon from Dellingr's dwelling. It could only be seen when Dagr returned and before Nott departed A dvergar named Thjodreyrir lived outside the doors of Dellingr's abode. Every day at dawn he'd arise and sing songs of awakening and blessings upon the worlds.

Nott and Dagr had beautiful chariots to command. Nott's dark chariot belonged to Narfi, and was pulled by her sable-colored steed, Hrimfaxi. As Hrimfaxi pulled Nott across the sky the drool from his bit dropped to Midgardr below, forming the dew on Midgardr at daybreak.

Dagr had a brilliant glittering chariot pulled by his two white steeds, Skinfaxi and Gladr. In his chariot he carried flaming sparks from Muspelheimr which eventually quickened into Alfrothul, the sun. Both steeds were so lustrous and bright-golden the shine from their manes, combined with Alfrothul, lit up the sky causing day.

For awhile Nott and Dagr will peacefully guide their chariots around Midgardr. But a time will come when three wolves will appear: Skoll and Hati Hrodvitnisson will chase Dagr; while Mana-Garmr will try to catch Nott. The three will pursue the two with gaping mouths hoping to close in and swallow them. Occasionally they will come close enough so mother and son can feel their breath and see their flaming eyes, that is if they dare to glance over their shoulders at them. And every so often Nott and Dagr will be swallowed up. Then, if the people of Midgardr cause enough of a clambering, Mana-Garmr, Skoll and Hati Hrodvitnisson, fearing for their lives will release Nott and Dagr who will flee as fast as they can from the slavvering wolves as the chase begins again.

Nott and Dagr will only feel secure when they come to the forest of the Varns behind the western horizon. This is the land of the Ruthenes whose practice of magic protects the two from the fearsome wolves.

Sol and Maane, Hjuki and Bil

There was a jotun named Mundilfari who thought his son and daughter were more beautiful than even the sun and moon. As such he decided to name his children after them, calling his son Maane, and his daughter Sol. Eventually Sol was given in marriage to Glenr, one of Surtr's sons.

Mundilfari's presumptuousness in naming his children after Dagr and Nott did not go unnoticed amongst the Æsir, and angered them so much they decided to honor Mundilfari by stealing away his two children and using them in the heavens. If Mundilfari thought it an honor to name his children after Dagr and Nott, just think how he'd feel if they were placed in the heavens with them?

Maane was given a horse named Alsvidr, also sometimes called Fjosvartnir, to ride while guiding Nott in her course around Midgardr. The path they traveled was called the manvegr, moon way, though some knew it as the milky way.

Living on Midgardr was a very cruel, vain old jotun named Vidfinnr. He forced his son and daughter, Hjiuki and Bil, to walk a great distance every day up a treacherous path to the top of a hill to Byrgir Well. Many thought the waters from Byrgir Well gave the drinker everlasting youthfulness. And Vidfinnr seemed to bear this out. Though he was very old his posture was straight, his step unhalting, his face unlined.

Hjiuki and Bil's task every day without fail, was to fill the cask sæger with the precious liquid from Byrgir Well. The well seemed only to have enough water each day to barely fill the pail. Then it was dry until the next morning. This made each drop even more precious.

After filling the pail the two ran the pole simul through the handle of sæger and balancing simul on their shoulders, walking one behind the other. With sæger hanging inbetween them from the pole, they returned with the prize to Vidfinnr. And woe unto them if they should spill even a drop of Byrgir's Force.

Then it happened. One day as they descended the hillside, Hjiuki tripped and tumbled down the hill. The pole slid from Bil's shoulder with such force she came tumbling after. The precious water covered the hillside quickly seeping into the ground. The grass watered by the liquid grew noticeably as the two sat side by side at the base of the hill. Hjiuki rubbing the rapidly forming lump rising on his head, wondered what punishment Vidfinnr would think up for them.

At that moment Maane was passing overhead. He had often seen the cruelty and blows Vidfinnr inflicted on the two children. Realizing their predicament he intervened to help them, though some say it wasn't much help and their situation afterward wasn't that much better. Reaching down he carried Hjiuki and Bil off into the heavens. Now they can be seen from Midgardr following Maane as the shadows on his face. Hjiuki and Bil's kidnapping sealed Vidfinnr's doom. Within days of the children's disappearance he withered and died of old age.

Sol, Maane's sister, was given two horses named Arvakr and Alsvin. It was her task to ride in front of Dagr, guiding him on his course around Midgardr, since the brilliance from Dagr's two horses and the sparks from Muspelheimr blinded him so much he couldn't see to steer a correct path. His formerly erratic path, steadied and became consistent.

To protect Sol and her two horses from Skinfaxi's and Gladr's brilliance the shield svalin was hung at the back of Arvakr and Alsvin. This shield also served as protection for Midgardr. Without it the brilliance from the sparks of Muspelheimr, Skinfaxi, and Gladr could very well have burned everything on Midgardr to a crisp. Two skins filled with an iron cooling substance called isarnkol were placed under the withers of Arvakr and Alsvin. As the horses ran their daily path around Midgardr the wind blew over the isarnkol, cooling and refreshing them.

More about Jotunheimr

Ymir's eyebrows hedging Midgardr were not the only fortifications protecting the inhabitants from unwanted intrusions by jotuns and other evil creatures. The Æsir carved out the river Ifing, which lay to the east between Midgardr and Jotunheimr. The unique property about Ifing was that it never froze over, so the jotuns had no bridge between the two lands. Ifing was useful in keeping the jotuns out of Midgardr, although it did not always succeed. But the Æsir's protection of Midgardr with Ifing also meant those on Midgardr were prevented from exploring the other worlds, unless the Æsir aided them.

Jotunheimr was also known as Outgardr and Utgardr. The ruler of this domain was Utgardr-Loki. It was a land of forests so high the tops of the trees stretched out of sight. Raging rivers cut deep paths through mountain ranges so steep one could never hope to cross over them. One of the largest mountains was called Glittering, located in the area called Glæsisvellir, which means Glittering Plains. The nine wavemaiden daughters of the jotun Geirrodr lived here. There were vast distances from one point to another, and a flickering fire raged around some parts of the land.

Many kinds of jotuns inhabited Jotunheimr. Some were also known as thursars and risars. They were known by their works; rockfalls, landslips and earthquakes were the mark of bergrisars, also known as bergthursars or hill jotuns; while flaring volcanoes, destructive lightning and the Northern Lights were caused by fire jotuns. But the most feared jotuns were the hrymthursars who caused avalanches, made glaciers, formed icecaps and froze rivers. Many on Midgardr worried the hrymthursar's attempts to freeze Ifing would one day work, then the way would lay open between the two lands.

The greatest hawk in Jotunheimr was known as Habrok. But there was also another fearsome bird living there. Hræsvelg was a terrible hrymthursar who took the form of an eagle. Sitting at the northern end of Jotunheimr his goal was to freeze Midgardr and all those living there. He spent his days and many nights flapping his wings, sending a terrible wind blowing out of the north across the neighboring land, causing harsh winters for those closest to the northern part of Midgardr.

Other horrible jotuns included Sterkoddr, who had six arms, Amr, Asvinr, and Gygien, who was a female.

Another dweller in Jotunheimr was Loki Laufeyjarsonr, the son of Farbauti and Laufey. They were also known as Bergelmir and Nal. Loki's brothers were Byleistr and Helblindi.

At the beginning of things Loki lived in Jotunheimr with his first wife, Glut, and his two daughters, Eisa and Einmyria. But, he found the land boring and took his boredom out on his wife and children who suffered regular beatings at his hands. On Midgardr when the flames crackled on the hearth those listening would swear they could hear the cries of Eisa and Einmyria. When the sun shone and yet it rained, those on Midgardr knew the rain was actually Glut's tears and Loki was beating his wife again. The times late in summer when the atmosphere was oppressive and you could see the waves of heat rising from the ground told them Loki was sowing his oats. And as moisture evaporated everyone knew Loki was collecting the moisture to make a drink.

Soon, though, Loki tired of his life in Jotunheimr. Leaving Glut, Eisa, and Einmyria behind, he made his way to the Æsir, claiming the kinship of his past friendship with Odin when they had become blood brothers, and more, and had sworn eternal friendship to each other. Odin when reminded of those promises of his youth exercised his authority and gave Loki permission to remain, despite the protests of other members of the Æsir. Loki then married Sigyn, who remained his faithful companion, no matter how ill she was treated. She didn't seem to mind he still had a wife and children in Jotunheimr.

The Ash Yggdrasyll, the Tree of Life, the World Tree

While Midgardr, Jotunheimr, and the other seven worlds were being created the ash Yggdrasyll, the Tree of Life, the World Tree, grew until it reached a state of full maturity. Its branches spread over all the nine worlds, forming a protective sheltering roof holding all the worlds together. When it falls, so does the universe. Now, in our latter days, it has reached and passed its maturity and is steadily declining. It will continue to weaken until Ragnarokr, the Doom of the Æsir.

Yggdrasyll had nine roots, one root going to each of the nine different worlds. The three main supporting roots reached to Midgardr, Jotunheimr, and Niflheimr. Five lesser roots grew to Muspelheimr, Vanaheimr, Alfheimr, Svartalfheimr, and Helheimr.

While exploring the roots of the Yggdrasyll the Æsir followed the ninth root to its end, a plain called Ida out of which arose Mt. Idavollr, the center most and highest peak on Midgardr. They claimed this as their land, called it Asgardr, and built their palaces at the very top.

The Rivers of the Worlds of the Tree

The river Thund protectively encircled Asgardr. Floating on the river was a dark shining flammable mist. In case of attack it could be ignited to repulse those trying to cross it. The black-terror gleam had a wisdom of its own and the ability to aim its flames at specific attackers.

Soon many rivers coursed from one land to another. Those flowing from Asgardr to Midgardr included Vadgelmir, Tholl, Sokin, Thyn, Vin, Sid, Eikin, Geirvimul, Rinnandi, Gipul, Gomul, Gopul, Rinn, Grad, Gunnthra, and Gunnthorin. Those flowing from Midgardr to Niflheimr included Vond, Thjodnuma, Strond, Vina, Nyt, Hronn, Nonn, Vegsvinn, and Naut.

The Wells That Nourished Yggdrasyll

The mighty ash Yggdrasyll derived its nourishment from three sources: Hvergelmir Well, Mimirsbrunnr Well, and Urdarbrunnr Well.

Hvergelmir Well was in Niflheimr. The waters from it nourished the Niflheimr root and helped the tree survive. Hvergelmir Well had swollen in size so now thirty-six rivers flowed from it; twelve flowed to Midgardr, twelve to Niflheimr, and twelve to Asgardr. Entwined about the root at Hvergelmir Well was a nest of poisonous dark-spotted serpents constantly gnawing away at the bark. They were Nidhoggr and his sons, Goinn, Moinn, Grabakr, Grafvolludr, Ofnir and Svafnir.

Mimirsbrunnr Well was located in Mimir's Grove at the Jotunheimr root in the land called Odainsaker, where Asmegin lived. It was a well of memory and knowledge and was guarded over by Mimir, taking its name from him. His long silvery beard reaching to his waist reflected his agelessness. Jotuns and Æsir both went to him for knowledge. Rarely did he grant them a taste of the water from his well, and then only after they had paid a dear price for it. But he drank from it daily. At dawn when the crimson sky changed the water to a golden-brown mead he drank a single draught from a golden horn. More than that would have destroyed him with too much knowledge. Because of his constant attention to the guardianship of the Yggdrasyll, it was sometimes called Mimameidr, the tree of Mimir.

Odin was one of the Æsir who had purchased a drink of the golden-brown mead from Hvergelmir Well. Long had he sought the drink, and finally he persuaded Mimir to give him a single swallow.

Odin bargained for a drink from Hvergelmir Well, "I must have just a single sip so the knowledge I gain will help me fight against the coming of Ragnarokr."

Mimir had heard it all before, "Many others have given me that reason. Why should I grant you what I did not grant them?"

Odin responded, "You should do so because of our fealty, one to the other. You are my mother's brother, you are my uncle."

Mimir realized he could not refuse a blood relative. But, if he had to grant a sip to Odin, it would be costly. "All right, then I will give you a sip. But it will cost you. The price will be your right eye."

Odin agreed.

Mimir dropped his drinking horn into the well, filled it, and pulled it back up by it's leather strap and proffered it to Odin who grabbed it and began greedily gulping down mouthfuls of the liquid, breaking their bargain of just a single sip.

Angrily Mimir snatched the drinking horn from Odin, "You have broken our bargain. You contracted for a single sip. You have just about drunk the horn dry."

Odin was without repentance, "No matter what I said or agreed to, a single sip was not worth the high price of my right eye. It is your fault I had to break an unfair agreement.

Mimir was furious, "Nonetheless you did agree to it. And so I curse the knowledge you have gained. You will forever dwell on the inevitable defeat of the Æsir. You will never be happy again. Your ill-gotten knowledge will defeat any happiness which comes your way. Because you know happiness is ethereal and ultimately you and those who follow you are doomed.

Mimir's Curse followed Odin the rest of his days. His countenance changed so that ever after he brooded on the hopelessness of life and the bleakness of the future to come.

Odin turned to leave but was stopped by Mimir who held out his hand for payment. "Honor your bargain. You've already gotten a better deal than you bargained for."

Furious, Odin gouged out his right eye with his thumb and gave it to Mimir, who threw it into the well where it stared up unblinking and unseeing as the clear water rippled over it. In time Mimir used the eye as a container for carrying the precious rejuvenating liquid from the well to Yggdrasyll and watering the tree with it. At other times the eye became his cup as he drank his morning sip of knowledge.

But Odin was not the only one who had gained a drink. Thor, Odin's eldest son, once stole a drink and subsequently gained a small degree of wit to go with his enormous brawn. Heimdallr, the Watcher of the Æsir, also bartered with Mimir. He traded an ear for heightened senses. It, too, was tossed into the water and lay unhearing at the bottom of the well near his father's unseeing eye.

The third well, Urdarbrunnr Well, was located at the Asgardr root. The waters of Hvergelmir Well and Mimirsbrunnr Well flowed into Urdarbrunnr Well, making it the most sacred of wells. It was so holy that it purified whatever was dipped into it, coating objects with a sacred white film. This well supplied the Yggrdasyll tree with its lifegiving force and its ability to sustain existence despite the destructive evil forces which were constantly preying on it. The fruit on the branches of Yggdrasyll was plentiful and was particularly good for the aid of women who were sick with child.

The Tribulations of Yggdrasyll

At a distance the four harts browsing beneath the boughs of Yggdrasyll at Urdarbrunnr Well looked pastoral. But this idyllic view was false. Up close one could be see they were nibbling at the bark and running about the tree biting off all the buds. They were Dainn, Dvalinn, Duneyrr and Durathorr. As they frolicked honeydew caught on their horns and dropped to Midgardr to nourish the bees.

The sons of Grafvitnir were pulling twigs off the trunk, adding to the tree's misery.

As Yggdrasyll's branches spread over the worlds, birds found their way to nest there, until at least one of every kind of bird was represented.

The topmost bough reached over Asgardr. On it roosted the satin eagle, Edgar. He was old and wise. The song he sung was on the birth of the worlds and their death. Those who heard it were moved to tears at the thought of what was to come. Perched between Edgar's eyes on his beak and thus obstructing his view, sat a hawk called Vedrfolnir, who gazed steadfastly into Asgardr, Midgardr and Niflheimr, reporting all he saw to Edgar. By itself on a nearby branch was the cock Vidofnir. He was silent, but one day his piercing songs would be the most feared sound heard.

Running up and down the mighty ash was a red squirrel named Ratatoskr, also known as Ratr. He carried gossip and vicious rumors between Nidhoggr and Edgar, doing his best to provoke them so they would take their anger out on the tree. At first he told Nidhoggr Edgar planned to fly down and pluck his eyes out. Nidhoggr responded by chewing more fervently at the tree trying to topple it so the eagle would be crushed in the boughs as the tree hit the ground. Ratatoskr ran up the tree to tell Edgar Nidhoggr was trying to bite the tree down so Edgar would fall into his waiting mouth. The eagle pulled at little branches with his claws and dropped them down on Nidhoggr hoping several would land in the serpent's eyes and cause him great pain, maybe even blind him.

The Building of Asgardr

Bifrost or Asbru

The Æsir now set about building their dwellings in Asgardr. First they built a rainbow bridge reaching from Midgardr to Asgardr and called it Bifrost, or Asbru. This most perfect of all bridges was made of the red from fire, the blue from air, and the green from the sea. These colors were constantly blending together in ever-changing hues. The Æsir set a perpetual fire at the foot of Bifrost to prevent the jotuns and other creatures of evil from crossing over.

Each day the Æsir rode over their bridge to Urdarbrunnr Well, sat beneath the branches of the Yggdrasyll, and held a Thing.

The only member of the Æsir not permitted to cross on Bifrost was Thor, the son of Odin and Jordr. Everyone feared Bifrost would bend and break under the weight of the mighty thundergod. Thor's journey to Asgardr, or the Thing, was by a different route. He was too heavy to ride a horse, so he either rode in his goat-drawn chariot, pulled by Tanngnjostr and Tanngrisnir, or waded the rivers Kormt and Ormt which flowed through the clouds, as well as the two streams that made up the river Kerlaug beneath Bifrost. As Thor crossed the river a poisonous mist would engulf him, and the Æsir awaiting his arrival on the far shore held their breaths until he reappeared, safe. Their greatest fear was that their most powerful defender against the jotuns would not make it through the deadly fog.

Heimdallr was given the task of standing watch on Bifrost. He was the son of Odin and nine wavemaidens who lived in Glæsisvellir, the daughters of the jotun Geirrodr. His mothers were Gjalp, Greip, Eistla, Eyrgjafa, Ulfrun, Angeyja, Imdr, Atla, and Jarnsaxa. Odin, adventuring under the name Ulvrung, had come upon the nine sisters on the white sand which covers the ocean's floor and had made love to all of them simultaneously. They immediately bore him a son who quickly grew to manhood on the diet the nine gave him. His meals included the strength of Midgardr, the wetness of the oceans, and the heat from the chariot of the sun. Soon he was able to assume his position as Guardian of the Æsir.

Heimdallr used many aids to defend Bifrost. One of the greatest was his keen sword named Hofud, which meant head. His golden horse was called Gulltoppr and carried him back and forth across the bridge each morning heralding the new day. Because of this Heimdallr was also known as Heimdellinger. His other ekenames included Hallinskidi, Irmin, and Hrutr. He was also known as the hviti ass, white god, because of the white armor he wore. Gjallarhorn was the name of his crescent-shaped trumpet. It would remain silent until the last great battle when its note would echo throughout the Worlds of the Tree to summon the Æsir and their allies to the last battle. Sometimes Heimdallr hung Gjallarhorn on the branch of the Yggdrasyll which reached over Bifrost to shade him. At other times it was hidden in the waters of Mimirsbrunnr, where it rested next to Odin's unblinking eye and Heimdallr's unhearing ear. Heimdallr had golden teeth which flashed when he smiled in recognition of a friend coming towards him. Some knew him as Gullintanni because of his golden teeth.

Heimdallr was more wakeful than a bird. And when he did sleep it was with one eye open so he was ever alert to guard Asgardr. His vision was so sharp he could see by day or night with equal acuity. His gaze beheld objects hundreds of rosts away. His hearing was so keen he could hear grass growing in fields and wool growing on the backs of sheep. And this despite the fact he had only one ear, having left the other with Mimir.

The Æsir built a hall called Himinbjorg at the keystone of Bifrost for Heimdallr. The mead cellars in his hall were amongst the best in Asgardr. He was often visited by the other Æsir who partook of his mead and made easier the loneliness of his watch. Heimdallr was well-liked and had few enemies.

To the other side of Bifrost, opposite Himinbjorg, sat seven maids.

With the task of building Bifrost and an abode for Heimdallr completed the Æsir and Asynjur, as the female of the Æsir were collectively known, met for a Thing at Urdarbrunnr Well. There they decided on the boundaries of Asgardr and decreed it to be a gridastadr, a sacred place where bloodshed and feuds would not be tolerated and it would be known for the peace which reigned there. It would be a land of eternal springtime with nothing ill-toward to mar the happiness there. Or, at least, that's how they thought it would be.

Alfheimr

First the Æsir created the land called Alfheimr for their friends the ljosalfar. In order to have their friends nearby they set Alfheimr midway between Midgardr and Asgardr. This enabled the ljosalfar to visit Midgardr and Asgardr with equal ease. They were always welcome in Asgardr and brought Heimdallr a cup of refreshing mead whenever they crossed over Bifrost.

The Other Halls in Asgardr

Now came the task of constructing the abodes of Asgardr proper. The Æsir first built a workshop and began the task of forging the extra hammers, anvils and other tools they would need for building Asgardr's halls. They took elements and combined them to make metals. Gold and silver were used extensively in Asgardr. All of their dishes and eating utensils were made of gold. Silver was used mainly for ornamentation.

Gladsheimr

Gladsheimr was the first hall built in Asgardr. It was inside and out like burning gold. There were had twelve thrones in the main hall with one throne higher than the others. This throne belonged to Odin. The other eleven thrones were used by the most important of the Æsir. General meetings and councils took place in this hall.

Vingolf

Then the vast hall Vingolf was built for the Asynjur. Those who met here included the Asynjes, also known as Frigg's Attendants. They were, Horn; Fulla, who was Frigg's messenger; Eir; Sjofn, who was appealed to in matters of love; Vor, upon whose name sacred oaths were sworn; Sage, also known as Saga or Laga, who spoke in poetry and was Odin's daughter; Lofn; Syn; Lin, also known as Hlin; Gefjun; Menglod, who knew the ways of healing and lived on Lyfajaberg; and Gna, who rode Hofvarpnir, a horse whose sire was Hamskerpir, and whose dam was Gardrofa.

Odin's Halls: Valaskjalf and Harr

Next they built Odin's main hall, Valaskjalf. It was an enormous white hall roofed in silver. The watchtower held Odin's throne Hlidskjalf. When Odin sat on Hlidskjalf he could look and hear out over all the Worlds of the Tree and learn what was going on. Nothing was hidden from him when he sat here. And to make him more comfortable he had a footstool of burnished gold on which to rest his feet. Frigg, Odin's consort, also had a throne in this watchtower. And from it she too could see and hear out over all the worlds. By this fact she tempered Odin's frequently harsh judgments with her own insight. At times, however, they came into conflict over what they saw and took opposing sides. Odin most often cast his gaze to the south and west, especially when he was trapped in his brooding thoughts, for in those directions lay hope. To the east and north lay evil beings working malicious deeds. His brow furrowed with worry at what he saw in those directions. The foul events he witnessed oppressed him and made him silent and dark in nature.

Harr was yet another of Odin's halls. In it were separate rooms for all manner of events from poetry reading to sporting contests, especially wrestling. At the end of the hall stood three thrones.

Fensalir

Usually Frigg could be found in her own hall, Fensalir which lay down by the sea far from the main portion of Asgardr. Bathed in eternal twilight its gold and silver rooms took on intense coloring, further emphasized by the pearls which adorned its walls. It was in this hall Frigg sat to spin her golden distaff. She gave the finished wool and flax to those housewives on Midgardr whom she found most worthy. Peasants in Midgardr hoping for some of this dear reward gazed into the sky at night watching her amongst the stars, spinning long threads to be made into cloth. They called the grouping of stars they saw Friggjar Rock.

Sokkvabekkr

Sage's hall was built and she called it Sokkvabekkr. It, like Frigg's hall, was near the sea.

Ydalir

Ullr, the son of Sif and Aurvandil, and also Thor's stepson, was the most proficient archer of the Æsir. He called his hall Ydalir, yew dales. It sat in a valley amongst a forest of yew trees and, although small, was found to be very comfortable by all who visited there. The bows and arrows made from the yews of his forest were the best in all the worlds.

Other Halls

Vidarr, the son of Gridr and Odin, was always silent and thus chose the solitude of the forest for his home. His hall was in Landvidi and was covered over with branches and flowers. Silence prevailed except for the occasional chirp of a bird or the sound of the rustling noise made by a fleeting squirrel.

A hall was built for Ullinn, and one for Lytir, who was worshiped most particularly by those in Sviothiod on Midgardr.

Brunnakr Grove

Near the southern ridge of Asgardr in view of Gladsheimr was a beautiful apple orchard called Brunnakr Grove. Its apple trees were still immature and as yet had put forth no buds. They awaited the arrival of someone to tend and care for them.

Gimle

Near Brunnakr Grove was a beautiful gold-thatched hall called Gimle. Only the most righteous and good dwelt there. It was prophesied it would still stand after the Nine Worlds of the Tree had fallen.

Feikstaf in Breidablik

Baldr, one of the twin sons of Odin and Frigg, was fair and good. He had white hair and light seemed to shine from him, blinding everyone to other's presences with his beauty. His decisions when he sat in judgment were so just, they were never disputed. He dwelt with his wife, Nanna Nepsdottr, in his broad-gleaming estate called Breidablik where evil was not allowed within its boundaries. His hall was called Feikstaf. The camomile flower grew there in abundance and was called Baldr's Brow because of its purity and healing power.

Baldr's twin brother was Hodr, who ruled over the darkness. His mood was as solemn as his brother's was radiant. Whereas Baldr's blue eyes shone forth rays of gladness and saw only the good in others, Hodr's unseeing eyes were black pools of blind resentment tinged with the green of envy. The two twin's appearance further contrasted in Baldr's golden curly hair and Hodr's black stringy hair. Baldr was loved by all, Hodr was seen and ignored. He hid himself away in the darkness of the forest and was not missed.

Glitner

Baldr and Nanna had two sons, Forseti and Brono. Forseti lived in a hall called Glitner. It was made entirely of gold with the roof thatch made of solid silver. Forseti sat on his throne, the lawgiver of the Æsir, dispensing his wise decrees, settling the arguments of all who approached him. He adjudicated disputes between the Æsir, as well as those on Midgardr. He was so fair and just that no one argued his findings. His mediation between enemies made them friends again. Solemn oaths were sworn on his name and kept. Oathbreakers felt his just wrath and died from their broken vows.

Bilskirnir

Thor the Thundergod was the eldest son of Odin and Jordr. Jordr, who was sometimes known as Hlodyn, lived in Verland in Midgardr. Thor was sometimes called Hlodynjar in her honor.

Thor was extremely handsome in face and figure. His appearance was striking since the red of his fiery beard and curly long hair reflected in the copper cuirass he often

wore. Frequently he wore a pointed crown which had flames and lightning shooting from each point. Although renowned for his strength, he was also known for his truthfulness and honesty, which he valued above strength. Soon after his birth Jordr realized she could not manage him. He could already lift and kick off the ten loads of bearskins which had been piled on his cradle to keep him warm – a worthy feat for a grown man and extraordinary in a child of just a few months. So she sent him to Vingnir and Hlor to be raised as their foster son. For this reason Thor was sometimes known by the ekenames Vingthor and Hlorridi.

Upon his return to Asgardr Thor claimed part of Asgardr as his birthright and called his estate Thrudheimr. Sometimes it was also known as Thrudvangar. He built Bilskirnir, his enormous hall, on this land. The outside of Bilskirnir was studded with shields and glowed red in contrast with the inside which was a gleaming purple. Bilskirnir had five-hundred-and-forty rooms, which made it the equal of the soon to be constructed Valhalla. Thor received a portion of the dead in battle for his hall. Here they quaffed mead and banqueted on enormous meals, and practiced their warrior skills in preparation for the last fateful battle.

Glasir Grove

Near Gladsheimr was a red-gilt leafed grove called Glasir, where many of the horses in Asgardr grazed. Such horses as Hjalmther, Lettfeti, Soti, Lungr, Vigg, Sinir, Gisl, Silfrintoppr, Hafeti, Tjaldari, Falhofnir, Gering, Skævadr, Gler, Jor, Gyllir, Glenr, and Skeidbrimir.

Valhalla

The last hall built was the most magnificent of all and also stood in Glasir Grove. The branch of Yggdrasyll with the satin eagle Edgar on it hung over this hall, so the final clarion call to battle would ring out loudly and clearly over all the Worlds of the Tree. Its roof slates were tiled with shields; its walls were shafts of spears so highly polished they alone could illuminate the hall. Above the western door, the main entrance, hung a wolf with an eagle hovering over it. Topping the main gate was a boar's head. There were five-hundred-and-forty doors to this hall and each door was wide enough to allow eight-hundred fully armored warriors walking shoulder-to-shoulder through at a time. The benches were strewn with warrior coats, fine armor and weapons, gifts to each warrior entering service there. This hall was Valhalla, the hall of the dead.

In the center of Valhalla was a mighty pine tree called Læradr which formed the hall's main support. Standing on the shield-laden roof was a hart named Eikthrynir who nibbled on Læradr's leaves. Dew dropped from Læradr onto Eikthrynir's horns. From there the drops fell into Hvergelmir Well and helped make up the poisonous waters of that terrifying well.

A warrior had to die in battle, on valol, the field of battle, to gain entrance to Valhalla. Preferably his or her death wound was by a javelin or sword. Many who wanted to be taken by the Valkyries fought as berserks, without armor and bare of clothing, but with a fierceness and battle frenzy which multiplied their strength. They fought naked to show their faith in the protection of the Æsir. As ulfhednars they attacked the enemy howling like wolves trying to gain the Valkyries' attention. Sometimes the Valkyrie Herfjotur caused this battle panic to come over the warriors for her own delight.

Odin took the princes who fell while Thor took the thralls. Frigg also collected some of the slain for her hall. The slain were called valr, and the chosen slain of Valhalla were usually called the Einherjar, although sometimes they were called the sigrthjod.

Odin dispatched Valkyries to the scene of the battle to collect the chosen slain. They were preceded by eagles and ravens. Warriors glancing up and seeing those noble birds realized Odin himself had taken special note of their battle. Soon the Valkyries appeared and watched over the battle, guiding spears to the hearts of the future Einherjar and causing swords to cut gaping wounds into Odin's chosen. Woe to the magnificent warriors who caught Odin's attention. Victory upon victory could only speed their journey to Valhalla. The Valkyries influenced the course of the battle and awarded victory and defeat as Odin had commanded. Occasionally they used Odin's magic bow which fired ten arrows at a time, each one finding its mark. The sweat from the splendid white horses the warrior maidens rode above the battlefield fell to the ground and fertilized it.

Often, when the Valkyries weren't riding to battle, they accompanied Odin on the Herlathing, the Wild Hunt, throughout Midgardr. They thundered across the sky traveling throughout the land, occasionally stopping at terrified households on Midgardr where they were offered mead, food, or, really, anything they wanted.

The Valkyries were equally at home serving mead in Valhalla as they were riding their mighty steeds over a battlefield. At a battle they rode fully-armed and wore dazzling white byrnies, their corselets, at times, blotched with the blood of the slain. Their golden hair flowed down their backs under silver helmets. They gleamed. In Valhalla their armor was hung and instead they wore white robes, and about their waists silver and gold belts for adornment. Some of the Valkyries were Odin's daughters, and were known as Herjan's Disir. Herjan was an ekename for Odin.

The Valkyries Gudr, Rota, and Skuldr always rode to every battle to choose the slain and order the fighting. Some of the other Valkyries were Hrist, Mist, Skeggjold, Skogul, Hildr, Hjor, Hjorthrimul, Thrudr, Hlokk, Gollr, Herjotur, Geironul, Geirahod, Randgridr, Geiravor, Rostgridr, Reginleif, Gondul, Gunnr who rode Goti, Herja, Radgridr, Geirskogul, Spearskogul, Hjalmthrimul, Thogn, Hrund, Thrimul, Godul, Sangridr, Gonul, Hlaka, Thrimu, and Svipul.

The Valkyries Hildr, who was also known as Skeggjold, Hjor, Hjorthrimul, Thrimul, Sangridr, Svipul, Gunnr, Gondul, Skogul, and Geirskogul had a great loom raised on spears into which they ran a red woof. This weft of victory was dripping with blood. The warp was made of men's guts weighted down with human heads. The shuttle was made of bare arrows, while swords were used for spools.

After the Einherjar had been chosen by the Valkyries they rose in the air to begin their difficult journey through the loudly roaring river Thund. They tracked through this river making their way to the wholly-barred Valgrindr Gate. And while they walked Thjodvitnir's fish swam and nipped at their heels. At the Valgrindr Gate they were given a brief respite but eventually had to wade through Thund again to reach Valhalla which was near the banks of Thund.

Hermodr, Tyr, and Vidarr met them at the entrance to Valhalla. From there they were conducted to the foot of Odin's throne where they received praise for their valor. If

a very special warrior was on his way Odin waited at the gate to Valhalla and met him personally.

Every morning the Einherjar were awakened by the crowing of Gullinkambi, also known as Salgofnir. They ate breakfast in Valhalla and afterwards climbed into their armor and made their way to the battlefield around Valhalla. They were shaded by golden trees which gave the area a relaxed and friendly setting. On the mock battlefield they fought each other, sometimes fighting against the same warrior they had fought against on Midgardr, and receiving and giving the same death blows as on Midgardr. But the Einherjar bore no grudges against each other, for their wounds and any death blows they received during practice healed almost as soon as they were dealt.

They fought all morning as hard as they could, then broke for lunch. After lunch they retired for a nap and then awakened and marched out onto the battlefield again and resumed their fighting until dinner, at which time the dead were bundled up and taken back into Valhalla where they came back to life and all those with cleaved heads and dismembered limbs were made whole again.

Odin had once carved a boar and given him life, calling him Sæhrimnir. It was this boar the Einherjar feasted on day after day. While the Einherjar were out fighting, Andhrimnir the cook killed Sæhrimnir, chopped up the chunks of boar, and tossed them into a giant cauldron called Eldhrimnir and cooked a succulent pork stew. And there was always enough for seconds, or even thirds, or more, for each of the Einherjar, for no one in Valhalla ever went hungry or in want of anything.

A nanny goat named Heidrun stood next to the hart Eikthrynir on the roof of Valhalla. She was raised up on her hind legs nibbling away at the needles and buds on the pine tree Læradr which overhung Valhalla. The mead, or hydromel, squirted from her two teats in such large amounts it filled a huge brewing kettle to the brim each day. Enough mead could be brewed so all the Einherjar could drink and drink without fear of it ever running low. By the end of the day the Einherjar were all roaring drunk. But no matter how drunk they got there was no suffering in the head the following morning, such was the magic of this special mead.

Nine Valkyries served the mead and boiled pork. They included Randgridr, Rostgridr, Reginleif, Hrist, and Mist. They had but one command from Odin, which was to keep the cups brimming and the plates filled. The Einherjar used their favorite drinking vessels, the skulls of their enemies. They were usually famished from their day of fighting and fairly gorged themselves on the stew, but there was always enough for all, with plenty left over. As the Einherjar ate, skalds sang of war and stirring Viking expeditions on Midgardr as well as the beginnings and endings of things.

Odin and Frigg joined the Einherjar for dinner, but Odin ate nothing. His solitary figure was seated at a table apart from everyone else. There Hrist and Mist poured blood-red mead in his cup. The food served him he gave with his own hands to Geri and Freki, his two wolves who sat on either side of him. He did not fear to hold his hands near their mouths. But they pulled and tore at the food so fiercely many thought he might lose a hand by this practice. There were few at the table brave enough to put their hands so near the constantly hungry wolves' mouths. Perhaps Tyr was one.

Hildr, one of the Valkyries, had given Odin two ravens, Huginn and Munnin. Her two daughters, Thorgerdr and Irpa, were accepted amongst the Æsir and lived in

Asgardr. At dawn, before breakfast, Odin sent these birds to all of the Worlds of the Tree to gather scraps and bits of information. At dinnertime they returned to him and perching on his shoulders whispered into his ears all the wisdom and news they had learned that day. Odin sat apart solemnly and aloofly to ponder the information he received. At times he could be seen sleeping over his mead which made the Einherjar think he had had too much to drink. But it was only his appearance which slept while Odin traveled to Midgardr in a wehr-form, such as a bird, beast, reptile, or even a man.

After dinner Sæhrimnir's bones came together and he was made whole and fat again and brought back to life so he was ready to be killed again the next day and be eaten once more by the Einherjar.

The day had been long and exhausting for the Einherjar who retired to their rooms to sleep and refresh themselves. When morning came they arose and had breakfast, after which they armed themselves again, marched onto the battlefield and started their battle practice for another day. This would go on daily until Ragnarokr when they would be called upon to defend Asgardr. Yet, would even lifetimes of practicing be enough preparation for the last great battle?

The Three Norns

After the Æsir finished creating and building Asgardr they led an idyllic existence which was called The Golden Age. It was always springtime and there was nothing but lazy peaceful days. The meadows waved with fields of self-sown grain and no one had to work. At this time, one of the favorite pastimes of the Æsir was a game similar to chess or draughts called Fidchell, played with toflur pieces. But when the Golden Age ended this game was lost.

But time passed and soon the three Norns from Jotunheimr arrived. No one knew from whence these three jotun maidens derived their power. There were some who thought they were descendants of the jotun Narfi. But the three never spoke of such things. Their duty was to look to the lives of others, not their own.

The three Norns were Urdr, Verdandi, and Skuldr. Skuldr was also a Valkyrie. Their hall was by Urdarbrunnr Well under the branches of the Yggdrasyll. Their task was to control the fates of the Æsir, jotuns, dwellers of Midgardr, and all else in all the other Worlds of the Tree. After their coming the predestined events leading to Ragnarokr began.

Veiled Skuldr, holding an unopened book in her hand and looking away from Urdr had golden threads which were taken from her by Verdandi. No one knew whence Skuldr drew the golden threads she never seemed to run out of. Verdandi wove the threads in and out to form a massive fabric. She wove quickly with the haste and carelessness of youth, tearing and blemishing parts of the fabric. Some parts she intentionally spoiled since she was jealous when someone had too much good fortune. A snip of a thread from her could prove disastrous for an individual. A snip, an accident; snip snip, a love affair gone wrong leaving the person lonely the rest of their life; snip, snip, snip, a life-threatening illness. Then Urdr, old and ugly and forever looking over her shoulder away from Skuldr, took the woof from Verdandi and smoothed its rough places and covered up some of the torn holes. But in the process she usually mended over some of the bright

places with a duller fabric. Then she rolled the fabric onto a great roller which grew thicker and heavier every moment.

If you happened upon the Norns, it was sometimes possible to get them to reveal your orlog, the future that awaited you. One day Odin and Vidarr journeyed to Urdarbrunnr Well to find out what lay in store for Vidarr. At first the Norns claimed they were too busy to deal with the matter at the moment. But with a little more persuasion from Odin they each spoke a short sentence telling Vidarr's future.

Skuldr spoke first, "Early begun..."

Followed by Verdandi, "...further spun..."

And finally Urdr, "...one day done."

Then they heard a voice on the breeze. It was Wyrd, the mother of the three Norns. Her breathy sentence concluded the prophesy, "And again joy will one day be won."

Odin tried to question them further so he could interpret the prophesy, but they refused to answer. He and Vidarr returned to Asgardr not realizing the prophesy spoke of a future battle, a death, the avenging of that death, and the glory that would come to the avenger in another time and place.

Another task of the Norns was to try and stave off the decay that had started in the Yggdrasyll. To do this they took water from Urdarbrunnr Well and ground it with gravel from near the well and sprinkled it over the rotted sections of the tree trying to rejuvenate it, or at least contain the rot. They also mixed Urdarbrunnr's water with clay and made a paste to spread on the hopelessly decayed parts of the tree trying to seal up the wounds of the tree and provide a path for water to flow to other healthy sections so branches would not shrivel and fall off. Both of these remedies had the effect of turning the Yggdrasyll white. Also, they took turns journeying to the spring Uppsah to fetch aurr which they also spread on the mighty ash. Theses remedies halted he decay, but did not stop it.

One day while the three Norns were mixing clay and water at Urdarbrunnr Well they noticed two birds had been born in the well. The Norns cared for them and they grew to become the most beautiful birds and were called swans.

Many of the Valkyries became so enchanted with the swans that sometimes they flew about the world in the guise of swans and were called Swan Maidens. At times while flying about in this form they would stop by a river or lake and discard their Swan cloaks so they could bathe. Anyone happening by could steal their Swan cloaks and transform the warrior maidens into mortal women until such time as they regained their cloaks. While in mortal form a Valkyrie was subject to the same passions as other women. But any Valkyrie who lost her virginity could never again fly as one of Odin's maidens; never again soar over the battle or see the flash of sword on sword, or hear the cries of victory and death. Instead she would be trapped as a mortal woman for the rest of her life.

But swans were important for another reason; with their birth creation was finished.

Chapter 2

Rigr the Walker

Odin was in his watchtower, seated on his throne Hlidskjalf, in his hall Valaskjalf, as he cast his gaze to the three Norns at Urdarbrunnr Well. Their coming troubled him greatly. More troubling, though, was what he saw when he looked into Midgardr. The men and women there were untroubled and unconcerned about life. They harbored no thoughts of glory, or of war, and planned for nothing beyond their immediate needs. Odin needed mighty warriors for training in Valhalla if the Æsir were to have a chance of winning the last great battle, and Midgardr was proving to have very few warriors. Something had to be done about this deplorable situation.

Odin sent a messenger to Heimdallr summoning his son to see him, informing Heimdallr he had a task for him. Heimdallr hurried to Odin's other hall, Gladsheimr, knowing Odin would receive him there. Odin rarely permitted others to see him on his throne in Valaskjalf.

Heimdallr approached Odin's throne with his head bowed, "Why have you sent for me, father?"

Odin answered, "I have looked into Midgardr and have seen those living there are unconcerned about the future. They have no ambition beyond tending their fields. They care not that jotuns have already intermarried with them and have produced some very evil monsters in the forms of men. I want you to journey to Midgardr and take on a disguise. Choose three deserving couples and see to it the three different orders of society come about through them. Hurry in this task before our enemies realize Bifrost is unattended and the way to Asgardr lays unguarded."

Heimdallr went back to Himinbjorg where he found Gulltoppr already saddled and everything ready for his departure. He mounted Gulltoppr and rode on Bifrost until he reached Midgardr. After reaching Midgardr he sent Gulltoppr back to Himinbjorg. It would not do to try to pass himself off as a poor traveler, if he were also riding the most magnificent horse in all of Midgardr. The other problem was that he was of the Æsir, and looked quite magnificent himself. He disguised himself down to the level of those

of Midgardr and called himself by the ekename Rigr, which means the walker. Then his journey started.

Ai and Edda

Rigr walked until he came to a seashore, and followed along it for the rest of the day. At twilight he saw a shabby rundown hut far in the distance. Since it was the first and only dwelling he had seen all day he decided to make his way towards it, finally reaching it after nightfall. The door was not latched so Rigr just walked in.

It was a very humble one-room abode. There was a small fire burning in a hole which had been dug in the middle of the dirt floor for the purpose. The smoke escaped through a hole in the roof. Sitting on a bench huddled about the fire were Ai and his wife Edda. They were a very old couple and wore clothing made from coarsely woven cloth. But they were friendly and welcomed Rigr.

"If you are a man of peace and goodwill then you are welcome to our cabin and are welcome to share what food we have," said Ai.

Rigr walked towards them and told them his name, "I am called Rigr and I come from far, far away. I am very weary and hungry and would like food and rest. In return I can offer you goodwill and stories."

Ai and Edda seldom saw anyone since their cabin was in such an out-of-the-way place and they had never met anyone who seemed as clever as this stranger. The promise of stories cheered them considerably.

"Make yourself at home, Rigr. We haven't had anyone visit us and tell us stories in such a long time. We would be most glad for your company for it grows lonely here at night," said Edda.

Rigr took them up on their offer and made himself comfortable. He sat on the bench between Ai and Edda nudging them apart in the process. There they sat and waited for dinner to finish cooking. While they waited Rigr told them stirring tales of creation and far off battles between the Æsir and the jotuns. Ai and Edda had never heard stories like the ones they heard from Rigr. Ai's mouth gaped open in wonder at what he heard.

"Your stories are the best we've ever heard. I could almost think they actually happened from the way you tell them," said Edda.

Dinner was almost ready. It consisted of a broth made of boiled calf meat and a very coarse bread made from bran. Edda reached over and tasted the broth. Satisfied it was done she ladled out some broth into an earthenware bowl and handed it to Rigr. She passed a bowl to Ai and prepared one for herself. Then she tore off pieces of the bread and passed them out.

Rigr told more stories during dinner. His supply seemed endless. After dinner while Edda cleaned up Rigr began telling about the noble Einherjar in Valhalla. He continued his stories well into the evening. At one point Ai began to nod off. As his head dropped down Edda punched him in the side and he started awake to the telling of bloody battles that seemed yet to come. Finally Rigr suggested it was time for bed, and met with no objections from the weary couple.

"We haven't an extra bed but you are welcome to sleep with us," invited Ai.

Rigr agreed to the arrangement. The night was proving to be very cold and it would be warmest in bed with others. As he had done when sitting on the bench, Rigr laid down in the middle of the bed forcing Ai and Edda to sleep on either side of him.

He stayed with them for three days and three nights, then bid them both farewell and left content with the thought that so far his mission was going quite well, and was not nearly as tedious as he had thought it would be. In fact, it had been quite pleasurable.

Nine months later Edda surprisingly bore a son whom she and Ai named Thræl, which means thrall. The couple had long since thought she was past childbearing age. But the boy lived and was dark-skinned with coarse black hair. In time he grew to be a very strong man. By the time he reached manhood his back had become twisted and bent from the heavy loads he had had to carry from the time he was old enough to walk. His skin was burnt like leather from having to work out of doors all of the time. His hands were wide and thick and heavily calloused from work. Likewise his feet were much too big, causing him to trip over them occasionally.

One day as he was bearing a bundle of kindling home upon his back he came upon a very ugly woman walking along the road. Her appearance was quite similar to his. She was very dark, had a bent back from hard work, and bowed legs. Her face was pushed in with a very flat nose, receding chin and receding forehead. The smile she gave to Thræl revealed that what teeth she had left were stained brown. Her name was Thir, which means drudge. Upon seeing her, Thræl lost his heart to her. They were soon married and had many sons and daughters.

They named their sons Digraldi, Drottr, Drumbr, Fjosnir, Fulnir, Hosvir, Hrimr, Kefsir, Kleggi, Klurr, Leggjaldi and Lutr. Their names meant fat, lazybones, log, herd, stinker, grey, shouter, whore-master, horsefly, coarse, big legs and bowed.

They named their daughters Ambatt, Arinnefja, Drumba, Eikintjasna, Kumba, Okkvainkalfa, Totrughypja, Tronubeina and Ysja. Their names meant servant, hearthnose, log, oak peg, stupid, fat legs, raggyshirts, cranelegs and harridan.

The life they led was a hard one, and the tasks they performed thankless ones. Their jobs consisted of putting dung on fields, herding swine and goats, cleaning, and other unskilled labors. From their offspring came the thralls and serving folk.

Gaffer and Gammer

Rigr continued on his way in search of another couple. He headed inland and the next evening after leaving Ai and Edda he came to a very modest stone house. He tried the door and finding it unlatched walked in.

Inside were Gaffer and his wife Gammer, both seated on a bench in front of their fireplace, each hard at work. Gaffer was building a loom while Gammer was spinning yarn on her distaff to have ready to use once the loom was constructed. Their clothing was neat and close cut. Gammer wore a simple smock. Gaffer had brown close-cropped curly hair and wore bangs. Gammer also had brown hair which she wore pulled back from her forehead. It was evident from their appearance they were two practical hardworking people. They looked up as Rigr entered.

"Welcome stranger. You look as if you've traveled a long way. If you are a man of peace then stay to dinner with us." As he spoke Gaffer nodded towards the stew was boiling away in a big pot in the fireplace.

Rigr seated himself on the bench between them. "My name is Rigr and I have traveled a great distance to meet you. I thank you for your hospitality. In return I will tell you stories."

Rigr told them stories of great deeds and stirring adventures. In return Gaffer also told some stories since he too had been in a few battles.

As Gaffer was about to embark on the telling of his favorite story of once having seen the Valkyries appear at a battle, he was interrupted by Gammer, who had heard the story many times before, announcing dinner was ready.

"Perhaps we can continue after dinner, then," said Gaffer hopeful of finishing his story for Rigr.

With that they sat down to a rather modest but well-provided for table. The first course served was soup followed by the stew made from veal stock. They drank cup after cup of homemade mead and relaxed. It was a long leisurely dinner during which Gaffer and Gammer came to like Rigr.

"You've brought a lot of pleasure to us this evening. Would you care to spend the night? It's late and there isn't another farmhouse for many rosts," invited Gaffer.

Rigr accepted their offer and for the rest of the evening he helped Gaffer with the loom he was building while Gammer continued with her spinning. When it was time for bed Rigr joined Gaffer and Gammer in their bed, lying down between the two.

Rigr was such pleasant company the couple invited him to stay longer. In all he stayed three nights during which he and Gaffer completed the loom. Then he bid them farewell and went on his way content with the knowledge things were going well in his recruiting of warriors for Valhalla.

A son was born to Gaffer and Gammer nine months later. He was red-haired and rosy cheeked. They named him Karl the Yeoman. He grew to be a man known for his honesty and his good and friendly nature. He grew to be a skilled craftsman and farmer. He could train oxen to pull a plough better than any other farmer in the area. And his crops yielded five-fold what other farmer's crops yielded on the same amount of land.

In time Gaffer and Gammer found a wife for him they thought suitable. She was a comely woman, slim and tall, named Snœr. To show the success she and Karl had had she wore a belt around her waist made of the keys to all of their properties.

The two lived a happy and prosperous life together. They had a large farm, good clothing, and no financial worries. In time they had many sons and daughters.

They named their sons Boandi, Boddi, Brattskeggr, Breidr, Bui, Bundinskeggi, Drengr, Halr, Holdr, Seggr, Smidr and Thegn who rode the horse Blakkr. Their names meant yeoman, farmholder, high beard, the broad, household, trimbeard, strong, man, farmer, goodfellow, craftsman and freeman.

The names of their daughters were Brudr, Feima, Fljod, Ristill, Snot, Sprakki, Sprund, Svanni, Svarri and Vif. Their names meant bride, bashful, good woman, the graceful, good wife, the fair, the vain, the slender, the proud and wife.

From their descendants came the craftsmen and farmers, the average folk.

Fadir and Modir

Rigr continued on his journey in search of one last couple. He walked and walked until the next evening when he came to a high knowe on top of which stood a castle. The entrance to the castle faced south. The castle bars were drawn so Rigr entered.

The front gate opened into an enormous hall down the center of which was a roaring fire. The floors were carpeted with a layer of straw. The furnishings were the finest possible. At the end of the hall was a large hewn and smoothly finished table surrounded by dozens of hand-carved chairs. The table was set as if for a banquet with gold platters and dinnerware, and silver and gold goblets. The castle was filled with every luxury imaginable.

Sitting at one end of the table were the owners of the castle, Fadir and Modir. Their clothes were finely and intricately cut. Their hands were smooth and delicate having never had to toil at anything.

Fadir was making ready for a hunting expedition he was going on the next morning. His elmwood bow was polished and newly strung, and he was now engaged in making arrows and whetting his sword. Modir looked on. The gown she wore was made of the finest silk. It was dark blue with a long flowing train. On the front of the gown she wore beautifully designed brooches which looked as if they might have been made by the dokkalfar. She spoke first and looked Rigr straight in the eye, never once flinching or avoiding his gaze.

"What is your name, stranger?"

"My name is Rigr and I come here to ask if I might stay the night before I continue on my long journey."

"You seem to be a man of peace so please join us. You are in time for dinner. It will be brought on soon. In the meantime tell us about yourself." Fadir spoke as he finished the last arrow he needed for the morning hunt. Noticing Rigr was admiring the bow he passed it to him for closer inspection.

"This is a truly fine bow, fit even for one of the Æsir." Rigr handed the bow back to him.

"Aye, that it is. The yew branch it's made from came from Asgardr itself. I'm going hunting tomorrow. If you are fit with a bow I have an extra one that I'll lend you. You seem to be a strong sort. And I think maybe you've hunted before."

Some servants came and reset the table at Modir's command. The platters, goblets, and dinnerware were removed and a fine lace tablecloth of embroidered linen was laid on the table. Then the table was set again with silver dishes.

First, loaves of pure white bread were brought out. While Fadir, Modir and Rigr began eating these the rest of dinner was brought and set before them. The main course consisted of roast poultry and cured ham. Their goblets were filled with a fine honey-wine mead from the best brewers in the land.

Dinner lasted all evening. As soon as one course was served another was brought on. Rigr felt it would never end, nor did he want it to, it was so sumptuous. But finally it came to an end. The three took their goblets of mead and retired to another hall where they talked until late into the night.

Finally Modir decided to put an end to the evening. "I think it is time for bed if you two are to rise early and get on with your hunting."

Fadir and Modir said good night to Rigr and went to their room to bed. But Rigr had other ideas. Without invitation he followed behind them and entered their room with them where he laid down between the two surprised hosts.

The next morning he and Fadir went hunting. And in the course of the morning Heimdallr killed more beast and fowl than Fadir had the previous year. They carried back what they could with them, but Fadir had to send his servants out to make many trips to bring back the day's kill. The servants spent many days preparing and preserving the meat for the coming winter. There was enough to feed the entire castle through this winter and well into the next winter.

Rigr stayed with Fadir and Modir for two more days, enjoying all the luxuries of the castle. He went hunting, played games, and had long talks with Fadir and Modir. After dinner each evening he slept with them. At the end of three days he took his leave.

Rigr returned to Asgardr and again resumed his identity as Heimdallr the Guardian of Bifrost, content he had fulfilled his father's expectations.

Nine months later Fadir and Modir had a son whom they called Jarl the Earl.

Soon after Jarl's birth Fadir went to see his son. Jarl was laying in his crib swaddled in the finest silk. He had a light complexion and a full head of hair which was as blond as the sun. But the most striking thing Fadir noticed about his son were his blue eyes. They were sharp and piercing and seemed to look beyond and into whatever met their gaze. Fadir tried holding a stare with Jarl but couldn't because of the intensity of his son's gaze and had eventually to avert his eyes. Jarl's effect on people was similar to a snake's mesmerizing effect on a bird.

Jarl's youth was spent learning the skills of a warrior; the use of a bow, how to hurl a javelin, fencing, etc. He also became an excellent horseman. Indeed everything he attempted he mastered. And he grew strong and straight.

Occasionally Heimdallr glanced into Midgardr and watched Jarl to check on his progress, waiting for the moment when Jarl would be old enough to accept his birthright. When that moment came Heimdallr asked leave of Odin to visit Midgardr once again, this time to see his son. His request was granted.

He came upon Jarl in a field practicing his warrior skills. Standing back he stood watching Jarl first wield his sword, hewing trees in two with one blow. Then he watched him throw his spear with accuracy and length. He was pleased with his son and walked up to him and gave him his birthright.

"Jarl the Earl, I've been watching you for a long time and I'm very proud of you and the skills you've developed. I have a gift for you." Heimdallr stared directly into Jarl's eyes.

Jarl was taken aback by the stranger who was the first person who had ever been able to meet and hold his gaze. "I could almost take you for one of the Æsir, such is your bearing. Who are you?"

"I am a warrior. I am also your true father. I've come to give you my name and your birthright. From now on you will be known as Rigr, and all the lands of Udal are yours to pass on to your sons and daughters, and they to their sons and daughters. I am indeed one of the Æsir, and you by right are one of them too. Be proud of your heritage and

carry it with you into battle. Now I'll teach you more warrior skills and how to read runes so you'll have great wisdom as well as strength."

Heimdallr turned and walked away. Rigr followed so that he might learn. They went into the dark foreboding Myrkvyrdr Forest where Heimdallr taught Rigr warrior skills, runes, and magic songs. After his lessons they returned to Rigr's practice field. Heimdallr took his leave and left behind a great and noble warrior to help guard Midgardr.

Rigr continued to practice his warrior skills and when he felt he was ready he gathered together a great army and claimed the lands Heimdallr had given him. He fought against men of evil and those who had laid false claim to his birthright. And he prevailed.

The new ruler built eighteen great halls throughout his lands so he would have places to stay as he journeyed around keeping the peace which reigned there. He was a wise and generous ruler who often gave away gold and silver, particularly to brave warriors. He tried to encourage the men of his lands to become warriors and helped them in whatever ways he could.

As he grew older Rigr began to yearn for a wife. On one of his journeys he had seen a fair lady. He enquired and found out she was Erna, daughter of the nobleman Hersir. Rigr sent a messenger to Hersir asking for Erna's hand in marriage. Hersir was so honored he immediately consented and sent Erna and her maidservant along with a generous dowry back to Rigr with the messenger.

They were married and had a happy life together. They had many sons.

Their sons were named Adal who rode the horse Slongvir, Arfi, Barr, Barn, Jod, Kon, Kundr, Mogr, Nidr, Nidjungr, Sonr and Sveinn. Their names meant offspring, heir, son, child, youth, king, kinsman, sonny, descendent, chip-off-the-old-block, son and boy.

All of their sons were taught warrior skills from the moment they could stand. Not only were they taught how to wield a bow but also how to plan a battle, for that is just as important.

Their eldest son was Barr. After reaching manhood he gathered together an army of the best warriors in the land and led them into battle and conquered new lands. He was proclaimed the first king of Denmark.

Their youngest son, Kon, took after his grandfather, Heimdallr, more than any of the others. He studied and learned the speech of birds and how to sing magic songs and read runes. He had the strength of eight men and became a great warrior.

One day as Kon was riding through the forest listening to the wisdom of birds a crow overhead spoke to him, "Why seek out our meager knowledge in the forest. You waste your time. It would be better spent seeking battle and conquest to increase your kingdom. Talking to birds will not do that. Talk to birds and you will conquer nests. Talk to warriors and you will conquer kingdoms." Kon set his jaw in silence as the bird continued. He knew the bird spoke the truth. "There are those whose dwellings and kingdoms are greater, whose conquests thought more of, whose treasures are filled with more gold, and whose prowess in their adventuring on ships grander than yours."

Sufficiently taunted, Kon yelled out, "Who are they?"

The bird chanted over and over, "Dan and Danp, Dan and Danp, Dan and Danp."

Kon raised an army and went immediately out on conquest. He won great honor and renown throughout many lands and added greatly to his kingdom. When his father, Rigr, died he took the name of Rigr and passed it along to the bravest of his sons. And honor and great deeds forever came to the son who bore the name Rigr.

Odin looked down from his throne Hlidskjalf and was well-pleased with the three orders of mankind. Now there were warriors being born to fight at the last great battle.

Chapter 3

The War Between the Æsir and the Vanir

The Æsir settled in Asaheimr in the chief city of Asgardr after the creation of the other worlds. One day Odin was sitting on his throne Hlidskjalf in his hall Vlaskjalf searching the other Worlds of the Tree for evil and checking on the handiwork of the Æsir. Something in the distance caught his eye, but he couldn't quite make it out. As he stared at it, trying to make it clearer, his son Heimdallr rushed into the throneroom and knelt before his father and spoke.

The Vanir

"I'm sorry to disturb you, father, but while at my station on Bifrost I saw something in the distance. I believe there are more gods, but somehow different from us." Heimdallr spoke rapidly. When he paused to catch his breath, Odin spoke.

"I've been aware of something in the distance which has been troubling me, but I've been unable to make it out. Now as I look, I can see you're right. I know now these other gods are the Vanir and their land in the distance is called Vanaheimr, also known as Uhland or Upphiminn, high atop the Yggdrasyll. They are bright and shining and were born in the pure upper air. They don't believe in combat, in war, or the glories of battle. They deal rather in witchcraft and wizardry and use these skills to fight their battles. They have a magic called vigspa which gives them foreknowledge of the events of a battle, and through that magically gained information they have been able to conquer most of their enemies. This makes them extremely dangerous to us. We must seek out whether or not they intend to be our friends or enemies. Right now they seem at peace. They seem more interested in their harvest than in us. Their ruler, Njordr, is very powerful. He controls the movement of the winds and seas. He has two newborn children, a boy and a girl, the result of his unnatural relations with Nerthus, his sister. Let's hope his twin offspring, Freyr and Freyja, are not monsters. I want you to go to them as my emissary and seek out their thoughts. To show our friendly intentions tell Njordr we are giving his son Freyr the land of Alfheimr as a tooth gift since he has just cut his first tooth. Maybe association with the delightful ljosalfar will assure Freyr's goodwill as he grows up. And here are some precious

golden bracelets, necklaces and jewels for his daughter, Freyja." With that Odin returned his gaze to other worlds and Heimdallr left in silence to undertake his journey.

Upon his return Heimdallr found his father at supper with the warriors in Valhalla. He sat with his father and during dinner they discussed the intentions of the Vanir.

"They've told me they mean us no harm, and if we keep to our ways they will keep to theirs, therefore no trouble should come about between us." Heimdallr paused as a Valkyrie filled his drinking cup.

"And what of Njordr? What is he like?" asked Odin.

"He's extremely handsome and glistening," began Heimdallr. "He fairly shines, clad in his sea green tunic. He wears a crown of shells entwined with seaweed upon his head, for his interest is the sea. But on occasion he can be seen with a hat of eagle or heron plumes. His hall is near the sea so he can bless the ships arriving and leaving at the port. Whereas you are fond of wolves and ravens, Njordr is quite different. The sea sponge receives his special favor and is sometimes known as Njordr's glove." Heimdallr paused as Odin fed his two wolves from his plate, then continued, "His sister, as you know, is Nerthus. She too is of the sea. Their two children are growing up well and strong. They don't appear to be monsters. They are both golden-haired with blue eyes and are quite beautiful." At the mention of this looks of disgust came over many sitting nearby, for the practice of brother/sister marriages was looked upon with disfavor by the Æsir and the warriors in Valhalla.

All evening the conversation in Valhalla centered on the Vanir and whether or not the noble Einherjar would be tested in brave combat against them. After dinner they fought and practiced to hone their warrior skills even sharper.

As time passed Heimdallr made many visits to Vanaheimr, becoming quite popular there. He dutifully reported the doings of the Vanir to Odin. "They still show no animosity towards us. Freyr and Freyja are growing up to be quite beautiful and well disposed towards the Æsir, as well as each other. They both have a talent and interest in the harvest and seem unconcerned with noble, warlike deeds."

Odin ignored Heimdallr's hints about the relations Freyr and Freyja might be having with each other or gossip which had recently been making the rounds in Valhalla about the two Vanir and some of the Æsir. He didn't reveal to his son he had also met Freyr and Freyja and had become good friends with both of them.

Freyja, who was sometimes known as Abundantia, had introduced him to a disreputable magic called seidr, which could only be practiced by a woman. Odin, using his shape-changing abilities, would meet with Freyja and change his shape to that of a woman so he could receive further instructions in the black art. If this were known Odin would be in great disfavor with the other Æsir. Yet Odin still risked it, for the knowledge and power he learned might be useful at the last battle. Over time his relationship with Freyja intensified and they had become lovers.

Angroboda

Soon after Heimdallr's most recent visit to the Vanir, Angroboda, a witch from Jotunheimr, came in disguise to Vanaheimr. She dwelt in the Myrkvydr Forest and was the daughter of the hrymthursar Hrimnir. Her uncle, Hrimnir's brother, was Egther, which means sword guardian. Egther had charge of several remarkable herds and also owned a powerful and

cherished sword of the jotuns. Her brother was Hrossthjof, whose name meant horse thief. In Vanaheimr she became friends with Freyja, but only for a purpose. For next to the Æsir, the jotuns hated the Vanir most.

Their friendship deepened, or so Freyja was led to believe, until she had complete trust in Angroboda. So it was without fear she followed Angroboda on a trip to Jotunheimr, where normally she would be loathe to go. Once in Jotunheimr Angroboda threw off the guise of friendship and became the witch she really was. Freyja was caught, trapped in the hands of the jotuns.

Freyja was goddess of fertility and fecundity. After her departure from Vanaheimr everything began to diminish. This was true not only in Vanaheimr, but also in Asgardr and Midgardr where crops refused to grow and animals, particularly swine, would not fatten up and their young were born dead, or if they lived they were grossly deformed and soon died. From high atop a mountain in Jotunheimr Freyja saw this and agreed to do anything for the jotuns if only they would let her leave. The jotuns, seizing on this opportunity, agreed to release her if she would promise to bring about a war between the Æsir and Vanir. Their strategy was this. While the evenly matched Æsir and Vanir would succeed only in destroying each other the jotuns would emerge as the real victor without having lifted so much as a spear. Their philosophy was if you can make two enemies fight and destroy each other, then you will be the winner and they will both be losers. Although Freyja harbored no ill will towards the Æsir she wanted her freedom and agreed for she felt it was the Æsir who would be vanquished and she would be free to return home. Perhaps Odin would recognize her and realize she was being used by the jotuns?

Gullveig

With Angroboda's help Freyja journeyed to Asgardr disguised as the witch Gullveig. Angroboda's sister and another daughter of the hrymthursar Hrimnir. Gullveig was goddess of gold and was being sent to corrupt the Æsir with greed and lust for this precious metal. No one recognized her when she arrived in Asgardr. She was fair to look upon; her light yellow hair, and indeed her whole body, shone temptingly like gold. Every one of the Æsir welcomed her as one of the Vanir. She accomplished what she set out to do in short order. Gold was soon being hoarded. Golden ornaments were stolen away and hidden in hastily constructed vaults, or melted down to make ringmoney which could be traded for things that formerly had been freely given. Halls in Asgardr which had been built with gold for its beauty were raped in the night for their treasure. Value was weighed in carats and greed prevailed.

Odin observing all this evil called a special Thing in Harr, one of his halls. Gullveig was brought to the meeting. Odin spoke, "We welcomed you here with kindness and you have repaid us by sowing seeds of discontent. What is your defense?"

She looked Odin in the eye, hoping he would see through the disguise and realize she was not sincere in her words or deeds. "I've brought nothing here that did not already exist. You've used gold throughout Asgardr to show the glories of the Æsir. If not for vanity, then you would have used wood to construct your halls. It gives the same shelter, protects from winds and storms just as well."

As she began speaking of everyone's greed, Odin cut her off. "I believe we understand well enough what you have done. You have presented no defense and there can be no excuse for what you have done." Odin looked around to confirm the rest of the Æsir were nodding in agreement, and continued, "I judge your actions to have been evil and against what the Æsir stand for. You shall be punished." Upon Odin's command she was spitted over the long fire which stretched the length of the hall. But she did not die. The Æsir found out what many know, evil is hard to destroy.

Instead Angroboda was reborn and escaped to Midgardr where she practiced her evil ways and taught the lust for gold to the inhabitants there. Cheating and murders occurred amongst those of Midgardr in whom this evil desire had been awakened.

Heidr

Soon after Freyja's/Gullveig's departure for Midgardr, Angroboda journeyed to Asgardr disguised as Heidr. Her attempts to renew the passion for gold first brought on by Gullveig failed. She also was taken to the hall, Harr where she was also judged, spitted and burned. Nor was she killed on the first try. She was reborn as her true self, Angroboda, and recognized as a jotun, whereupon she was immediately seized and burnt again. This time Loki rushed at the flames and searched through them looking for her heart. He found its half-burnt remnants and swallowed the meagre meal. Thus the seed of her evil nature was planted in him. Some time later Loki departed Asgardr for a cave in the Myrkvyrdr Forest where he gave birth to three children. They were in order of birth Fenriswulf, a grey wolf; Midgardrsormr (also known by the jotuns as Jormungandr), a serpent; and Hela who was half dead and half alive. Who could possibly love such a monstrous brood? Loki was pleased.

The War

But despite the spitting and burning of Freya/Gullveig/Angroboda/Heidr, the Æsir and Vanir still were not at war. A few jotuns took matters into their own hands and journeyed to Vanaheimr carrying the news of Freyja's (in all her forms) burning to the Vanir. "Noble Freyr we bring you this news of your sister's death and offer to help you seek vengeance, for the jotuns are upset by it also. We've always considered Freyja and all the Vanir as our friends and any injustice to the Vanir is an injustice to the Jotuns."

Freyr looked upon the jotuns with suspicion. They rarely ever came to Vanaheimr without trouble following. But there was nothing he could do about the matter. Freyja seemed to have disappeared, and had not been heard from for awhile. The last anyone could remember she had mentioned she was going to Asgardr for a visit. Convinced of her death, Freyr was honorbound to avenge it. With the jotuns standing right there he had to take immediate action so as to show no weakness before them lest they entertain thoughts of conquering Vanaheimr.

Freyr went to the center of Vanaheimr and called out, "Fellow warriors, and all my relations both near and far, I have had news of the murder of my sister and your kinswoman Freyja by the gods of the Æsir. We've sought to live in friendship and peace with them, and have kept our part of the truce. But now with this action by them we can no longer honor that truce. I ask that all of you accompany me in an assault on Asgardr.

The call to action was swift, and within the remaining hours of sunlight the whole of the Vanir were journeying to Asgardr prepared for battle. Odin had watched the jotuns visit to Vanaheimr and now looked with interest as the jotuns at the edge of Jotunheimr parted company with the Vanir.

The Jotuns informed Freyr they were going to head towards the East and then quickly circle around Asgardr and attack from the other side. Freyr was not a warrior and certainly lacked training in battle strategy. So, he really couldn't disagree with their plan. And, even if he disagreed with the Jotuns, there was nothing he could do. So, he watched as the jotuns turned towards the east. And that's the last he saw of them. They did not circle around, they did not attack Asgardr from the other side. They headed back to Jotunheimr to watch safely from atop mountains that offered them a clear view of Asgardr. Watched as their two enemies fought each other. They were of one thought: My enemy who fights my enemy fights for me. The Æsir would not be the last tricked into fighting another's war.

Freyr led the Vanir on to Asgardr. Odin called the Æsir to battle.

The next morning they met on a field of battle. On one side of the field Odin sat atop his horse with the warriors of Asgardr behind him. Freyr with his force behind him sat astride his horse opposite the Æsir. He and Odin rode to the center of the field to discuss the payment of weregild for the death of Freyja, and perhaps avoid bloodshed in an honorable manner. Freyr mentioned a suitable sum.

Odin responded sarcastically, "I assume you would like that in gold?"

Freyr did not recognize the sarcasm and responded, "Of course, gold would be fine."

Odin laughed and refused payment, "The only weregild the Vanir will receive from the Æsir will be the iron from the tips of our spears and the edges of our swords, and the wood from the shafts of our arrows." The discussion was brought to an abrupt halt when Odin raised his sword Notung in one hand, and flung his spear towards the Vanir with the other. The battle had begun.

The Vanir fought with vigspa, their battle magic; the Æsir with brute force. Mountains and icebergs were used as missiles – the Æsir hurling them with sheer physical strength, the Vanir projected them with magic. At one point Njordr was able to burst Asgardr's wooden walls with his battleax and victory seemed certain for the Vanir. But the Æsir were able to force their enemies back almost to Vanaheimr. The balance of the battle shifted back and forth from Æsir to Vanir so frequently it was hard to tell which side was winning. So it came about both groups of gods had won and lost the same number of battles, but neither was close to winning the war. And while the Æsir and Vanir, overcome with exhaustion, rested, Njordr and Odin met to talk things over since Freyr wished to have no further dealings with Odin. In the distance they could see the jotuns watching and waiting with more than just a little interest.

Njordr spoke first, "Odin, our methods may be different but we are all gods. Gods who are destroying each other, while there in the distance stand the jotuns, our true enemies, ready to pick up the spoils."

Odin nodded in agreement, "What you say is true. The jotuns will be the only winners of our battles, for it is only a matter of time before the Vanir and Æsir succeed in destroying each other. I think we should hold a Thing and discuss our differences."

So a Thing was convened with both Vanir and Æsir in attendance. Prior to the Thing Odin had sent his ravens, Huginn and Munnin, out in search of Freyja, whom they found on Midgardr. She was brought back to Asgardr, where the story of how she had been used by the jotuns was learned.

The Thing devolved into a confused shouting. A loud clatter of voices arose from the Vanir. They were answered by equally vociferous voices from the Æsir. The clang and clatter went on in circular arguments that seemed impossible to settle. At times the battle was almost renewed.

"The first matter to be discussed is the payment of weregild for the death of Freyja."

"But she is no longer dead, so we have no obligation to pay."

"That makes no difference. You did kill her at one point."

"Who is to assume the cost for all the damage done to the Æsir?"

"Ha, your damage was nothing compared with what we suffered."

"Our walls have been shattered. You call that nothing?"

"What about the lost lives of our fellow warriors?"

"Warriors? How can farmers of suspicious personal habits be warriors?"

And it went throughout the rest of the day, the night, and the next day.

Tempers flared as each side traded accusations or claimed the greater losses and suffering. If the meeting had been held other than on sacred ground the two groups might have come to blows again.

Finally, Forseti, known for his efforts at mediation and problem-solving stepped forward to speak. Of all the Æsir, the Vanir trusted him to be fair. All quieted to listen as he spoke.

"It has not yet been a day since each side, deadlocked in battle, was shouting that because they had inflicted the greater damage to the other, victory should be awarded to them. Now each bemoans losses which far outweigh the losses suffered by the other side. From listening to the quarreling, I believe both sides' losses are fairly equal. As for those casualties suffered in battle, let's bring them back to life so there can be no further complaint about the matter. This leaves us with the final problem of a lasting peace. Our battles are too recent for us not to still distrust one another. Therefore, I propose we exchange hostages. And if either side breaks the peace then the lives of those hostages will be forfeited."

This seemed fair and everyone immediately agreed to the terms.

Then there was great discussion about whom was to be exchanged. The Vanir wanted Thor so he could help protect them from the jotuns. But the Æsir were reluctant to give up their own chief defense against the jotuns.

Finally, it was agreed Hœnir, the aurkonungr or marsh king, and Mimir would be sent to the Vanir in exchange for Njordr and his two children, Freyr and Freyja. Freyr also took with him his two servants, Byggvir, his valet, and Beyla, his maidservant.

Kvasir

With all of their differences settled and peace established, the Thing came to an end. But before leaving, they set up a gold communal cauldron in the middle of them and all of the

Vanir and Æsir spat into it as they left. This peace token was called Hraki. The Æsir took Hraki and fashioned the spittle into the form of a man whom they named Kvasir.

Kvasir became the living symbol of the truce between the Æsir and the Vanir. Because Kvasir was born full grown he lacked childhood memories. He had no reminiscences of toys or parties, no fond recollections of pretend battles with other children. And, more importantly, no childhood friends.

So he set out to visit the Worlds of the Tree making friends along the way. He possessed the childish wonder of discovering new things, and walked throughout the Worlds of the Tree, where he was always welcomed seeking the stories of others' childhoods. He was the first poet and often spoke in poetry.

Njordr, Freyr, and Freya in Asgardr

Njordr, Freyr and Freyja were welcomed into Asgardr and given the duties of sacrificial priestess and priest of the Æsir and were known as the blotgodar. Great halls were built for them and they were treated not as hostages, but as friends. Many of the Æsir were particularly glad for Freyja's return.

Njordr lived in his hall, Noatun, near the sea where he stilled the mighty tempests of Ægir with his calming hand.

Freyr lived in solitude in Uppsala. His palace, covered with precious gems, stood off by itself. A rose tree forest shaded it so that it was set in darkness. Freyr often stood and look out over the lake that bordered his property, staring at the white swans swimming in it, thinking about his loneliness and hoping to someday meet someone who would end it.

Freyja's domain was Folkvangar, and her palace was called Sessrumnir. After moving to Asgardr she became involved with the Valkyries and frequently lead them to battle and was known as Valfreyja when she did so.

Mimir and Hœnir in Vanaheimr

But things went differently in Vanaheimr. At first the Vanir looked favorably upon their two hostages. Mimir, Odin's uncle, was a personage of great wisdom and renown. Hœnir was swift, long-legged, extremely handsome and noble in bearing. Because of this he replaced Njordr as chief of the Vanir. Although not overly intelligent, Hœnir enjoyed the wise council of Mimir who gave him sound advice on all occasions. Eventually Hœnir became so dependent on Mimir's council he could not reach a decision unless Mimir was standing at his shoulder whispering what to do in his ear.

Hœnir's pretense to knowledge could not go on forever.

One day Mimir was gone when a dispute arose. It was so serious it could not be put off until Mimir's return, as Hœnir wanted. A Thing was held and Hœnir had to attend and give council. Fearing he would give out disastrous advice, all he would say was, "Let the others decide." Hœnir used this to dodge all question during the first part of the Thing pointing out others who had greater expertise in the area in question. Pressed for further decisions throughout the meeting he would only utter the same phrase, "Let the others decide."

The Vanir began to feel the Æsir had deceived them in the exchange of hostages. Some of the Vanir laid in wait and when Mimir returned he was set upon and his head

chopped off. Mimir's head was tucked under Hœnir's arm, and he was then sent back to Asgardr as a present for Odin.

Odin received the head of his friend and uncle with sadness and decided the knowledge Mimir possessed could not be allowed to die. He immediately set about to preserve the head.

In seclusion, in the form of a woman, he performed seidr on the head. She first covered it with herbs and other preservatives to halt and reverse the decay. Next she chanted mystical incantations and carved runes of life on it. Soon the head gained the power of speech.

After he was once again changed from a woman to his old form, Odin carried the head back to the well of Mimir near the Yggdrasyll and balanced it on the stone lip of the well, away from the wind. Odin would be able to ask it for advice when advice was needed, for Mimir had become even wiser from learning the wisdom of the dead.

Even though the Æsir's hostages had been returned and accepted back, by rights Njordr, Freyr, and Freyja could return to Vanaheimr. But the three decided to remain in Asgardr, although their travel frequently took them back to their homeland.

So, the War Between the Æsir and Vanir was over. But what of the damage to Asgardr from the battles? Gaping holes in the battlements remained.

Chapter 4

The Rebuilding of Asgardr's Walls

Even though Heimdallr stood guard on Bifrost and Odin watched from Hlidskjalf, the Æsir still felt insecure. Njordr had easily burst their walls with his battle-ax during the late war. And the walls, still scattered in rubble around Asgardr, reminded the Æsir the city was still vulnerable to attack from the jotuns.

Odin called for a Thing at Urdarbrunnr Well. All the Æsir were present excepting Heimdallr who was standing watch on the bridge, and Thor who was away in the east slaying jotuns.

As ideas were being discussed, Heimdallr arrived to introduce a stranger who had arrived in Asgardr. "Odin, there is someone who wishes to see you. He says he can build a wall for us so strong the strength of all the jotuns and hill trolls combined could not burst it."

Impatiently waiting behind Heimdallr was a large bearded man seated atop a white stallion. Æsir, Vanir, jotun? They knew not. His deep-set eyes glinted out from under shaggy brows. His stern face revealed little. "I'm a master mason and can build you the most sturdy wall in all the Worlds of the Tree.

After some consultation the Æsir agreed to let him try if suitable payment conditions could be agreed on. Hœnir spoke, "And if we contract for your services what is the wage you'll extract from us for this mighty wall?"

The mason replied, "It'll be quite cheap, considering what you are getting in return. I'll build your wall in eighteen months, a time equal to three winters. My price is the hand of Freyja, who has only recently come here to live, so she'll not be missed that much. Also, I would like the sun and moon thrown in."

The Æsir were dumfounded at his request. Heimdallr spoke for them all when he told the mason what he thought of the bargain, "If that's cheap, as you say, then what would you want to build us an expensive wall? But come with me while the rest of the Æsir discuss the matter." Heimdallr took the mason on a tour of the old wall. As the mason knelt down and picked at the rubble he could hear the Æsir shouting in the distance. He

just smiled. He knew they needed a wall, and he was the only one offering to build one for them.

Back at the Thing, Loki spoke first. "We should insist he build the wall in one winter with no one to help him. And it must be completed by the first day of summer. If as little as a stone of the wall remains incomplete we will not be required to pay. There's no way he could possibly comply, and we'll have a wall for free, or at least most of a wall, and still have Freyja, the sun, and the moon. We'll be able to finish constructing what he leaves undone ourselves."

Though the Æsir were always distrustful of Loki, his proposal seemed to make sense. Especially the part about cheating the mason out of his payment. They called the mason back to the Thing.

Again Hœnir spoke, "We'll agree to your wage request providing you agree to our terms. You must build the wall without help during the course of only one winter. And upon the first day of summer if the job is unfinished then you will forfeit all of your wages and depart in peace."

The mason replied, "I'll agree to one winter if I can have the assistance of just my horse, Svadilfari, or three winters if I have to do it all on my own."

The Æsir discussed his counteroffer and pretty much decided against it. It was too risky. Svadilfari was huge and looked like he could do the work of a hundred jotuns.

Then Loki sided with the mason. "After all, it's not likely he'll finish the task even if he does use his horse. And we'll still come out ahead, with less of the wall to complete ourselves, Does anyone here really think he can build a wall in one winter, even with Svadilvari's help?" Loki knew he had won when he saw all the Æsir shaking their heads no. The greed of wanting a wall for nothing won the argument. The mason was awarded the contract.

As it happened the next day was the first day of winter. The mason started to work immediately at midnight. His plan was to haul rock by night and build the wall by day. The base of the wall was built on lerbrimr, which meant Ymir's limbs. The wall itself was called gastrofnir.

While the mason toiled away at building the wall the Æsir hired Solblindi, the son of Valgrindr and Thrymgjoll, to fashion a strong gate to insert in the wall. Solblindi assured the Æsir the gate was strong, "I guarantee my gate will withstand the battering of even the most obstinate jotun pounding into it with his head over and over. His head will crack long before my gate bursts open."

The gate was set in the wall in such a manner that its movements were regulated by chains which raised and lowered it to allow or deny passage across into Asgardr. Anyone ignorant of the specific workings of the chains trying to gain entry by prying open the gate would have quite a surprise in store for them. With clang and clangor the gate would fall on them, crushing them flat in the process. The gate also had a magical lock which, when tampered with, could cause the gate itself to become links of chain that would trap and hold any who tried to unlawfully enter Asgardr.

The mason was working very quickly and the wall was going up more rapidly than the Æsir had thought could be done. And a lot of this had to do with his horse, Svadilfari.

The Æsir watched in amazement at the mountainous rocks Svadilfari was able to drag back to Asgardr. And astonishment mixed with fear came over them when they saw

Svadilfari was indeed a clever steed. Once he dragged a rock to Asgardr he could also mortar it into place in the wall. It had never even occurred to the Æsir that Svadilfari would be able to actually help construct the wall. Even at night while the mason slept the horse kept working on fortifying the wall.

By the end of the first morning both mason and horse had squared many stones and placed them in position. By the end of the first day they had finished laying the entire wall's foundation, circling all of Asgardr.

Heimdallr had a perfect view from Bifrost, and muttered to himself, "They've done all that in just one day. I fear Freya's going to have a hard time of it."

The mason and Svadilfari worked unceasingly throughout the winter. Three days before summer the Æsir hurriedly held another Thing to discuss the alarm they felt at the progress the mason had made.

Lodurr gave a report to the assembled, "The two have worked harder and accomplished more than we ever imagined. The job is finished right up to the fort gate. The only work remaining for the mason and Svadilfari is to set a giant slab above the gateway. Something that might take just a morning to do."

Hermodr put their concerns concisely, "So they have half a day's work left, and three days in which to do it. Freya, the son, and moon, may be with us only a few days more."

Hermodr asked, "Who got us into this mess?"

Loki spoke so no one could remind the others he had pushed the mason and Svadilfari on them, "Rather than dwell on the past let's spend our time thinking what we should do. In fact, should we even pay him at all? Obviously, he mislead us into thinking he couldn't do the job as fast as he's doing it."

Hermodr responded, "How did he mislead us? He told us he could do the job? We didn't think so and hoped he wouldn't be able to do it. He's kept to the contract. He's never lied to us."

Loki responded, "But why should we be obligated to an unfair contract? We based it on the fact no one would be able to fulfill it. Now, he has used extraordinary means to fulfill it. I say, break the contract and pay him for his time and trouble and be off with him."

Gradually the Æsir come to feel wronged by the mason and Svadilfari's hard work and believe they had been tricked. But, they felt they should be fair. Most agreed they should ignore the original conditions of his employment, and should give the Mason a decent amount for his work.

Hermodr persisted though in bringing up arguments against their breaking the contract. But the others were not firmly for a forced renegotiation and pointed out the obvious. Lodurr put it quite succinctly, "What can he do if we refuse to pay him according to the contract? Even with Svadilfari he couldn't hope to fight all the Æsir and win?" Everyone agreed and the matter seemed to be all settled except for a vote.

Forseti had been sitting, listening, to the Æsir propose dishonor after dishonor. Finally, he could take no more of it and jumped up and spoke, "I can't believe what I've been hearing. We are honorbound to this commitment. We can't just break our oaths because someone is doing what they said they would do. We are the Æsir. We stand for honor and justice. Yet so many of you blithely propose we break a contract, as if the breaking of a contract were an every day acceptable way to do business. If we can't honor our contracts

how can we expect others to honor theirs? Whatever we do, it will set an example for those in Midgardr. Do we want our example to be lies and deceit? Or, do we want our example to be honor and truth?

Forseti's words seemed to bring everyone back to their senses. Well, almost everyone. Loki had quietly moved back around the side of a building deciding it would be better if the Æsir forgot he had been the one who suggested the mason, had convinced them to let him use Svadilfari, and now was urging them to become oathbreakers.

Forsetti was final in his admonition, "The mason entered into the contract in good faith. If he completes the contract on time, we must pay him in good faith. Anything else would bring dishonor to the Æsir."

Embarrassed they had even thought to break the contract the Æsir started bickering, trying to affix blame for the predicament in which they found themselves. If they couldn't break the contract, they'd affix blame to someone for their thinking about breaking it. Gradually, their argument settled down until one name only could be heard upon their lips – Loki.

Hermodr looked around, but couldn't find Loki. "Where is Loki? He was just here. Someone bring Loki here."

Lodurr saw Loki standing in the shadows and sent a servant over to bring Loki down front and center before the Æsir.

Hermodr accused him, "You advised us to accept the terms set forth by the mason. So, now it falls to you to get us out of this mess, but with honor."

The Æsir turned on Loki and threatened him with death unless he was able to find some solution to their predicament.

Thor, recently returned from the east, spoke, "If I had been at that first Thing I would not have made such a stupid deal."

It was a measure of how far the Æsir had sunk if Thor was speaking intelligently. He was known more for his brawn than brain.

Instead of trying to defend himself Loki started taunting the others. "You didn't have to take my advice. After all it is your own greed that has gotten you into this mess. You thought you could have the wall for free. Now you might loose Freyja, the sun, and the moon. You have only yourselves to blame."

But because of the threats being aimed at him and his proposed banishment from Asgardr Loki agreed to come up with a trick to cause the mason to default on the contract. As Loki was leaving the Thing the words of Forseti followed him, "Default the contract without causing the Æsir to loose honor."

Being by nature mischievous and sneaky, planning a ruse was easy for Loki. With barely any thought he knew what he was going to do. And it would be fun for him, too.

Back at the fort gate the mason was in high spirits. Placing the slab on the fort gate with a few small boulders for fillers would be a simple matter for he and Svadilvari. So, he might as well get to it.

He and Svadilfari walked to the quarry. Soon all the necessary material was loaded onto the cart and they headed back towards the wall. But before they had gotten far a white mare trotted into view. She whinnied and pranced around the stallion tossing her head and flicking her tail back and forth invitingly. The effect was immediate on Svadilfari. He roared up, kicking over his traces, overturning the cart at the same time. In a flash he was off chasing after the mare.

The mason ran after his horse all night, but couldn't catch him. When dawn came he decided to try to complete the work himself. Carrying the large slab was out of the question, but he could always fill in the last of the wall with lots of boulders. So he toiled all day and into the evening. But without Svadilfari he was unable to move enough boulders to complete the work.

He went to the Thing to meet with the Æsir and discuss payment. But the Æsir held firm. No payment.

Hermodr insisted on the Æsir's position, "You didn't complete the contract, so, we are under no obligation to pay you. If you had completed the contract you'd expect us to fulfil our part wouldn't you?"

The mason didn't know about the discussion the Æsir had had about breaking the contract, or he would have had a better argument. As it was, his only resort was brute force. He filled with fury and his size doubled before the Æsir's astonished eyes. Yet he still kept growing. Then he took on his true form and was recognized as a brother of the bergrisar, rock jotun, Thjassi. Throughout the evening and dark hours of the morning his size increased with his rage. The Æsir looked on as he stood atop the wall threatening to tear it down as well as threatening to destroy Asgardr and all those inside. He was so angry he neglected to notice the rising sun, the one thing his true form as a bergrisar could not stand. Abruptly his thunderous threats stopped. With his arms raised in anger he turned to stone, tipped forward and fell from the wall down an embankment into Midgardr where he broke into a mass of mountain ranges, pebbles and gravel.

The problem was solved. The Æsir completed the wall and felt very safe. None of the Æsir noticed that Loki was nowhere to be seen.

Loki was still transformed. He, now a she, was still a white mare. And she was pregnant by Svadilfari, who was no where to be seen. Svadilfari had soon run off after his romp with the white mare and the mason's death. And learning of the white mare's pregnancy added to his speed of departure.

Eventually, pregnancies come to term, even unusual ones. Loki gave birth to an eight-legged foal he named Sleipnir. Eight legs give a lot of extra speed, so Sleipnir was the fastest horse of all and had magical runes of wisdom carved on his teeth. In an effort to return to the Æsir's good graces Loki gave the steed to Odin. Odin looked at Sleipnir's long body standing on his eight legs, and he reminded Odin of a coffin born by a bearer at each corner. This was the perfect steed for a seeker of the dead like Odin. Odin was pleased and signalled his agreement that Loki was forgiven.

Once again Loki was accepted amongst the Æsir. Temporarily, all was forgiven, but not forgotten.

Chapter 5

The Death of Kvasir

It was now seven years since the Great War between the Æsir and Vanir, and during that time Kvasir, the man formed from the spittle of the gods, continued to grow in knowledge. In fact he was so wise there wasn't a question he couldn't answer. He had grown to be a kind and gentle man who suspected evil of no one and spent his time traveling throughout all the Worlds of the Tree trying to help everyone. And those who offered him hospitality and kindness were greatly rewarded because he would impart to them wisdom and knowledge.

Fjalarr and Galarr

On one journey Kvasir came to the house of two dvergues named Fjalarr and Galarr. Thinking good of everyone, Kvasir didn't realize they were craven, envious, wicked little men. When they saw Kvasir approaching in all his noble bearing, they hated him instantly.

Fjalarr turned and whispered to Galarr, "Let's kill him. Then see if his wisdom will do him any good." Galarr hastily agreed, for there was nothing he liked better than a little mischief.

As Kvasir came towards them they beckoned for him to enter their place. Fjalarr spoke first, "Although we are only humble dvergues we will gladly offer you food and lodging if you'll spend the night with us, for we haven't seen anyone passing this way in months, and haven't heard any recent news."

Kvasir, grateful for the accommodations, replied, "I would be honored to stay with you. If there are any questions you might have I would be glad to try to answer them for you."

Galarr seemed to jump at the offer. "We have need to ask you a very urgent and dire question about a matter most important to us. It's a very private and important matter."

Fjalarr added, "Yes, very important," and shrugged at Galarr. He had no idea what the important question was, but, he continued conspiratorially, "We can't ask the question here." He looked around and from side to side, and then over his shoulder checking to see whether anyone was listening, and continued, "We have to go to the forest so we're certain no one else can hear our question. It concerns a very private matter."

Although it was odd they were anxious not to be overheard when no one had passed their way in months, Kvasir suspected ill of no one and readily agreed to accompany them to the dark interior of the forest to be certain no one would be around and they could ask him their question in private. He had met many odd people in his short lifetime and always humored their requests.

After they were a fair distance into the forest Fjalarr signaled for Kvasir to bend down so he could whisper the question in his ear. As Kvasir bent down, Galarr, standing behind him picked up a nearby broken off tree branch and was able to raise up on his tiptoes and strike their guest on the back of his head with all his dwarvish might. The blow killed Kvasir instantly. Fjalarr gleefully ran behind a tree and brought out several containers they had previously hidden. They drew off Kvasir's blood into them. The first, and largest, was a bronze kettle named Odrærir, which means heart-stirrer. The two vats they used were called Son, which means blood, and Bodn, which means offering.

Galarr ordered Fjalarr about, "Gather twigs and then branches and make a fire. Go back to our place and get the large kettle."

Fjalarr didn't feel like carrying a heavy cast-iron kettle through the forest,"Why must I do it. You do it. Or, better yet, let's drag Kvasir back to our place. He's much lighter than a kettle."

Galarr was to the point, "You'll do it because I told you to do it. And make certain you bring the LARGE kettle. Not the smaller one."

Fjalarr did as he was told. His rebellion was over.

The two set about their brewing mixing honey and rum with the blood and boiling it until it was a dull yellow color. Then with incantations the two dvergues transformed the liquid into a magic mead capable of giving great knowledge and the gift of poetry to any who drank it. Eventually the mead would be known as the "foundation of poetry."

The two dvergues returned to their cabin with the kettle and two vats, hiding them and not making use of the mead's magic power. Boasting back and forth between one another they recounted their adventure and embellished it through the night until it had become a deed of heroic bravery. However, they didn't dare tell anyone else what they'd done for fear of retribution by the Æsir or Vanir. Since Kvasir had last been seen heading their way they put about the story he had sat down to dinner with them, complained of a headache from the knowledge bursting within his head and had fallen over dead. Their story held since no one believed two small dvergues would dare cause harm to one so favored by the Æsir and Vanir. So pleased were the two at having gotten away with Kvasir's murder they decided to kill someone else.

Gillingr and his Wife

Fjalarr spoke first, "Whom shall we kill next? What about a ljosalfar? I can't stand them anyway. They're always so happy, singing all the time and hopping and skipping about like that."

"And always smiling. Ugh," added Galarr. "But," continued Galarr, "why should we waste our talent on a mere light elf? What about a jotun? Or maybe even Thor himself?"

Fjalarr trembled a little at the thought of tackling Thor. "I think a jotun will do for now. Maybe we should practice a lot more before we think of killing Thor."

"What jotuns do we know?" asked Galarr as he paused to think.

"There's that hill troll on the other side of the valley. What is his name?" asked Fjalarr.

"You must mean Gillingr. All right, he's a good choice. Let's invite him to dinner next week," suggested Galarr.

"Why not this evening? You know how anxious their sort is for a free meal," spoke Fjalarr fairly jumping up and down with the thought of another murder.

Galarr went to the kitchen to make certain they had enough food on hand while Fjalarr sent off an invitation. A little while later they heard the thunderous footsteps of Gillingr and his wife approaching. Their very cabin shook.

Gillingr roared as he came up to their cabin, "Although you didn't include her in the invitation, I'm sure you don't mind that I brought my wife with me. She's a light eater, only as much as a bird. I don't know how she does it."

Fjalarr mumbled to Galarr, "It must be some bird."

Galarr agreed. "Some really big monstrous bird. However, there's nothing for it. We'll have to kill them both."

The four passed a pleasant evening. Galarr and Fjalarr were amazed at the appetites of their guests. Gillingr and his wife had eaten everything on the table plus all the food they had set aside in their larder for the next several weeks. And this despite it hadn't been cooked. They didn't care. It was food, they were hungry, they ate it.

Fjalarr called Galarr aside, "What now? We're out of food"

Galarr looked through the window at the smelly, rotten garbage heap, "Go get that and ladle it on their plates. Tell them it's free-range stew."

Fjalarr took the cover from the wicker enclosure they used out back for their personal elimination, and scooped as much of the garbage heap on it as he could.

"Here, you two, more scrumptious food for you."

While the two greedily scooped up mouthfuls, Fjalarr went back out and brought back the rest of the garbage heap.

Gillingr complimented the two dvergues, "Hmmm, this is the best meal we've had in a long time."

The two still seemed hungry so Galarr offered to go out and get some more food. Then he realized there was no more. The two jotuns had eaten everything in their home, including everything they'd put by for winter. And, then, they'd even eaten the garbage outside.

Gillingr stretched and said, "That's very kind of you. Even though I think I'm hungry enough to eat ten times what I've eaten tonight, I do feel a bit tired and think my wife and I had better be getting back to our mountain."

Galarr and Fjalarr both jumped at this. They had been cleaned out of food and still hadn't had the fun of killing the couple. Fjalarr thought quickly and said, "It's so late, why don't you and your lovely wife spend the night here with us? Then we could all go out fishing tomorrow and have an early breakfast. That way when you leave you'll be well-fed and well-rested. We don't want it said that we ever sent our guests away tired and hungry."

Gillingr and his wife both nodded in agreement with this idea. After all, a free meal was a free meal, and here was another one being offered to them. That had never happened before. They were never invited back places, and so hardly ever went out. Gillingr's snoring was well-known in the area since there was hardly anyone within ten rosts who had not failed to hear it. And yet they were also being asked to stay overnight. How could they refuse?

Early the next morning Galarr and Fjalarr both gave up trying to sleep. Galarr shouted to Fjalarr, "Are you asleep?"

Fjalarr answered back, at the top of his lungs, "Are you kidding? I've never had such an awful night in my life. Even our cabin's shaking from the noise. I hope the walls stay up."

Galarr replied, "I don't see why not. Gillingr's snoring is keeping everything up."

Galarr was now up and dressed, "We had better get things ready. The sooner we get it over with the sooner we can get back to sleep."

The two began preparing for the fishing expedition. When all was in readiness they woke up Gillingr, and soon all three were on the boat rowing out to sea. Gillingr seemed a bit worried. "Please row carefully, I can't swim."

The two dvergues gave each other knowing glances and could hardly contain their joy at hearing this bit of news. "Don't worry, the sea is calm today, and we should catch a fine lot of fish," remarked Fjalarr.

They fished all morning with great success. The dvergues moved about in the boat as much as possible, stomping back and forth and bumping against the sides of the boat trying their best to tip it over. After awhile Gillingr began to get nervous. "What's wrong, Gillingr?" asked Galarr. "The sea is calm and you can have a huge breakfast when we get back."

Gillingr replied, "It's just that I've never been out on a boat before, and we've been out here so long, and you two keep moving about so much. And the sky keeps moving so much. I'm getting a bit scared. I never knew boats rolled back and forth like this. I don't think I want such a big breakfast after all. Maybe we can start back now? I think I'm going to be sick." Gillingr began to turn green and hung his head over the side of the boat.

Fjalarr patted the jotun on the shoulder. Gillingr was touched by the sympathetic gesture. In reality, the dvergar was trying to shove Gillingr overboard. But he was too huge for the blows to have any effect and they were mistaken for friendly taps.

"Don't worry," said Galarr swaying back and forth all the more. "I'll take the boat back in. Besides, we've caught enough fish to last Fjalarr and me for a week. We've enough fish to feed ten jotuns all at once. You certainly were able to bring in the big ones for us."

Gillingr smiled and moved his head side-to-side as he watched the two dvergues, swaying. It was too much and once again he had to lean over the side of the boat.

But instead of steering the boat back, Galarr headed it out towards the edge of a violent whirlpool. Gillingr blanched when he saw the swirling water funneling downward to Ægir's land. Galarr then steered the boat safely back towards shore. As they neared some cliffs both dvergues jumped up and down pointing towards the overhanging rocks. "Look over there, Gillingr," yelled Galarr. Gillingr was gripping the sides of the boat, too terrified to move. Slowly he turned his head and as he did so the two dvergues capsized the boat.

Both dvergues immediately swam back to the boat, righted it, and climbed back in and started rowing away from Gillingr. All Gillingr could do was cry for help as he ineffectually flailed his arms about. Galarr and Fjalarr steered the boat out of reach of the jotun and looked on as his terrified yells ceased and he sank beneath the waves. Soon the churning of the water stopped. The two dvergar made their way to the shore and waited.

It was only a short while before his bloated body washed ashore. They managed to drag it into a cave beneath the overhanging rocks. No one would ever find him there. They also unloaded all of their catch and stored it there, not wanting to take the chance Gillingr's soon to be grief-stricken widow would turn out to be the sort who eats after hearing bad news.

Next it was off to deal with Gillingr's wife. They rowed back to their home and informed Gillingr's wife that she was now a widow.

Galarr spoke first, "He fell out of the boat."

Fjalarr broke in, "We rowed over to him to try and help, but he pulled at the boat."

Breathless, Galarr finished the story, "He tugged so hard that it overturned. Fjalarr and I almost drowned. It was all we could do to save ourselves. Look how soaked we are. We weren't even able to save the fish we caught for breakfast."

Gillingr's wife started crying and shrieking and gnawing on the end of her apron. Fjalarr was glad they had hidden the fish. He was certain she was an upset eater.

She carried on so until the two dvergues were nearly deafened. They tried to comfort her, but nothing helped. Finally the two looked at each other and nodded in agreement about what to do.

"Follow me," yelled Fjalarr as he walked out the door. "I'll point out the spot where your husband drowned. Maybe that will make you feel better."

Galarr excused himself. I'll start breakfast. I'm sure I can find enough for us to eat, since the one with the biggest appetite is no longer here." Gillingr's widow renewed her crying upon hearing these words.

Galarr went to the kitchen and started to work. After making a clatter of noise with some pots and pans he ran up to the second floor. Fjalarr and Gillingr's widow were just walking out the front door.

"Stand over here," motioned Fjalarr, positioning Gillingr's widow beneath the second story window. "There, now look out to the sea just to the left of those overhanging rocks."

Fjalarr backed up looking first at Gillingr's widow and then at the second story window. He yelled out to her, "Maybe if you moved a little to the left you'd get a better view." Unsuspecting, she did so, but a little too far. "No, back to the right a little. Now back up a little. There, perfect. Do you see anything?"

She squinted but couldn't see a thing, which didn't matter, for at that moment Galarr dropped a millstone out the second floor window, hitting her on the head, killing her instantly. This had been quite a day for the two dvergues.

Fjalarr stepped out of the way, satisfied. "There, now she can be with Gillingr eternally."

They put her in their boat, rowed to the far shore, and dragged her body to the cave where they had buried Gillingr, and very quickly dug a grave for her. If they worked fast there would still be enough of the morning left to get back to their cabin with their catch and have a leisurely breakfast of fish and bread.

Suttungr

Back in Jotunheimr Suttungr, Gillingr's and his wife's son, began to worry about his parents' whereabouts. He had expected them back the previous evening. The dinner invitation sent

by the dvergar had seemed suspicious to him. After all, their own sons didn't even invite Gillingr and his wife over for dinner. Why would dvergues want them over for dinner?

He made his way to the dvergues' cabin. The two weren't there. He looked around and found markings indicating something large had recently been dragged away from the area. He followed the trail to the water's edge and looked across and saw the two dvergues doing something. He couldn't quite make out what, but Fjalarr looked up and seeing him scurried into the cave. It all seemed very suspicious.

Suttungr couldn't swim, so he just sloshed across the inlet. In the cave he saw the two dvergues finishing his mother's burial. He saw the other freshly dug grave. The two dvergues had thought they had more time. They counted on Gillingr's son having to find a boat to cross the inlet. They were so startled to see him, they confessed the murders straightaway and begged forgiveness.

Galarr pleaded louder than Fjalarr, "Honest, it was just an accident. First there was the boat and Fjalarr accidentally overturned it."

Fjalarr, seeing the blame was not too subtly being shifted to him started telling his version of events, "And then Galarr accidentally dropped a millstone from the second floor window onto your mother's head, crushing it flat."

Suttungr was enraged, "My parents died by water and rock, and so shall you two die, but not nearly as quickly. I shall enjoy watching you both take a long time to die."

He grabbed up each dvergar by the scruff of the neck, one in each hand, their feet kicking furiously in the air, and carried them far away from the shore and set them on a narrow shoal. "Lucky for you two it's low tide. Even at high tide you'll be able to survive, for a few weeks. But gradually the waters will rise until this area will be completely covered at high tide. It's much too far for you to swim back to shore, so you'll both eventually tire of treading water and one-by-one be swept out to sea. I know you dvergues don't need much food, but maybe all that treading will give you appetites. Perhaps Ægir and Ran will invite you for dinner? I've heard about what happens to those who visit their table. Now don't you two worry about me. I'm going to go over there and sit on those overhanging rocks and watch the show. Seems to be a lot of fish there for me to eat."

He left the two dvergues huddled together for warmth. Soon it would be dark. Long gone were their hopes for a nice fish breakfast.

As the days passed the water rose higher and higher at each tide. They could hear Suttungr's laughter off in the distance. Finally the water was just passed their waists. They yelled and screamed for help. Their calls awakened the sea mews who flew from their safe nests near the shore to the rock where the two dvergues were. They started screeching and mocking Fjalarr and Galarr, imitating their cries for help. Often had the two dvergues thrown rocks at them, or had stolen the eggs from their nests to use in their morning breakfasts. Now the sea mews had a chance to get even. Meanwhile Suttungr sat on the high rocks of the cliff. He played with the baby birds that had been left behind in the sea mews' nests. His pants legs were rolled up and he paddled his feet on the breakers. The water he kicked splashed out to the dvergues. This made him laugh even more as each wave drenched the dvergues and threatened to wash them away entirely.

Thinking perhaps to purchase their freedom, Fjalarr made an offer of weregild. He yelled, "Suttungr, you know all dvergues have hoards of gold stashed away. Give us our freedom and we'll show you where our hoard is."

Suttungr heard the offer through the wailing from the sea mews and the crashing waves and mistook what they had said for something disrespectful about his mother and kicked a giant wave towards them.

Galarr yelled out, as loudly as he could, "We are master smiths who can forge magical tools and weapons. And since there are all types of battles we can also forge our gold into beautiful necklaces which even the most hardhearted of female jotuns couldn't resist. Surely there is some jotun you wish to impress or fight?"

Suttungr made out enough to understand the offer. "I'm a jotun, what do I need with tools? My fists are my weapons. So far I've successfully avoided the companionship you would help me win. The closest I've come to being trapped has left me saddled with a daughter. I like what I'm doing now, drinking beer and watching you two drown."

What he had said gave Fjalarr another idea. "What if we were to give you the finest tasting brew around? Not only is it better than beer, it will also make you smarter than you could ever have imagined. Why grieve so for parents who spent the evening with us complaining about you and your brother Baugi, and how neither one of you two could find the time to visit them."

Suttungr defended himself, "That's not true. I visited them often. Baugi never went to see them. But they always forgave him and not me. He's the youngest and was always their favorite." Jotuns, Æsir, Vanir, dvergues, siblings have the same problems throughout the Worlds of the Tree.

Galarr nodded in agreement with Suttungr. "You see. Why avenge parents like that? Why not gain more from their deaths than just watching us drown? What good will that do you a year from now"

Fjalarr could feel they were winning him over, "The mead will bring you many moments of pleasure, once you have it."

Galarr added, so as not to be forgotten should the jotun agree to the deal and they be rescued, "Surely such a payment would be adequate weregild for your parents' deaths? And only one of us can undo the intricate magic chains and locks protecting the mead from thieves. If you try to take it without knowing exactly how to do it, then it will spill and seep into the ground and be lost to you." Galarr lied. The mead had just been carelessly left in their containers on the floor of the kitchen in the two dvergues' cabin.

Suttungr expressed some interest, "Tell me more. What is this mead? What makes it so special?"

Fjalarr boasted of its properties and even lied about tasting it, "It's called the Precious Mead, hinn dyri mjodr. We've tasted it and no mead in the world is so good. It consists of honey, Kvasir's blood…"

Suttungr frowned at this and Galarr quickly added, "And plenty of rum. In fact, it's mostly rum. We used a lot of rum when we made it. It'll make you drunker than you've ever been before. All that rum."

Fjalarr continued, "But it's a special kind of drunkenness. If you're the sort who sings and tells stories, everyone will sing along with you or laugh at your stories."

The two could see he was nearly won over. Galarr added the finishing touch, "Best of all is the fact you can drink as much as you like, and the next morning you'll never know you had been roaring drunk the night before. Friends can run around early the next morning rattling pots and pans in the kitchen and your head will be as clear as if you'd gone to bed with a glass of warm milk the night before.

Thinking there might be something to what the dvergues were saying Suttungr reached over and plucked them from the rock to safety. In a few steps he was back at their cottage where the still shivering dvergues were dangled a little bit and then dropped onto the ground. They both ran into the house and returned carrying the three vessels containing the Precious Mead. As he departed the two dvergues shouted their gratitude at being let go. But once Suttungr was out of earshot they went back to their mischievous ways.

The Precious Mead of Inspiration

Soon Suttungr was back at his castle high atop a mountain on the border of Jotunheimr. His castle was appropriately named Hnitbjorg, which means lock rock. In fact his castle was actually carved out of the mountain. Many of the rooms were hollowed out deep within the mountain. It was in one of these lower chambers that he stored the vessels containing the magical drink. There it could be kept cool and fresh. But fearful the Precious Mead could still be stolen, he turned Gunnlod, his beautiful daughter, into a hideous looking hag and locked her in the treasure chamber to guard his hoard. There she sat, grieving for her lost beauty and longing for someone to love her.

Kvasir's absence from Asgardr was soon noticed. He never left for long periods of time without telling the Æsir where he was going and how long he'd be gone, so they began to worry foul play had befallen him.

After a few casual inquiries a ljosalfar related the story she had heard that Kvasir had died of too much knowledge while staying with two dvergues named Fjalarr and Galarr.

But that evening at dinner in Valhalla the true story came out. As Odin sat aloof at one end of the table one of his ravens flew in and landed on his shoulder. It whispered in his ear of Kvasir's murder by Fjalarr and Galarr. Odin left the hall and went to the Mimirsbrunnr Well to seek advice from his old friend and uncle. Mimir told Odin the rest of the story, informing him the Mead of Inspiration was now in the hands of the jotun Suttungr, but that he had not yet tasted it.

Odin hurried back to Asgardr and called an immediate Thing at Urdarbrunnr Well. Everyone knew it must be important because Odin interrupted everyone's dinner.

After everyone was assembled he spoke, "Kvasir was killed by two dvergues and his blood made into a Precious Mead, a Mead of Inspiration. That mead is now in the hands of the jotun Suttungr. He hasn't yet tasted it, but if he does he will gain knowledge and understanding that is best kept only amongst us. Right now Suttungr doesn't realize how much we want the mead. If we send for it or demand it from him then he'll know how important it is to us and I'm sure his price will reflect that."

Thor spoke, "Obviously someone must go in disguise and try to win it."

"If they cannot win it they must steal it, for we can't do without it. It's much too valuable to let anyone else have," spoke Tyr.

Ullr rose and reminded the Æsir never to trust the words of Fjalarr and Galarr again, "For it was they who spread the rumors Kvasir had died of his own wisdom when in fact they had killed him."

The next day Odin left Asgardr disguised as a common farm laborer, carrying a scythe over his shoulder and wearing a broad-brimmed hat pulled low to cover his missing eye. All day he walked through Midgardr, until he finally crossed over Ifing into Jotunheimr. Soon he came to the farm owned by Baugi, Suttungr's brother.

As he passed by Baugi's fields he came to nine ugly thralls who were mowing the field making hay. When they saw Odin they stopped work and ran over to talk to him. Baugi's fields were so out-of-the-way that strangers hardly ever passed by.

Odin spoke first, "I hear Baugi is a hard taskmaster. Is he fair?"

One of the thralls replied, "He's not as bad as some and better than most. As long as our scythes stay sharp we're able to mow fast enough to please him."

Odin took a whetstone from his pocket, "I can help you there. Let me sharpen your scythes for you." The thralls sat down to rest as Odin set about sharpening the scythes. Sparks flew as he honed each blade until they were all razor-sharp. The thralls were amazed. Their scythes had never cut as well, even when they were new.

They all ran over to Odin offering to buy the whetstone. All the thralls cried out their offers.

"Sell it to me."

"No, not him, he never pays. He'll buy the whetstone from you and then steal the money back, and maybe even cut off your head with his sharp blade."

"I've more money than the others since Baugi paid me extra for following him past the Myrkvydr Forest and helping him burn out some of the other farmers."

All the workers began to quarrel as to the one who should get it. Each thrall tried harder and harder to outbid the others. And in their excitement they told Odin much about their own wicked deeds.

Odin at last cried out above the confusion, "I'll sell the whetstone for a thousand pieces of ringmoney. Choose amongst yourselves who shall have it." Odin threw the whetstone down in front of the group.

The nine thralls still carrying their now razor-sharp scythes over their shoulders ran at once to be the first to pick up the whetstone. In their eagerness they chopped off each other's heads. Odin stepped over the thralls, picked up the whetstone from the center of the fallen workers, and went on his way. By nightfall he arrived at Baugi's house and asked for shelter. He introduced himself as Bolverkr, which means baleworker.

"My name is Bolverkr and I'm looking for employment. As you can tell by my name I'm not totally unskilled in the dark arts. I assure you I can earn my night's lodging many times over."

Baugi was in a foul mood, having come upon his dead thralls in the field earlier that afternoon. "You alone would hardly be of any use to me. My thralls killed each other this morning. It wouldn't be so bad if they had finished cutting the hay first. I need more than just you to get my hay harvested. Where am I going to find more men? I've killed most of the people around here. Any others that were left have run away. Those nine out in the field were my special followers, whether mowing hay or mowing men. So you can see I need more than just you to do my work."

Odin stood up to speak. Baugi hadn't noticed before how big Bolverkr was. He seemed all of a sudden to fill the room with his presence. "You should try me before you judge and taunt me. I can easily do the work of your nine thralls. In fact if I fail to complete their jobs in less time than they would have, then you won't have to pay me."

Baugi's mouth dropped open in astonishment at the offer, "It's not possible. But if you could do what you say, I would gladly pay you whatever you wanted."

Odin pretended to be uncertain about the pay, then he said, "Is it true your brother Suttungr has a most wondrous drink in his cellar? I've always enjoyed drinking and would gladly finish your harvesting if you would get me a drink of his brew."

Baugi was surprised Bolverkr knew about the secret mead. "How do you know about Kvasir's Blood?"

Baugi didn't notice Odin's slight wince at the name the jotuns had given the Precious Mead, or that he didn't respond to the question, but merely said, "That is my price," and started to walk towards the door to leave.

Baugi rushed around to stand between the door and Bolverkr to stop him and spoke as he barred the way, "I would certainly pay you one small sip if I could, but Suttungr guards it jealously. He won't even give me a sip, let alone share it with a complete stranger."

Odin offered him an alternative payment, "Well then, will you promise to help me steal a drink of it without Suttungr knowing about it?"

Baugi readily agreed, for he felt he had nothing to lose and everything to gain. Here was a chance to get his fields harvested for nothing. He was certain there was no way Bolverkr would be able to break into the chamber. "I can certainly promise that. But you'll have to be very clever indeed to gain the prize."

They sealed their agreement by swearing oaths, each promising to keep his part of the bargain.

All summer Odin worked toiling in the field and had the hay harvested and stacked before the corn was ripe. Next he gathered corn, threshed and culled the grain and filled Baugi's granaries to overflowing. Not only was Bolverkr fast, he was efficient. Never had Baugi had such a harvest.

Baugi stood and watched in amazement as Bolverkr did the work of more than nine men. By the beginning of winter Odin had finished his part of the bargain. All the crops were in and the field had been prepared for the next spring. Baugi offered to take Bolverkr to Suttungr's castle. "You certainly have worked harder than my nine thralls would have. I'll do what I can to persuade Suttungr to give you a drink."

Baugi and Bolverkr went to Suttungr and told him of the bargain that had been made to get Baugi's fields tilled. After hearing what they had to say Suttungr refused saying, "It's not my bargain and I'm not responsible for paying my brother's debts. NO." Suttungr started yelling at his brother, becoming angrier and angrier, "Baugi, you're a fool. You would waste my most precious possession on a mere farm laborer when the Æsir themselves would pay dearly for it. Both of you get out of my sight, and leave my mead alone."

After they had departed a distance from the castle, Baugi spoke first, "I'm sorry that you'll not be paid for you are the best worker I've ever employed."

Odin seemed unconcerned. He hadn't really expected the mead to be handed over to him without a fight. "Don't you remember the second part of your promise? If a sip is not freely given to me then you would help me steal a drink."

Baugi responded, "Certainly, I'll help you. But I don't see how. The mead is deep in this mountain, guarded by the ugly Gunnlod." He slapped at the overhanging rock they

were standing under, emphasizing the hardness of their task. "There's only one way to get to the treasure chamber and that's through the castle which is guarded either by Suttungr himself, or some of his servants."

Odin seemed to be talking more and more unlike a farm laborer with every word he spoke, "Don't worry, we'll find a way to get in. Let's go to the bottom of the mountain and get as close to the treasure chamber as we can from the outside."

They reached the foot of the mountain where Baugi paused and said, "We're as close to the treasure as we can get without actually standing outside the door to it. But I don't see how you're going to cut your way through this rock. It would take a family of dvergues a year to dig a tunnel to the treasure chamber from here."

Odin seemed unconcerned, "If you follow my instructions I'll have all the mead I want."

Odin took the gimlet rati from his pocket and handed it to Baugi. "This auger is different from any you've ever seen before. It has magical properties which allows it to expand as long as necessary to cut through stone and reach the other side. I need your jotun strength to bore through the mountain."

Baugi doubted this last statement, but began to bore nevertheless. He worked and worked until he became too tired to continue. Thinking to fool Bolverkr he drew the auger from the hole and tossed it down saying, "There, that's that. But it's such a tiny hole, I don't know that it will do you any good." All the while he was thinking, "If Bolverkr is somehow able to change his shape and crawl into the hole I'll just plug up this end and trap him." Baugi was beginning to have doubts Bolverkr was just an ordinary farm laborer.

Odin was suspicious, too. He blew into the hole and was not surprised when bits of stone and dust flew back into his face rather than through the hole to the other side. Odin spoke angrily to Baugi, "I thought you honored your word and would not cheat one who has worked in good faith as hard for you as I have?"

Baugi picked up rati and began furiously drilling again. The stone seemed to become harder the longer he drilled. But eventually the auger broke through to the other side and Baugi, still pushing with all his might, fell against the mountain.

Odin once again blew at the hole and this time the dust blew out the other side. He spoke quickly to Baugi, "Stand watch. Signal me by whistling if Suttungr or his guards happen along." Quickly changing himself into a snake he slithered into the hole.

Odin's action was so quick Baugi didn't at first see the wehrsnake slither into the hole. At the last moment he caught a glance of it and made a thrust into the hole with the auger. He missed and could hear Odin yelling back to him from the other side, "Too late, too late."

Instead of running to warn Suttungr his mead was being stolen, Baugi ran back to his home. He wanted no part of the anger Suttungr would have for him.

Once inside the dank cave Odin changed himself into a well-shaped young jotun and surveyed his surroundings. Suttungr had certainly not spared any expense in the room. Stalactites and stalagmites hung from the ceiling or jutted up from the floor. Water dripped down the walls. It was just a cavern which Suttungr had taken no pains to turn into an apartment for his daughter. The air smelled of moss, mud, and bugs. Bats hung overhead, asleep in a room where not much happened.

The problem confronting Odin now was how to win the mead and get out of the chamber with it. The only exit appeared to be the one leading through the castle. But, ultimately, the task proved not to be as difficult as he had thought.

When Gunnlod noticed the handsome warrior, she seemed unsurprised and unconcerned for she had been warned thieves might try to break in and steal the drink from her. "Have you come to drink the mead?"

Before she could continue Odin interrupted, "Oh, no, I wouldn't risk my life for some silly mead. I've tasted the best meads in all the Worlds of the Tree. I'm sure this is just average. If it were of higher quality more care would have been taken in bottling it. I didn't even know there was mead here. I've come to see you, for I've heard of the great beauty trapped in her bower. And I can now see the words I've heard describing your appearance were no exaggeration." Odin caressed the side of her face while thinking to himself, "For you are indeed every bit as ugly as they have said." Odin smiled at her.

Gunnlod was flattered and rested her head against his hand. Perhaps the spell her father had cast had somehow been broken and she was beautiful once more. She had long since destroyed all of the mirrors in the chamber, so there was no way for her to look at herself.

Odin walked over to Gunnlod's golden couch, the only concession to comfort in the room, and laid down on it. "I've come a long way and am very tired."

She laid down beside him. "I'm tired of being shut up here alone. I won't tell my father you're here. Please stay with me…forever."

Odin didn't answer. Instead he carefully undressed her, took one look, and blew out all the candles, and silently cursed the full moon still lighting the bower.

They made love all night. The next morning Odin sat up, stretched and remarked how thirsty he was. "I certainly could do with a drink."

Gunnlod ran over to the three vats in the corner of the chamber and undid the bars and bolts securing them to the floor and brought the vat Odrœrir to him. He drank it down in one gulp. "You certainly have a great thirst?"

She expected him to get up and leave since he had won a taste of the mead. But to her surprise he didn't. Instead he motioned for her to return to bed. Another day and night passed. The next morning the same thing happened. This time she brought the container Bodn to him, whereupon he promptly drank it in one gulp and again motioned for her to return to bed. On the third day she gave him Son, the final vat.

She begged him, "I've never been so happy as in these last three days. Stay with me forever and be my husband. I'll give you whatever you want. My father has other treasures you can have."

Odin spoke, "I'll stay with you forever, for I've never met another like you. But your blue eyes remind me of the sky and I must have one last look at it and one last breath of fresh air before I spend the rest of my life down here with you.

Gunnlod, being slightly slow-witted and full of love, which we know, in itself can make one's wits disappear, opened a secret door at the top of a large rock. It was obvious she had never tasted the mead.

Looking up the shaft he could see a tiny speck of blue which was the sky. Odin transformed himself into an eagle in the wink of an eye. Carrying the mead in his crop he flew spiraling ever upwards into the open air.

Gunnlod started shrieking for him to come back. "Please don't leave me, my love. Whatever will I do cooped up here? I thought you were different?

The entire castle was summoned by her cries. Suttungr immediately realizing what had happened he put on orne-ham, his eagle-guise, and gave chase to Odin.

Odin flew higher and higher hoping he could fly high enough to clear the mountains of Jotunheimr. He flew towards Asgardr, flapping his wings with all his might.

While in Asgardr, the Æsir were waiting, watching to the north for his appearance.

Odin flew nearer and nearer. Heimdallr was the first to point out the figure was no more than a speck in the sky. Soon the Æsir could see Odin and the great black eagle in pursuit gaining on Odin with every flap of its wings.

At the first sight of Odin some of the Æsir placed three large containers in the courtyard. Others stood ready on top of Asgardr's walls with swords drawn to defend the land. Ullr slowly fitted an arrow to his bow and raised it ready to aim and fire.

As Odin approached the walls he regurgitated the mead. Most landed in the three golden vessels, but some spilled outside Asgardr's walls. Everyone can drink of this spilt mead which is known as the skald-fiflahlutr, the fool-poet's portion.

Odin was now lighter and flew higher and faster. He seemed to be putting more distance between himself and Suttungr with every flap.

As Suttungr neared the wall Ullr raised his bow to shoot. But before he could loose his arrow he heard another of the Æsir yell out, "Look there to the east. I see the glint of…"

Another yelled, "Uppr dagr!"

They all looked and could see the rising sun. A beam of light struck Suttungr. Orne-ham, his eagle-guise, fell to the ground followed rapidly by Suttungr who had been dayed-up and turned to stone. The jotun fell out of the sky with a great crash.

That evening the Æsir celebrated their victory in winning the mead. Odin spoke, "At last we have Kvasir's Blood back where it belongs. Let's all drink of it so we may increase in wisdom and better be able to fight the jotuns. And on occasion we'll give a sip to some in Midgardr, and those who drink will become poets and shall tell of our victories and perhaps our defeats."

But the mead was in Asgardr only a short while before a jotun named Midvitnir, meaning mead-wolf, stole it and carried it to the realm of Surtr in Muspelheimr. He kept it in Brimir's mead hall called Okolnir. There the liquid was kept in Heidraupnir's skull and Hoddrofnir's horn, both guarded by Sokkmimir, Mitvitnir's son.

Once again Odin, this time in the guise of Svidrir, went in quest of the Precious Mead. He stole Surtr's fiery sword, med sviga læva, and hacked off the head of Sokkmimir with it. Odin had difficulty lifting the enormous containers and carrying Surtr's sword at the same time. So, reluctantly he had to leave the sword behind. Much as he would have liked to have taken both prizes back to Asgardr he had to make a choice. He chose the Precious Mead, and flung the sword back into the furnaces of Muspelheimr, where it was eventually found and returned to Surtr, who harbored an even greater hatred of the Æsir now that the mead had been stolen from him, and his son Sokkmimir's head had been chopped off.

After its second return the Precious Mead was guarded constantly and never again stolen.

Chapter 6

The Stealing of Sif's Hair by Loki

Loki, hidden behind some shrubs, watched as Sif completed her bath. Her long blond hair covered her from head to foot. It flowed like the silk on the ears of corn in the fields of Midgardr over which she spread her protection. She was one of the most beautiful of the Asynjes. This in itself was enough to make Loki want to possess her. But there was also the added satisfaction that she was Thor's wife. To take his enemy's wife as mistress was a revenge worthy of his evil.

As she walked by him he stepped out from behind the shrubs. At first he tried flattering her with compliments about her beautiful hair. He knew she was exceptionally vain about her hair. Yet, try as he might, ultimately she spurned his advances and continued on her way back to Bilskirnir, the hall she shared with Thor in Thrudvangar, Thor's estate in Asgardr.

Loki was not one to accept rejection. Later that afternoon he journeyed to Bilskirnir where he found Sif laying outside on a couch fast asleep. Thor was not around or Loki would never have thought to do what he did next.

Loki crept up to Sif and cut off all her hair, then fled the hall, his arms raised in victory with the golden tresses flying behind him. His prize was captured, his revenge was sweet. But, quickly he realized he was being too bold. He didn't want a confrontation with Thor, so he gathered up Sif's hair and stuffed it into a pouch.

Thor returned to Bilskirnir later that afternoon. Sif was still enjoying her afternoon nap. However, Thor never made a delicate entrance. The ground shook with each step, and he yelled out for his love, "Sif, where are you? I'm back."

His thundering footsteps and voice woke Sif. She got up from her couch and it was a moment before she realized something was wrong. Her head felt lighter. She screamed when she realized her veil of hair, usually flowing to the ground, was gone. She was bald. Not wanting Thor to see her in such a state she hid behind a pillar outside the palace.

In the meantime Thor was surprised Sif had not run to greet him as was her usual custom. Then he heard her scream. Fearing for her safety he searched through every room of the hall, which was no easy task considering Bilskirnir had 540 rooms. When he still

couldn't find her he started searching outside the building. The first place he looked was her couch, where she usually rested in the afternoon. He could see she had been there. A goblet of half-drunk mead was on a side table, and the cushions were arranged just as she liked them. Then, he heard a quiet whimpering. He followed the sound and looked behind a nearby pillar. There was Sif facing the pillar, her head against it as she tried to muffle her crying. She had on a veil covering her head. At first Thor couldn't see what the problem was.

Thor walked up to her, "Sif, what's the matter? I called for you when I saw you weren't here to greet me."

She turned to face him, pulling back the veil, revealing her bald pate. "It was Loki. This afternoon he stood too near and made some vile suggestions to me, which I rebuffed. He left, very angry. But, I thought that was the end of it. But, while I slept he got his revenge. He cut my beautiful hair. Oh, I miss my golden tresses. My beautiful, beautiful hair. Loki took it."

At first Thor didn't completely comprehend what she was saying. Then the realization sunk in that Loki had propositioned his wife and then cut off her hair when she had refused his advances. Everyone agreed Sif had the most beautiful hair in all the Worlds of the Tree. Now it was gone. His wife was bald.

Thor's eyes reddened with anger. He yelled for a servant to prepare his chariot. His two goats, Tanngnjostr and Tanngrisnir, had already been unhooked and were enjoying a nice rest, eating and drinking as much as they wanted. Suddenly servants pulled both by the horns and hooked them back up to the chariot. Thor boarded, grabbed the reins and slapped at his two goats. They didn't like that one bit. Just moments before they were contemplating a nice restful evening. Now they were being slapped and urged to run faster than they had all day. But, nothing for it. What Thor wanted, Thor got. The two goats bolted forward rising into the air pulling the chariot with Thor in it behind them.

The heavens thundered as his chariot rolled through the skies. His voice boomed out one name over and over again, "LOKI! LOKI!" The name reverberated from cloud to cloud. As Thor approached a cloud it changed from light and frothy to dark and menacing. Lightning played back and forth amongst the clouds, and from ground to cloud. Many on Midgardr were frightened at the sudden change in the weather. What had been a pleasant evening outdoors now sent people scurrying for shelter.

None of this was a surprise to Loki. He knew once Sif told Thor what he had done, Thor would come looking for him. Why had he done it? He had gained nothing. He couldn't use Sif's hair and had thrown it away. All he'd accomplished was to make Thor angry with him. It had been a really stupid thing to do.

No undoing it, though. Now he had to deal with the consequences. If he could just hide long enough for Thor's mood to blow over. He had played pranks on just about everyone he knew. Wherever he thought to hide, there was someone nearby whom he'd wronged and who would love to give him up to Thor. Instead of hiding on land where others might see him and report to Thor, Loki, decided to hide in a nearby lake. He changed himself into a salmon, jumped in, and swam over hoping to hide amongst all the other salmon. The salmon were so thick Loki was pushed upon the backs of some of the Salmon. Not only wasn't he hiding, he stood out. He tried to scramble back down into the

water. Thor passing overhead looked down and spotted the strange salmon who seemed to be irritating the other salmon so much they quickly swam away from it.

Loki looked around. He was now in the open lake, all by himself. Before he could swim back over to the group, he look up to see Thor changed himself into a sea gull, and swoop down towards him. Loki tried to dive down, but Thor was on him before he knew it and had snatched him up, carried him over land and dropped him. He bounced against a rock and started flapping around, suffocating in the air.

Thor landed and changed from a seagull into his real shape. He bent over the struggling salmon. "I can tell it's you, Loki. Not because the other fish wanted nothing to do with you, but because of your eyes. Fish don't have the evil eyes you do."

Loki gave it up and changed back into himself and immediately struck Thor. But, Thor was Thor and Loki was rather puny. The blow glanced off him. Then Loki grabbed Thor by the neck. This was not a good idea either, because then Thor did the same to Loki. And Thor was a fighter. Thor was on the verge of strangling him when Loki confessed to having cut Sif's hair.

"Yes, I cut your wife's hair. I don't know why I did it. It was just there. She was just there. It seemed like a good idea at the time. You know how I am, Thor. Sometimes I just do things without thinking."

Thor was unimpressed with the confession, grabbed Loki by the throat and began strangling him again.

Loki gurgled out a proposition, "I cut it, but if you'll not harm me and let me go I promise to restore her hair." Thor's grip loosened slightly. Loki's voice was stronger now, "I know a group of swarthy elves who will be able to make a crown of golden hair for Sif, far more beautiful than her real hair ever was."

Thor thought about the proposition, ignoring Loki's implied insult, "But in the meantime Sif has to endure being without her hair, being b-b-b-bald…"

Loki noticed Thor could hardly bring himself to say the word. So, here was a weakness he could exploit. Thor was proud to have a beautiful wife with beautiful hair. It seemed to be more important than the person Sif was. He didn't want a bald wife. He didn't want to be seen with a bald wife.

Loki now knew how to manipulate Thor and quickly countered, "I promise that before nightfall I'll be back with a golden mantle worthy of a goddess."

After swearing many solemn pledges by Var and Leiptr, Loki was finally let go. He left Asgardr and made his way through Midgardr until he came to some towering mountains. In the caves beneath these mountains dwelt some dvergues and their cousins who were members of the race of Svartalfheimr, or dark alves. Loki descended through gradually narrowing passages. He followed the winding, twisting stairway as it led deeper and deeper down, until he could hear the echoing of hammers on anvils. The rhythmic clanging became almost hypnotic as he stood listening. Then continuing on, the passage suddenly opened into a cavern lit by the crimson glow of the furnaces. Hot breezes blew across the fires as the bellows pumped up and down. Little muscular dvergues glistening with sweat ran about on busy errands. Loki watched as the dvergues turned rocks into pure gold, and flint into rubies. The juice from freshly picked violets was used to turn ordinary pebbles into sapphires. Emeralds were made from the green of meadows, and pearls were made with the tears of widows and young maidens. All sorts of precious metals and jewels were being

produced and then taken away to be hidden under rocks, some close to Midgardr's surface for the tempting of those above, others deep down and hoarded away never to be found.

These dark alves were Ivaldi's sons, and were known for their work in gold and brass. Dvalin was the name of the dvergar who did the actual forging, and was the person whom Loki now approached.

Dvalin seemed irritated to be bothered. Every moment away from his smith was one less jewel to hide. "Speak quickly, Loki. Your time is measured in carets, not seconds."

Loki made his proposition to them, "If you make me a crown of golden hair that will grow like real hair and glow with the brilliance of the sun itself, I'll give you whatever you desire..." Seeing their eyes light up he added, "...within reason."

The little men huddled and excitedly talked amongst themselves. They quickly agreed to the task and started haggling over price with Loki. Dvalin spoke, rubbing his hands back and forth in anticipation, "This is a difficult thing you ask. Our price will be one jet black newborn horse, without any trace of white." Greed shone on the faces of the other dvergues as they nodded in agreement, for this was truly a dear price.

Loki considered the request for a moment, then said, "Perhaps, but I'll need the hair by this evening."

The dvergues started a clamor of talking amongst themselves. Phrases echoed throughout the cavern, "That's impossible." "What does he think we are, slaves?" "You need time to do quality work." "We were promised a party tonight for having finished that other job for that Midgardr king so his wife would be happy." "I was going to go and sit with my gold this evening."

Dvalin waved his hand to silence them and spoke, "It might be possible, but our price will be different. Instead of the horse we want a newborn baby from Midgardr. One who doesn't cry as much as the last one you brought us. It's wailing is louder than all the clang and clamoring of our anvils. The sound keeps us up. We cannot rest. We're all very tired."

Loki thought for a moment and declined, "No, I don't have enough time to find one."

Dvalin really wanted the job so the two haggled back and forth until finally the price was agree upon. Loki was to bring them a newborn jet black colt and a newborn jet black goat, both rare creatures indeed.

As the cunning Loki turned to go and was climbing the steps of the narrow passage, Dvalin shouted after him, "And make certain you don't paint over any of the white spots like you did that other time. They have to be completely and naturally black. We're going to check this time before we hand over our work."

The dvergues immediately set to work. First, before starting on the golden hair they had to finish a spear called Gungnir and a ship called Skidbladnir, both of which were already in the process of being forged. Then they set about making Sif's replacement hair.

Dvalin spun gold thread finer than he had ever worked before. And after it was sewn into shape, charms and spells were sung over it so that once placed on a head it could never be stolen by force or cunning. It would quicken and grow as natural hair does, but be more beautiful to behold, reflecting the light brilliantly in a way natural hair never could.

Loki quickly headed to a farm in Midgardr where he was certain he could steal a black colt and goat. And he was right. In no time at all he returned to the dvergues expecting to just pick up the hair and leave. He was worried because the sun was beginning to set.

Instead, he found the golden tresses just being finished. He reached over to grab the hair and dart off, but was stopped by Dvalin.

"You must wait until the annealing process is over. The strands need to be tempered to strengthen them so that not even you will be able to steal the hair once it is on Sif's head. And it must cool so you don't misshapen it when you touch it. Stand over there out of the way and wait until I hand you the hair."

Loki was irritated and worried that he might not get back to Asgardr in time. "Why have you taken so long with my job? I expected the hair to be ready when I got back so I could give you the colt and goat and leave immediately. I'm bound by solemn oaths to return before nightfall. I might not make it if I have to wait any longer."

Dvalin signaled for the two animals to be taken away and inspected. Two dvergues took them to the other side of the hall and began sloshing and cleaning them. Dvalin pointed to them and spoke, "I am warning you, they are being cleaned with a magical liquid. If you've painted over them in any way we'll find out. And we'll keep them and the hair.

Loki questioned Dvalin, "Why has it taken so long to finish Sif's hair?"

Dvalin looked over at the two dvergues who were signaling that both animals were jet black. "Master Loki, we had two jobs in progress we had to finish before starting work on your job. To interrupt them at that critical juncture would have destroyed them. We would have had to start all over again tomorrow, losing a day's work. And look how magnificent they turned out." Dvalin pointed to the finished objects.

Dvalin continued, "Here's the spear Gungnir and the ship Skidbladnir. They are priceless treasures." He looked at them with pride.

At that moment a dvergar brought over the finished hair, "And look Sif's hair is finished and you have plenty of time to get back to Asgardr. Everything has worked out fine."

Loki saw a greedy opportunity, "Any treasures made on my time are my treasures and belong to me."

Before Dvalin could react, Loki grabbed all three items and hurried to the surface with them. The sun, though setting, was still shining enough for uppr dagr. The dvergues dared not pursue Loki lest they be dayed-up and turned to stone.

Loki made his way back to Asgardr with the three objects. He was going to put them to good use.

The sun had just set as Loki entered Asgardr so he had met the deadline, just barely. He went to Valhalla where all the Æsir were gathered and immediately began boasting about his treasures. He had decided to generously give all of them to the Æsir, hoping to store up a little goodwill for the future.

Loki stood in the hall next to the long fire. Sif's Hair, the spear Gungnir, and the ship Skidbladnir were laid out nearby. The Æsir, seated at tables around him look at the objects Loki had brought back.

Loki boasted pridefully, "The handiwork of the sons of Ivaldi is the best there is, and I have the best treasures they have ever made. The work of all other dvergues and alves is useless chattel since all other forgers are false and too stupid to know the proper secrets of

working with precious metals and stones. Only Dvalin's followers have the gifts to make such wondrous treasures."

Now, there were other families of dvergues. And it so happened that standing near Loki was a dvergar named Brokkr whose brother, Sindri was thought by the dvergues themselves to be the finest craftsperson in all the Worlds of the Tree. Brokkr spoke up to defend his brother's talent, "My brother Sindri could work more wonders with iron, brass, and gold, than all the sons of Ivaldi any day."

Loki began to laugh, "You think so? Well then, go to him and have him make a weapon more worthy than Gungnir; something to carry the Æsir faster than Skidbladnir; and something to wear more powerful than the beauty of this golden hair. And if they're judged better than my gifts then you can have my head."

Brokkr jumped at the offer. "Then it'll be your head against mine."

Loki burst into laughter and yelled after him as Brokkr ran off to see Sindri, "You're short enough already. Just think what you'll look like without a head."

All of a sudden the dinner had just gotten more interesting. Some of the Æsir who had been dosing from having consumed quite a bit of wine, perked up. Some seemed to have missed what happened and were poked by tablemates.

"Here, open your eyes and ears. Do you know what just happened? Brokkr has challenged Loki. And the wager is for each other's head."

"Wha? What's that about someone's head?"

"Oh, go back to sleep, you'll know tomorrow."

The only one who seemed disappointed was Sif, who had another day of baldness to endure.

Brokkr found Sindri at his forge in a giant underground cavern. Sindri's forge was different from the one Loki had visited in Svartalfheimr. For one thing he was the only worker in it. It was more modern and the fires were hotter and blazed with less coal so the place wasn't nearly as dirty as Dvalin's forge. When the flames from the smithy roared up corners were dimly lit to reveal piles of tools, completed jobs, and precious metals for use in upcoming jobs.

Brokkr spoke, "I've made a wager with evil Loki. I've bet him my head against his that you are the best smith. He was brash enough to boast that the works of the sons of Ivaldi were better than yours, when everyone agrees that you are the best smith around."

Brokkr further informed him of the nature of the treasures made for Loki by Dvalin. Sindri was eager to win Loki's head so he set aside what he was working on and began work on three objects with which to win the wager.

Brokkr was kept busy working the bellows to increase the heat from the coals. Sindri took a golden swine skin and placed it in the hot furnace. "Keep pumping at the bellows until I return. I'm going to go and work magic incantations and runes so that our work will win the wager."

After he left a golden gadfly flew into the smithy. Looking at its mischievous eyes one could easily tell it was actually Loki in disguise. After buzzing around for awhile it alit on Brokkr's arm and stung him. Though Brokkr could hardly bear the pain he still continued to pump the bellows.

Sindri returned and pulled a boar with bristles of pure gold from the furnace and named it Gullinbursti, though sometimes it was called Slidrugtanni. He then took some red gold and placed it in the furnace with the same admonition to Brokkr, "While I'm gone, and until I return pump the bellows harder than ever." Sindri left for a second time.

Again the gadfly returned and stung Brokkr, this time on his neck. But the dvergar resisted its sting and continued to pump the bellows.

This time upon his return Sindri removed a shining arm ring from the furnace and called it Draupnir. Then finally Sindri threw a bar of iron into the fire. "This is the most difficult task of all. You must pump harder still than all your previous efforts." With that he left for a third and final time.

And again the gadfly returned. He alit on Brokkr's nose and stung him so sharply across the bridge that blood ran into Brokkr's eyes. Even though he couldn't see what he was doing he continued pumping at the bellows. The gadfly bit and bit again and again. Finally the pain was so great Brokkr raised his hand to brush away the insect. The fire immediately cooled as the flames quickly died down. It was at this moment Sindri returned.

"You've almost ruined it, and this is the most valuable prize of all." Sindri pulled a hammer from the fire. "See, the handle of Mjolnir is too short, because you let the fire die down."

In order to salvage the hammer Sindri affixed a loop to the end of it to make it easier to throw.

Sindri handed all the gifts to Brokkr. "Here, take these gifts to the Æsir and bring me Loki's head in return. Then we'll see what I can make of that when I throw it into the furnace."

All of the Æsir were assembled for a Thing to watch the judging of the prizes to be presented before them. Three judges were appointed, Odin, Thor and Freyr.

Loki and Brokkr stood opposite each other with their treasures beside them. Loki presented his treasures first. "Odin, I take this spear called Gungnir and give it to you. It is a unique spear in that when aimed and thrown it never misses its mark. And any oaths sworn with a hand upon its point cannot be broken. Next, I give this golden hair to Thor so the lovely Sif can be adorned once again with beautiful golden locks, her tresses falling to the ground."

Thor took the hair and walked over to the tree Sif was standing beside and stood in front of her so that the other Æsir could not see as he removed the veil covering her bald head. He placed the golden hair on her head and stepped aside. It immediately began to grow like real hair and fell down her shoulders in a beautiful cascade, billowing to the ground, waving like golden wheat.

Next Loki gave Freyr the ship Skidbladnir. "This ship is of such great expanse that all of the Æsir fully armed can fit aboard it. And it will never fail to find a breeze, and will sail as well over land as it does over the sea."

The Æsir moved around looking and touching the ship. Loki continued, "As if those weren't wondrous enough traits, it also has one other unique feature. If you will notice," said Loki pointing to the sides of the ship as if he were trying to sell it, "It's made up of

thousands of interlocking pieces which can be folded in on each other even as you would fold up a handkerchief, and the entire ship can be reduced to the size of a napkin and pocketed." In a sweeping gesture he did just that and placed the ship in Freyr's pocket with a flourish. Loki stepped back and smiled, confident he had won the wager. He made a slicing motion across his neck as he smiled and pointed at Brokkr.

There was a murmuring amongst the Æsir about the great value of the presents which had been presented to Odin, Thor, and Freyr. It certainly was going to be hard for Brokkr to better Loki's gifts.

Brokkr stepped forward with his first present. "I'll also give my first treasure to Odin." He handed the arm ring to Odin. It was made of red gold and shaped like a snake holding its tail in its mouth, with a garland of precious gems enfolding the rim of the arm ring. "Every nine days this ring, called Draupnir, drops eight other rings just as valuable and as beautiful as it is." Odin put the ring on his right arm and seemed pleased.

Everyone was admiring the arm ring while Brokkr picked up his second gift. "To Freyr I give this red-golden boar named Gullinbursti, called Slidrugtanni by some. It can run swifter on air, land, and water than any other animal. It can even run faster than your horse, Blodughofi. And its brilliance will light up the night so you can see where you're going." Freyr smiled, pleased with the gift.

Lastly, he picked up the hammer and handed it to Thor. "Finally, I give this hammer to you, Thor. It is known by several names, such as, Vigdi, Mullicrusher, or Thrudhamar. But its most famous name is Mjolnir. It will complement Megingardr, your belt of strength, nicely, since its ornamentation matches your belt. No matter how far you throw Mjolnir, it will always return to you, and will never miss its target. Because it is made with special charms you can compress it to a small size and hide it secretly in your shirt."

Thor put on his iron gauntlets called jarngreipr so that his hands would have enough strength to wield Mjolnir. No one else in Asgardr was strong enough to use the hammer, although Vidarr almost could. Thor took the hammer in his right hand, but frowned at the small handle. Brokkr continued, "Its only fault is its small handle, and that is my fault not Sindri's."

Thor swung the hammer over his head. Great peals of thunder boomed through the sky, while lightning flashed, and dark clouds rolled quickly over Asgardr, a land where it had never rained.

The Æsir all shouted that the most valuable gift was the hammer because of its ability to protect them from the jotuns. Brokkr was the unanimous winner.

Brokkr yelled above the clashes of lightning, "I'll take Loki's head now. Will someone kindly get it for me?"

No one stepped forward.

Loki spoke, "You'll have to get it yourself which could prove very difficult. However, I'll gladly give you anything else you want in exchange for my head. I offer you great treasures as weregild if you will allow me to purchase my head."

Brokkr, intent on revenge and his trophy refused the offer, "Neither rings of gold nor jewels beyond imagining are as valuable as your head is to me. I already have those things. I'll have your head or I'll have nothing."

Loki answered, "Then you shall have nothing. I should have stung you harder when I had the chance. Catch me if you can."

The realization that it had been Loki who had almost cost him the wager and his head infuriated Brokkr all the more. He ran towards him, but by the time he reached the spot where Loki had been standing Loki's magic shoes that could fly over land or water had carried him off.

Brokkr appealed to Thor, "It was the trouble with your wife that brought about this wager, so will you return Loki to me so that I can recover the head that is rightfully mine?"

Thor looked towards Forseti, the lawgiver of the Æsir. In matters of legal interpretation, his word was final. "Have I an honor debt to bring Loki back for Brokkr?"

Forsetti did not even hesitate a moment to think about it and nodded yes.

Thor went in search of Loki, soon found him, and returned with him to the Thing.

Thor held Loki down. Brokkr stood over Loki and raised a sword ready to sever Loki's head. Loki had to do something. His mind raced and as the sword was raised he yelled out, "You can have my head, for you have won the wager, but my neck is no part of the wager, so you can't have that. I appeal to Forsetti for a ruling."

Thor reached over and stopped Brokkr's arm mid-swing. Brokkr had intended to just ignore that Loki had spoken and cut off his head. Better afterwards to say he hadn't heard Loki saying anything when he cut his head off. Better to ask forgiveness than permission. Now he had to deal with arguments on what he thought was a clear cut matter. Loki's head was his, and that was that. But, the Æsir didn't think it was so simple.

Most of the argument was against Loki as a person. He had over time harmed everyone there. Some harm was mischievous, other harms had been deliberate and cruel.

Brokkr listened, and if it had just been about how bad a person Loki was, then the head was his. But, some of the Æsir like Heimdallr, Baldr, and Forsetti set about looking at the matter impersonally and rationally.

The Asynjes were all against Loki and for his head being handed over to Brokkr. Every woman there had been insulted by Loki in some way or other. All had been verbally assaulted. But there were those who had been physically assaulted, too. Even Loki's wife was against him, for he had beaten her repeatedly.

But, the loudest voice against Loki was Sif's. "Why do you dilly dally about? It's clear he has lied and cheated everyone here. He's fought all of you men, and assaulted all the women. What does it take for there to be justice? If we deal with him how, we won't have to face the terrible things he can do at the ending of all things."

The Æsir didn't want to think about that. Many knew some of the horrors awaiting them and preferred to think they were too horrible to happen.

But Sif's speech seemed to have swayed the majority who agreed with her and began chanting for Loki's head.

"Chop! Chop! Chop! Chop!"

But the madness of crowds seldom leads to justice. It only leads to escalating madness from the other side.

Forsetti gave his opinion.

"Such matters are hard to accept, but, agreements have to be interpreted in a strictly legal sense. Often, we don't like the outcome. However, if it were your head on the chopping block, I'm sure you'd want to make certain all the legal niceties were followed.

"The agreement was agreed to by Brokkr and was that if Sindri's gifts were judged better than the ones Loki brought, 'then you can have my head.' Brokkr's gifts were adjudged

better by acclamation. Loki fled, but after being brought back gave the circumstances under which the agreement was to be fulfilled. This is what Brokkr agreed to, only Loki's head. So, nothing else must be injured in retrieving the head. Unfortunately, the very act of retrieving Loki's head will injure the rest of his body."

The Æsir murmured, Brokkr fumed, and Loki seemed to be breathing a little better, confident the air entering his mouth would reach his lungs.

"Don't blame Loki if he was cunning enough to suggest this agreement. Blame yourself, Brokkr, for not being wise enough to discern the trickery. My ruling is that you can only have Loki's head if you can find a way to sever it and not harm his body as you cut it from his neck. My decision is final." Forsetti stepped back. Standing next to him were Heimdallr, Nanna, and Odin, adding their assent to the judgement.

Many of the Æsir started discussing how this might be done. How could they get Loki's head and not harm him. Several mentioned Mimir, only for it to be pointed out Mimir's head still lived, but his body did not. So, his circumstances weren't an apt comparison.

After much debate they reached the conclusion there was no way Brokkr could sever Loki's head without hurting his neck or fatally injuring the rest of the body."

Furious, Brokkr pulled out his sword and ran to Loki, who was still being held down by Thor. Either Thor was too dull or deliberately didn't protect Loki, but Brokkr grabbed Loki's lower lip and tried to poke a hole in it with his sword. But, the sword was too old, rusty, and blunt to do any damage.

Brokkr spoke out loud, "I wish I had Sindri's awl here so that I could work on the head that is rightfully mine." To everyone's amazement, the awl suddenly appeared. The dvergar quickly made several holes in Loki's lips and laced them together with a leather thong, which was called vartari. "There, your lips are sewn so tightly shut you can never bother anyone with your speaking or boasting again. I may not have your head but at least others won't have to listen to what comes out of it."

The Thing broke up with much comment about what had happened.

Odin, Thor, and Freyr were pleased with all their gifts.

Brokkr felt cheated out of Loki's head, but was satisfied at having put an end to Loki's boasting.

However, such was not really the case. Since magic charms had never been worked on the leather, Loki was able to later tear the binding from his lips. Though his lips were ever after scarred and uneven, and he always had a snarl on his face, he was still able to carry on with his boasting and mischief-making.

Chapter 7

Loki's Brood

It seemed like such a long time ago, but if you'll remember, before all the todo with Brokkr, Loki, that mischievous taunter of the Æsir, had eaten the heart of the evil witch Angroboda and that deed had precipitated the War Between the Æsir and the Vanir.

Now, by some mysterious way, Loki found himself pregnant. He had been having strange food cravings. Had become upset at the slightest provocation; and instead of threatening the other person, would just burst into tears. And, then, there was the weight gain. He was becoming huge. At the first kick he knew he was pregnant and left Asgardr for a quiet deserted island. None of the Æsir knew the truth of his delicate condition. That is, except Odin, who could see all from his throne Hlidskjalf in his watchtower in his hall Valaskjalf. And, Huninn and Muninn delighted in sitting on his shoulders in Valhalla telling him how they had watched Loki earlier throwing up the strangest things he had been eating.

Loki got huger and huger. Mountainous. And he had the same thoughts many pregnant women have, "When will all this be over? Are these children never coming out?", after which he went and ate more lutefisk, topped with clotted cream. He now loved lutefisk. Ate it all day long. And the clotted cream made it extra special.

Eventually, it was his time and he bore three children as a result of that foul meal of Angroboda's heart. And what would one expect from children bred from Loki and an evil heart?

Fenriswulf was the eldest. He was followed in age by his brother Midgardrsormr, sometimes known by the Jotuns as Jormungandr. Hela, their sister, was the youngest. Thus, Angroboda's evil lived on in her wretched offspring.

Although it might have been hoped the three would turn out alright, such was not the case. How could they have become anything but evil considering the fact their parents were both dark with malicious deeds that had hurt and destroyed countless others? Both Loki and Angroboda, having had a sworn vengeance to bring about the destruction of the Æsir, could hope their children would accomplish that feat for them.

Loki could feel Odin looking at him and knew his children would not be safe on this island. It was inconvenient to get to, but it could be gotten to. There were no magical protections around it. So, Loki moved with all his children to Jotunheimr where the Jotuns welcomed his children as future slayers of the Æsir. All the Jotuns of every kind, from hrimthursar to bergriser pledged protection to Fenriswulf, Midgardrsormr, and Hela. Loki eventually deserted them as soon as his belly had gone down, leaving them in a cave, and returning to Asgardr as if nothing had happened.

So, the three all grew to adulthood safely within the protected bounds of Jotunheimr. As they grew older the evil of the land worked its way into them, possessing them totally.

Odin, seated on Hlidskjalf in his watchtower in his hall Valaskjalf, gazed out over the nine Worlds of the Tree. To the east of Jotunheimr he caught sight of a darkness outside a cave in one of the remote areas of that land. As his eyes focused on the image the sight became clearer. He was looking upon Fenriswulf, Midgardrsormr, and Hela. Today was the first time they had ventured out of the cave in which they lived.

"So," Odin thought, "that's what became of them. I knew it was too good to be true to think they had drowned in the sea when Loki returned to Asgardr alone."

The three siblings had become too big for their shelter and had decided to move on and find a larger cave. Odin watched as their shadows cast an evil darkness towards Midgardr. Though he had heard rumors of their existence and had sensed an evil presence when gazing in that area, until now he had never seen them . Their size and power awed him. They were far bigger than he had imagined. Something had to be done. He sent for Thor, Tyr, Hermodr and Loki to give them orders on how to control the situation.

"There's a great evil in Jotunheimr that we must contain before it becomes too powerful even for us," spoke Odin. "My ravens have whispered to me of a presence not to be trusted from that quarter. I have now seen them for myself. They are more powerful than even I thought they could be, and they are still growing. Therefore, we must take action immediately. You four are to set off this very day for Jotunheimr and seek out these three and bring them back here where we will be strong enough to overpower them." Then turning to Loki he added, "If you refuse to help us in this matter out of some sense of misplaced parental duty, I shall ban you forever from the hallowed grounds of Asgardr. Your loyalty should lie with us, not with those monsters which you've spawned."

Thor, Tyr, and Hermodr started a bit and looked at Loki. This was the first they heard he had anything to personally do with Fenriswulf, Midgardrsormr, or Hela. But, to also find out he was their father, this was truly startling. Just think if they knew Loki wasn't their father, but their mother?

Although Loki had ties with both Asgardr and Jotunheimr he preferred living in Asgardr. His enemies were fewer because Asgardr was hallowed land where blood could not be shed. He didn't have to look over his shoulder so much. Loki was ambitious and constantly plotting the overthrow of the Æsir. His plots had their best chances of success if he remained in Asgardr keeping track of what was going on and setting one god against the other whenever chance arose. For him the betrayal of his children was of small consequence. After all he could always bear more children. Then, again, there was always the possibility his children might triumph.

The four journeyed eastward towards Jotunheimr. Their travel was made difficult because of the high mountains surrounding the outer perimeter of the land. Some of the mountain ranges were natural. But on occasion one could glimpse a mountain range which upon closer inspection revealed itself to be a group of jotuns who had been fighting each other so hard they hadn't noticed daylight approaching and had all been dayed-up, turned to stone mid-blow.

Eventually the four came to the cave where Loki's children lived. Loki spoke first, "My children, I have a wonderful adventure planned for you. It's time for you to be with your father. It is time now that you accompany me to Asgardr to see where I live. It's a beautiful place and you'll like it there."

His children slowly backed into the cave, not trusting their mother who had deserted them, who was now saying he was their father and welcoming them to accompany him back to Asgardr. They had been warned by others in Jotunheimr never to go to Asgardr because their powers would be greatly diminished there. Why was their mother/father doing this to them? The three were terribly confused.

Hermodr, Tyr and Thor were growing impatient and took Loki aside to talk with him. Thor was all for forcing the three monsters to go back with them. "I'm strong enough to bash them all on their heads with Mjolnir and carry them back with me. When next they open their eyes they'll see the glories of Asgardr."

Hermodr felt Thor's remarks were a bit boastful. As the two started arguing between themselves Tyr stepped between them. "We're here to fight the jotuns, not ourselves. I'm sure you can do all that you say, Thor. But wouldn't it be better on all of us if they came with us willingly, rather than making things difficult for us by having to carry them? Remember how high those mountains were?" Thor stepped back thinking of carrying Midgardrsormr over the mountains. Tyr continued, speaking this time to Loki, "I feel it's up to you to persuade them to come. Remind them they should honor their father, or mother, or whatever you are to them."

Loki went back to his children and spoke to them, "You're my children and I ask that you obey me in this. I wish to have you three in Asgardr with me so I can teach you the things a parent should teach his children. I want to do this without having to journey this far to see you each time. If you don't obey me in this then I'll never see you again and disown you."

His children were still young enough to want attention from their parent, and not old enough to openly rebel for that attention. They trustingly agreed to accompany their father back to Asgardr.

Upon their arrival in Asgardr they found its streets lined with the Æsir watching the strange procession to Odin's hall. Hermodr and Tyr were in the front followed by Midgardrsormr, Hela and Fenriswulf. Loki followed them watching his three children to make certain they created no mischief. Thor brought up the rear of the parade keeping an eye on Loki to make certain he created no mischief.

As Hela walked past, some of the Æsir marveled at her beautiful profile. But when she turned to face them they were shocked by the rotted half-dead side of her face which had been hidden from them in profile. As she approached closer some of them noticed a smell about her, as if one were standing next to the freshly shoveled earth from a newly dug grave. She smelled of a long dead corpse left in the sun to rot. Luckily there were no

mortals from Midgardr in the crowd. For anyone from Midgardr looking upon her baleful face would have immediately been turned to stone.

Midgardrsormr's tongue occasionally lashed out threateningly at the crowd as he turn and raise up over their heads. Poisonous slobber dripped from the corners of his mouth.

And lastly Fenriswulf walked past. Occasionally he stopped in front of some of the Æsir. Staring at them he hunched down, growled and drooled as if preparing to attack. But then he calmly moved on.

Soon they reached Odin's hall where he spoke to them. "You're now in Asgardr where your power is greatly diminished. Therefore, I am going to deal with you now so you'll no longer threaten the Æsir and the good people of Midgardr."

Midgardrsormr

Turning to the serpent, he continued, "Midgardrsormr, I shall deal with you first." With that Odin caught up the serpent by his tale, swung him round and round overhead, gathering momentum, and finally hurled him into the sea, his body writhing in the air as he fell towards Midgardr. There he stayed and grew large enough to encircle Midgardr entirely until eventually he caught his own tale in his mouth. He grew lazy in the sea and would sleep for days and even weeks on end. But when he did awaken, it was with a great hunger. So he'd stretch and raise his head to the surface causing the ocean to churn with unabated fury. The waves crashed into shores all over Midgardr. He capsized and wrecked ships at sea so he could feast upon the sailors who drowned. Some were not quite drowned when he swallowed them down. Then sated and fed the world serpent settled down to sleep some more until once again hunger woke him. It was known that with the arrival of Midgardrsormr on Midgardr, disease and pestilence came into the world, emanating from his body.

Hela

Next Odin dealt with Hela. "You're ambitious, Hela, and I think you would like to rule the Æsir and those in Midgardr. However, I have something different in mind for you. Aim your thoughts lower, for you shall be a queen, but your kingdom will be in Niflheimr and your rule will be over the nine worlds that go ever deeper down in that land. Your subjects will be those who have died cowardly straw deaths, whether on their sick beds, in their sleep, or of old age; those whose only crime has been a bloodless death. You will have command over all perjurers, oath-breakers, murderers and adulterers. But in your land those whose only crime is that they died a cowardly death will not be punished, nor will they be rewarded either. As for the others, do with them whatsoever tortures you can devise."

At this command the ground opened around her and swallowed her up. She slowly sank down to Niflheimr, to the furthest of the nine regions, to Helheimr.

For others, helveg, the road to the underworld, is more difficult. You must travel downward and northward for nine days and nights past the Myrkvydr Forest with its iron-leafed trees, and through Svartalfheimr, the land of the dark alves. There you will come to the Gjoll River, a stagnant black stream cut between two precipitous cliffs and ravines. At this point you will find the entrance to Gnipahellir Cave. Chained at the entrance, next to the bottomless pit, is a hel-hound named Garmr. He constantly howls and strains at his chains, longing to break free. His chest is soaked with the bloody slaver caused by eating those who have tried to escape from Niflheimr. Only the offering of a helcake can calm him. The only ones in Niflheimr having such a treat are those who while living had once given bread to someone in need.

It is easy to drift on the Gjoll River, past Garmr, into the cave. For all are welcome into Niflheimr, it is the leaving that's the difficult part.

Further along the river one comes to Gjallarbru, the echoing bridge. This magnificent crystal structure is roofed with burning gold and is held in place by a single strand of hair since the dead are so light more is not necessary. Standing guard on the bridge is the skeleton maiden Modgudr, the daughter of the jotun Vafthrudnir and his sister Imr. Here she exacts her toll of blood before allowing anyone to cross over. The blood from the dead and their entourage will be drained from their bodies into Gjoll to raise its level so the funeral ships passing underneath will not be run aground. Frequently the dead will ride the horses burned at their pyre with them over the bridge while their unattended ship floats under the bridge on its way to Niflheimr.

Beyond Gjallarbru the way is barred by a gated wall known by many ekenames, amongst them are Helgrindr Gate, Valgrindr Gate, and Nagrindr Gate, or corpse gate. Beneath this gate lives the hrymthursar Hrimgrimnir, and perched above the gate is the cock named sooty-red whose deathly crow stirs the slain.

As the doomed travel further past the gate, the land becomes colder and colder. Nearby is the river Leiptr over which solemn oaths are sworn. And closer still coming out of the east is the icy-cold river Slidr, whose churning waters are filled with swords, knives and other instruments of battle. Those bound for torture in Niflheimr get a foretaste of what's in store for them by having to wade these treacherous waters on their journey. The swords and knives slice at their bodies, cutting deep wounds which will never be healed. But once their punishment in Niflheimr begins they will think back and long for the mild discomfort of Slidr rather than endure the trials Niflheimr has for them.

If one listens closely one can hear the sound of glaciers cutting and grinding out paths for the river Elivagar as it flows from the well Hvergelmir. It is here, near the well Hvergelmir, one can find the wharf called Nastrond, the strand of corpses, where a ship called Naglfar, made of dead men's nails, is being constructed to carry the dead to the last great battle. This is why it is so important to trim the nails of the dead, so construction on the ship can be slowed.

Those entering Niflheimr from this direction, who have led impure lives, have to wade through freezing streams of venom flowing through a cave covered over the roof and sides with nests of wattled serpents. The twined snakes stretch out from the walls and ceilings, mouths opened and fangs extended hoping they can bite into the dead. Their poison can no longer kill, but sharp fangs can still hurt.

But the worst is yet to come. After passing through the cavern the dead are swept down a waterfall into the well Hvergelmir. As they struggle to stay above the churning waters they might catch sight of Nidhoggr and his sons Goinn, Moinn, Grabakr, Grafvolludr, Ofnir and Svafnir. Though Nidhoggr is wrapped around Yggdrasyll chewing on the root, occasionally he lets up long enough to reward himself with a snack and places his yawning mouth into the stream where a few of the corpses complete their journey in

the cavern of his mouth. He treats himself to the corpses of the dead who have washed into Hvergelmir, first sucking on them and finally, mercifully, swallowing them, for no matter what the horrors the corpses will not be rewarded with a final death.

From there the waters of Nastrond open into a lake called Amsvartnir. Centered on this lake there is an island called Lyngvi. And on this island is the crag Gjoll.

On the other side of the lake is Nidafjoll, the hills of darkness. Here one reaches the three worst regions of Hela's kingdom. They are Hel, Niflheimr, the name all the lands are known by, and Niflhel. Niflhel is by far the worst. Here is Helheimr, the region where Hela has her abode. Damp fog rises up and almost engulfs the area. Inside is her hall called Elidner, which means place of storms.

Her land is a horrid place of punishment for perjurers, oath-breakers, murderers and adulterers. Although no sun has ever shone on it, its doors face to the north to make certain the sun can never gain entrance. The abodes of Asgardr were frequently covered with silver and gold. But for Hela a wickerwork of serpents are entwined around each other covering the walls and ceilings. Their venom drips down upon those inside and burns the flesh of those hit by that poisonous slavver. Sometimes the venom fills the hall so much those inside cannot avoid it and have to wade through it to go from place to place.

Hela's entranceway is called stumbling, her table is set with hunger, while the knife which cuts the meal is called starvation. Ganglati, which means indolent, is her servant, while Ganglot, which means lazy, is her maid. They both take their time waiting on her guests. And if her guests should starve in the meantime, well those things happen. Her bed is sickness, while the hangings about the room, called Arsal, are anguish and evil.

The suffering for those doomed here is terrible. Their hands are riveted against the walls. Their hearts have been cut out and hang outside their chests. All the while ravens tear at their eyes, while their clothing is engulfed in flames, yet the cloth never burns fully away. When the suffering is too much and they call out for drink they are served by the velmegir, those whose deeds in life had not been quite so wicked as those they serve.

The goat Heidrun in Asgardr, whose milk goes to the brave Einherjar in Valhalla, also gives drink to the chained in Niflheimr. Her urine runs down her legs forming a river which flows to Niflheimr. The velmegir wade through venom and fill their cups with this drink and carry it to the chained.

All the while Hela feasts on the brains and marrow of dead men

At the end of the hall, standing between two rocks, are skulls and bones piled into the form of a throne for Hela. At each of the entranceways hangs a skeleton. Placed in the bones of each skeleton is a candle which gives off what little light there is in the hall.

Hela was in her new realm only a short while before its effects could be seen. Above she head been well-formed, with a beautiful figure. But, here, with only the sparse flesh from stripped bones as her meal, or what little marrow was left inside, she soon grew lean and bony.

Her subjects trembled when she raised her hand and pointed out one who was to be taken and put through the worst tortures imaginable to provide entertainment for her enjoyment. It was then as she watched that she sneered, which was the closest she ever came to a smile. Although she had a heart it no longer beat. And when she embraced someone, that person died in her arms. She could often be seen riding her spectre-like three-footed white horse amongst her subjects in Niflheimr and in Midgardr. And if one of those subjects was unlucky enough to be spoken to by her he felt the icy wind coming forth from her mouth. At worst a subject would die from the cold. At best, they might loose a hand or foot to frostbite. But, all would know she had been nearby.

Sometimes when she rode through Midgardr she brought pestilence and famine with her. It was said by those in Midgardr she used a rake when only part of a village was destroyed and a broom when the entire village was destroyed.

Yet even in this region of dank, musty smell, of threat and violence, one could see a magnificent hall of gleaming gold off in the distance on Nide's Plain. This sight gave hope to some in Niflheimr. Maybe there was a future they could aspire to, a way out of their hopelessness? Or, maybe not. For most the hope lead to even greater depression.

As time passed the hatred in her continued to grow. She resented her kingdom. She was better than this. She was greater than a kingdom of skulls and bones. She aspired to a kingdom with an outdoors and light and dark, not this relentless shadow. She plotted and waited for the chance she knew would come, the time when she would have the worst possible revenge on the Æsir. The thought of this future moment of triumph made living in Helheimr bearable, if not worthwhile.

Fenriswulf

Finally, back in Asgardr, Odin turned his gaze to Fenriswulf. "You're strong and could one day be a powerful ally for us. Therefore, I have decided to allow you to remain amongst us and grow up in Asgardr. Perhaps the nature of this sacred land will influence you to help our cause, for at the last battle we will have need of someone with your strength."

Fenriswulf merely glowered at Odin and licked his lips. He skulked off to a corner of the room and laid down. He'd be the restful dog for now. The dog that could be patted on his head. But, he plotted.

Fenriswulf grew stronger day-by-day. He grew more ferocious and evil day-by-day. He growled at any who came near, low, rumbling and frightening. Eventually only Tyr had the courage to feed him, since Fenriswulf had recently acquired the habit of taking extra nips at the hand holding food for him.

At first Odin ignored Fenriswulf and told people he'd grow out of it. But, he didn't and only got worse with daily complains to Odin by many of the Æsir. Finally, Odin agreed that Loki's offspring were becoming a real threat, so he reluctantly called a Thing.

The Æsir met at Urdarbrunnr Well. Fenriswulf crouched in the distance gnawing on a bone, seemingly aware his future was being decided. His ears were perked as he tried to overhear the conversation.

Odin explained the situation to all present, "He's becoming stronger every day, at our own urgings since we are the ones providing the food." Odin ignored the fact this was all at his orders.

Some of the Æsir yelled out the suggestion that Fenriswulf be killed. But Odin struck down the idea, "No, he has a right to live. As yet he has done us no actual harm. Threatening to bite off a hand is not the same as actually biting off a hand. One is a thought, the other a crime. All of us have thoughts that might send us to Niflheimr, few of us actually do deeds foul enough for such a punishment. No, we must come up with

another solution. While we consider what to do we must remember Asgardr stands on sacred ground and blood may not be spilled."

Then Thor yelled out, "Let's chain him."

This seemed the ideal solution. Thor volunteered for the task and worked throughout the night in the smithy at his estate forging a chain. Those in Midgardr looked to the sky and saw glowing fires, while the earth trembled with every blow Thor struck with Mjolnir. When the adamantine fetter was finally finished it was called lædingr.

The following morning the chain was spread out and Fenriswulf was called to it. One of the Æsir yelled to Fenriswulf, "You boast of your strength, but I bet this chain is strong enough to hold you."

Fenriswulf responded to the taunting and let the Æsir bind him with it. Then Thor struck two mighty blows to the last link and riveted it to the strongest stone in Asgardr. The Æsir stood back, confident the problem had been solved. Fenriswulf rose up, stretched lazily, easily snapping the chain in a dozen places. Then he walked away, bored with the matter.

The Æsir hurried back to Urdarbrunnr Well for another Thing. Fenriswulf once more lurked in the distance. And the Æsir were so embroiled in their arguments they didn't notice Fenriswulf had slowly been crouching closer and closer, to within hearing distance while they discussed the situation.

Hermodr spoke first, "Clearly Fenriswulf is stronger than we thought."

The rest of the Æsir agreed with him.

Eventually the conversation got back to trying to bind him, and their failed previous effort with the chain Thor had forged.

One of the lesser Asynjes suggested they get someone else to make a new chain, "Our plan would have worked last time save the fact the chain wasn't strong enough. We need a dvergar chain forged in an underground smithy, and created with magical incantations."

Thor disagreed and spoke up to defend his smithying skills, "I made a chain last time I thought would be sufficient. All of us had underestimated his strength. I vow I'll forge another chain that will be impossible for Fenriswulf to break."

Thor was given a second chance.

That night Thor returned to his smithy. The people of Midgardr gazed into the sky and saw it ablaze with Thor's hammer blows. This spectacle delighted and awed those on Midgardr for three days and three nights. At the end of that time, as dawn broke, Thor came forth with dromi, a chain twice as strong as lædingr had been.

Fenriswulf was again sought out. Thor spoke to Fenriswulf since it was he who had been most insulted by the breaking of lædingr. "Here is another chain. Test your strength against this one, if you dare."

Fenriswulf walked around the chain looking it over, again sniffing at it, inspecting it. He knew what the Æsir were up to and didn't want to fall into their trap. But he saw that he was much stronger than dromi, so again he permitted himself to be bound. The Æsir looked on smiling for they knew this was the strongest chain ever made and Fenriswulf would finally be harmless to them. "You may bind me once more. There is no dvergar smell about the chain, so I know Thor alone worked on it. And, I can easily break anything he makes."

Thor reached for Mjolnir, but was stopped by Odin, "Remember, my son, no blood may be shed on our hallowed ground."

Thor backed away, but the other Æsir could tell he was furious.

They bound Fenriswulf tightly, wrapping the chain in many layers around his body. Again Fenriswulf surprised them. He rose up, gave a shake and a great heave. Dromi's links broke, seemingly more easily than had lædingr. Once more he just turned and walked away.

Odin called another Thing. He spoke to Skirnir, Freyr's messenger and friend, "I want you to journey to Svartalfheimr, the home of the dark alves. Once there seek out the sons of Ivaldi, who made Sif's hair, Gungnir and Skidbladnir. Have them make an enchanted chain that Fenriswulf cannot possibly break."

Thor frowned, but said nothing. He knew he would not be given a third opportunity.

Skirnir was off immediately. He crossed over land and sea until he reached Svartalfheimr. Deep within a cave he called out for the sons of Ivaldi, "Nar, Nain, Niping, Dain, Bifur, Bafur, Bombor and Nor. Come here. I have need of your skills." Soon he was surrounded by an assembly of dirty faces whom he recognized as those whose names he had just yelled.

Skirnir spoke, "The Æsir have sent me here to request you make an enchanted chain to be used for the binding of Fenriswulf. It is to be so slight when Fenriswulf sees its skimpiness he will be willing to test it. But it has to be strong enough that he will be unable to loose himself from it."

The dvergues went off and talked amongst themselves for a few moments. They were happy to help bind Loki's son and get some revenge for the cheating they had suffered at his hands. They still remembered he had stolen the spear Gungnir and the ship Skidbladnir.

There was a lot of scurrying about in all directions. All the while Skirnir sat idly in the darkness while they forged. The work went on for two days and two nights. But at the end of that time the dvergues came forward and handed him the chain gleipnir saying, "It will grow stronger and stronger each time the prisoner attempts to break its bonds, for its strength is derived from the effort of the struggle to be free. There is no charge for this magnificent chain."

Skirnir, had in fact, not offered any payment for the chain. Still he nodded acknowledged their generosity. He was pleased and thanked them, "The Æsir will never forget the generosity of the sons of Ivaldi."

Skirnir hurried back to Asgardr where he met the rest of the Æsir at Urdarbrunnr Well for another Thing. There he spread out the grey chain for all to see. Most of the Æsir had doubts about its strength. It looked exceedingly frail for chain since it was as smooth and soft to the touch as a silken thread.

Thor held up the chain, "Bah, it's no more than a ribbon." He pulled at it to show how easily he could break it. But, much to his surprise, as he pulled and strained, it held. He tried ever harder, his face reddening with the effort, and veins bulging in his thick neck. He grunted and groaned, but all the chain did was cut into his hands.

Skirnir attempted to convince the rest of its strength by explaining what had gone into the forging, "It's made from the noise of a cat's footfall, and we all know how stealthy that is. Add in the beard of a woman and the spittle of a bird which are things we know don't exist. Its flexibility comes from the sinews and nerves of a bear; its strength from the roots

of a mountain. Finally, its weight comes from the breath of a fish. There is nothing in the entire world that can break this silken twine."

The Æsir sat in discussion all afternoon. As night came upon them they looked overhead as Maane followed Nott, when suddenly a great roar shattered the sky as Fenriswulf made a leap for Maane in an attempt to swallow her. Fortunately he was still not quite strong enough to reach Maane, but he came close enough to give the Æsir a scare.

Tyr spoke, unmoved, "Fenriswulf has awakened and wants something to eat. I'll go to feed him." He left the gathering and went to Fenriswulf laden down with dead animals for the dog's supper. Once more the roar was heard, then the monster quieted down and all that broke the silence was the cracking and crunching of a meal being consumed.

Fenriswulf's attempts on Maane had given the Æsir a legitimate reason to bind him. So they could now proceed with righteous justification.

The next morning the Æsir took gleipnir and rowed in Skidbladnir out to the lake in Niflheimr known as Amsvartnir. There on the rocky island known as Lyngvi they walked to the hill called Siglilnin. There they prepared things while some of the Æsir went back to fetch Fenriswulf.

They slowly, warily approached Fenriswulf. Hermodr asked if he'd like to go on a fishing expedition. "We've been bringing you food. Wouldn't you want to experience the hunt and catch some for yourself? Some of us are going fishing and you're welcome to join us."

Fenriswulf replied, "I'll not leave the safety of Asgardr. I feel something is about. The Æsir are out to hurt me. I know I'm safer here in your midst on the sacred grounds of Asgardr than in any of the other Worlds of the Tree. I'm staying where I am."

Hermodr continued, "But everyone has gone on an outing to the island of Lyngvi. There will be no one here to feed you this afternoon since Tyr is there fishing in Amsvartnir. He told me he was going to catch a lot of fish for you since you love the taste of fish that's just out of the water, still flipping around struggling for a breath in their death throes." Fenriswulf seemed to be weakening in his resolve. Hermodr continued pressing the point, "You know how you like fresh fish. Just think how they'll taste after sitting in the sun in Skidbladnir during our return journey, rotting and beginning to smell. Stay here and you won't be fed until quite late, you know. Go with me and you'll eat until you're as full as full can be. Even Thor has offered to help catch fish for you. For once you'll have as much food as you want. There'll be feasting and celebrating like you've never seen before."

This was too much for Fenriswulf to resist. Although he was fed every day, the Æsir never seemed to feed him enough. He was always hungry. It was too tempting to not go with the promise of finally being fed until sated, until he wanted no more.

Fenriswulf accompanied Hermodr to Lyngvi where he lolled about while the Æsir caught fish after fish and threw them to him. He liked fishing. All he had to do was every once in awhile raise his head, open his mouth, and catch a flopping fish. He was fishing without even getting wet. He wiggled on his back some more, stretching. He was happy. And he would only be happier if someone would come over and scratch his belly. They had done that when he was younger. And he had liked it. But, that would never happen. Everyone was now much too frightened of him for that. But, still, it would have been nice. He reached up and batted down a fish that had been thrown at him and swallowed it in one gulp.

At one point Thor brought out gleipnir and mentioned the fun they had had trying to bind him. "You certainly have made fools of the Æsir with your strength. You've broken both lædingr and dromi, two chains that looked far stronger than this simple thread. It's deceptive, though, since we think it's too strong for any of us to break. It's probably too strong even for you to break." With that Thor handed the thread to one of the other Æsir who tried to break it and failed. That god passed it to another who also failed. And yet another and another. They all failed in their attempts at the string.

"Still," Thor continued as the string was passed back to him., "You're so much stronger than all of us. I've wagered with Hermodr you can break it. Will you show us? I'll split my winnings with you."

Fenriswulf eyed gleipnir suspiciously. "If I do break it I'll get no credit, and if it's made with magic I might never free myself from it."

Thor tried to reassure him he could easily break it, "If you can't free yourself, which I doubt, then we'll untie your bonds."

Fenriswulf replied skeptically, "That's what you say now. But once you get me bound how can I be certain you'll set me free if I can't free myself? I'll only submit to being bound if one amongst you will lay their hand inside my mouth. And then if there be any deceit that member of the Æsir will lose his hand."

The Æsir now realized Fenriswulf was much more dangerous and cunning than they had first supposed. It was imperative he be chained. They drew aside to discuss amongst themselves who would be the one to lose his hand, for that was the certain fate awaiting the brave Æsir who volunteered. They all agreed it couldn't be Thor since he was the only one who could wield Mjolnir effectively, and he needed both his hands for that. While they were discussing the matter, comparing the advantages and disadvantages of each of them losing a hand, Tyr walked over and stretched out his right hand, his powerful sword hand, and laid it in Fenriswulf's mouth. "Not only do I submit my hand, I am a warrior and submit my sword hand. If I were to lose it, what worth would I be?" Fenriswulf was impressed. The rest of the Æsir were aghast.

None of the Æsir moved, so much was the shock of seeing Tyr's hand laying across Fenriswulf's tongue. A tongue seemed to be licking at the hand, curling around it and tasting it. Tyr broke the silence, "Who will bind Fenriswulf? He is ready. We both await."

This got the Æsir moving. They hurriedly bound the cord tightly around Fenriswulf's girth, feet, legs, and head until finally he was restrained. They hoped somehow Tyr would be able to jerk back his hand before Fenriswulf realized he was truly and firmly bound.

Fenriswulf rose up and stretched as he had done twice before. This time he was surprised, as were the Æsir. The thread did not give immediately like dromi and lædingr had.

Astonished they watched as Fenriswulf strained against the thread. The more he tried to break gleipnir the tighter it wound about him and the harder it grew. Fenriswulf's eyes burnt red with anger when he realized he had been tricked. He finally yelled through clenched teeth for the Æsir to unbind him. Teeth clenched on Tyr's hand. "You have won. Now keep your promise and unbind me."

The Æsir were all laughing at his struggles to free himself. His twisting and turning wasn't at all graceful since he had to maintain his grasp on Tyr's hand.

Tyr wasn't laughing. His hand was still tightly held in Fenriswulf's mouth.

One of the Æsir answered the wolf, "We said we would unbind you if you asked, but we didn't say when. So we have not betrayed our oaths. We will unbind you someday. At some point. In the future. The far future. We'll be thinking about it."

Fenriswulf started up again trying to get free. He began rolling on the ground, heaving and stretching, but all to no avail. The chain held and cut even deeper into his body. The Æsir looked on satisfied. Then they saw Tyr struggling with Fenriswulf.

Tyr was wrestling with the wolf trying to free his hand. He was using his other hand to pull at Fenriswulf's lower jaw, trying to pry it open. In anger Fenriswulf bit down hard on Tyr's hand and swallowed it. Tyr fell back, blood gushing from the stump. Ever after Tyr was known as the hinn einhendi ass, the one-handed god, and the wrist was known as the wolf-joint. Because of his having wrestled with Fenriswulf, those on Midgardr who practiced this sport called upon Tyr for strength and courage.

The Asynje Eir, the healer of the Æsir, walked over to Tyr, grasped his arm and began chanting magical incantations. The stump stopped bleeding and healed over. She quieted the pain.

With practice Tyr learned to wield a sword with his left hand just as dangerously as he had with his right. His only problem was the difficulty he had in handling a shield with his right arm. He could easily enough put his arm through the bands holding the shield. But, it would slip because he couldn't grasp the leather handles to steady the shield as he raised it to fend off blows. As often as not the shield slipped off his arm, leaving him exposed to his adversary's blows.

Once Fenriswulf was down the Æsir grabbed hold of him and attached the rope hræda to the bonds and wrapped this around Fenriswulf. They had to be careful. Gleipnir was wrapped around Fenriswulf's body. But his head continued to whip back and forth as he tried to bite anyone he could.

The chain gelgja was attached to the end of hræda and threaded through the hole of the great mountain called Gjoll, which was held fast to the center of Midgardr. And to ensure it could not be moved, the boulder thviti was pile-driven down on top of Gjoll to further secure it. The Æsir were taking no chances.

Fenriswulf was exceedingly mad and continued lunging at the Æsir. But they had backed away and were out of his range. He howled and struggled. His mouth gaped open as he strained to reach them. At one point Thor ran up and thrust a sword between the wolf's jaws. The pommel lay on his lower jaw while the point pierced the roof of his mouth. This caused him to let out howls of pain. When he tried to close his mouth the point of the sword cut deeper into his palate until finally a bloody slaver flowed forth from the sides of his mouth forming two rivers called Van, which meant hope, and Vil, which meant despair. Because of this he earned the ekename Vonargander.

After satisfying themselves Fenriswulf was safely bound the Æsir returned to Asgardr.

Fenriswulf was out of sight. But at night when all was quiet they could hear his howls and could feel tremors as he strained against gleipnir. They prayed the thread would hold. Because even though they didn't feed him as much, they were still honorbound to feed him some. And no matter how meagre his meals he continued to grow. And he would keep growing and becoming more fierce, until he's loosed at Ragnarokr.

Part Two

The Adventures

Chapter 8

Utgardr-Loki

A king of Uppsala in Sweden once built a great temple and dedicated it to the Æsir. An eternal flame burnt on an altar within the temple to symbolize the gratefulness the people of Midgardr had for the protection given them by the Æsir.

Now this homage to the Æsir made some of the jotuns in Jotunheimr jealous because no one ever honored them for anything. Rather blame was all anyone spoke about when jotuns were mentioned. Blame for everything: bad crops, cattle dying, sickness. Even bad weather. And these were things the jotuns had no control over. The jotuns decided this king needed to be taught a lesson.

Recently a blockage of ice in Ifing had formed a temporary bridge which a jotun had recently come across and realized it was possible for a few of the lighter jotuns to cross over into Midgardr.

Soon a contingent of jotuns were on their way to Uppsala, to the temple. And they had quite a surprise with them. Captured in a jar was a burst of icy wind from one of the hrymthursar. Their plan was to hold the jar up to the eternal flame, open it and blow out the flame. That would show those on Midgardr just how eternal a flame could be.

And their plan went exactly as they had planned. They stood around staring at the smoke waving up from the wick. That was it? They had crossed Ifing, journeyed in the cold, exhausted themselves, and all they had to show for it was an unlit candle? Now that they'd done it, blowing out a candle didn't seem to be satisfying enough. They couldn't get the thoughts out of their heads. That was it. A smoking wick. They'd crossed over Midgardr at great peril to blow out a candle? Seemed silly now. They looked at each other. After all, they were jotuns. And jotuns liked to throw big things around. And, if something was damaged, then so be it and all the better.

Tearing down the temple had been much easier than they thought it would be. Soon they were heaving the stones in all directions, killing many of the priestesses and people of the village. But, rampaging can be exhausting. Satisfied with their day's work, and a little tired, they returned to Jotunheimr. Soon after, the weather warmed a bit, the ice melted and the way into Midgardr was once again protected by the river Ifing.

Odin saw all of this while he sat in his watchtower seated on his throne Hlidskjalf in his hall Valaskjalf. He called a Thing by Urdarbrunnr Well. Of all the Æsir who met there Thor was the most angered by the attack on the temple. "That temple was honoring us. To despoil it defiles our own sacredness. This cannot stand. They must be punished."

He turned to Odin, "Give me leave to do so and I'll go to Jotunheimr and seek out those who destroyed this monument to the Æsir. I'll teach them a lesson they'll never forget. I'll bash their heads in."

Seemed like a plan. Not a great plan, but at least they'd be doing something to show how angry they were that a temple dedicated to the Æsir had been destroyed.

However, it didn't seem feasible for Thor to go to Jotunheimr by himself. Everyone voted and it was decided Loki would accompany Thor because he had been to Jotunheimr many times and was more familiar with the territory. And there was his ancestry. He was as much jotun as he was Æsir. They thought this was an advantage, not however, seeing the jotuns might think Loki placed more importance on the jotun half of his ancestry. For his part Loki just smiled.

Soon Thor's iron chariot was readied for the journey. With Thor holding tightly to the reins and Loki gripping handholds on the chariot, Thor's two milk-white goats, Tanngnjostr and Tanngrisnir, pulled the chariot up and away through the sky towards Midgardr.

At first the people of Midgardr heard the dull rumbling of the chariot in the distance. As it drew closer the rumbling became a thunderous roar. Gazing skyward their eyes saw a blinding sight. The gold-shod hooves of the goats reflected across the sky. At times Thor waved Mjolnir overhead causing great jumps of lightning to strike out across the sky from cloud to cloud. The display was deafening and awesome to behold. Thor was traveling west to east as was his custom across Midgardr to battle the cold storms coming out of the east from Jotunheimr. Although Thor sometimes brought rain, the drops were warm and comforting. His storms nourished, while those sent by the jotuns ravaged the crops of Midgardr.

Thjalfi and Rosva

They journeyed eastward across Midgardr until they came to a farmhouse near the river Ifing, where they sought shelter for the night. Thor went to the doorway and knocked. When the peasant, who was named Egil, answered Thor asked, "Could you lodge two weary travelers for the night?"

Most people of Midgardr were generally hospitable and this peasant was no different. "Gladly will I give you a rest from your journey."

Then his wife broke in, "But food is something scarce here. Most of our farm extends across the river into Jotunheimr. Though we can cross Ifing to tend the part of our fields in Jotunheimr, the jotuns cannot follow us back across Ifing. This just angers them and they frequently come to our fields to steal our crops. I'm afraid we have very little for you to eat, but we will gladly share what we have with you."

Thor replied, "Don't let that worry you, we'll gladly provide you with food in exchange for your hospitality. Put a kettle on to boil while I take care of the rest."

With that Thor went back to his chariot and proceeded to kill both his goats as the peasants' two children, Thjalfi, the swift, and Roskva, holdfast, looked on. They were both blond and blue-eyed, and just entering into their teenage years. Thjalfi was slightly older than Roskva.

Thor stripped the two he-goats, Tanngnjostr, gap tooth, and Tanngrisnir, crack tooth, of their skins, which he carefully spread across the hearth inside the cottage. Then he drained their blood into a jug, added honey and other ingredients to make a delicious mead to serve with dinner. By now the water was boiling in the kettle and Thor put the meat and bones of his two goats into it and proceeded to cook a delicious stew.

The goats cooked very quickly and it wasn't long before everyone sat down to table to eat. As they picked up their tableware Thor admonished them, "Eat hearty. It matters not to me if you eat all of my goats. However, under no circumstances should you break any of the bones. When you have finished throw the bones into the skins spread out over there on the hearth."

Each made the sign of Thor's hammer over their food and blessed the Æsir. Thor hallowed the meal by swinging Mjolnir overhead after which the meal was dished out on plates to everyone except Thor. His appetite was so great that ordinary plates were insufficient. Instead he used his shield as a plate in order to hold enough for his meal. Tilting it up, everything on it ran over the edge and into his mouth, except some that fell on his shoulder and to the floor. He was not the tidiest of eaters.

Loki sat next to Thjalfi, and saw his chance for some mischief and whispered into the young lad's ear, "The only reason he has told you not to break the bones is because he wants all the marrow for himself since that's the tastiest part. Look at how he wolves down the greatest share for himself. Also, these goats are special and the marrow possesses magical gifts. I'm certainly going to break into mine." With that he made motions as if to crack apart one of the bones. But he didn't really.

After eating all the flesh from his portion Thjalfi hesitated, but finally the urge was too irresistible and he broke the thighbone on his plate to get at the marrow. It was indeed delicious. But as he looked around he saw the others were tossing their bones into the skins on the hearth without breaking them, including Loki whom he realized had not actually cracked open his bones, after all. So Thjalfi hurriedly tossed his bones in with the others hoping no one would notice the broken thigh bone and was relieved when it looked as if no one had.

Early before dawn the next morning Thor gathered up the skins and bones and took them outside where he swung Mjolnir overhead to hallow them. Immediately everything fell together and his goats were made whole again. He whispered runes over them and chanted secret incantations which caused the goats to rise up and stand, living once more.

The others in the household had been awakened by the thunderous sounds caused by the swinging of Mjolnir and came out in time to see the goats rise up. Tanngnjostr began prancing around playfully, glad to be living again. But Tanngrisnir walked slowly, painfully, measuring each step carefully. Thor noticed it limping. Realizing one of the peasants had disobeyed him he filled with rage and spun around raising Mjolnir overhead ready to strike down the four standing before him. Lightning bolted up to the sky. Gone was the amiable guest from last night. Standing before them was a very angry God.

Egil and his family all fell to their knees trembling, begging for mercy. Thor motioned for them to get up. Egil spoke, offering as weregild all they had, "I don't know how it happened, but I offer to you and your friend everything we own to make up for this terrible, terrible thing that has happened."

Thor yelled back, "Has happened? You act as if it were an accident. It didn't just happen. Someone caused it. Someone cracked the bone of my goat. Who was it?" Thor looked from father to mother to son to daughter. "WHO WAS IT?"

Thjalfi stood to one side trembling with fright. In order to spare his family he finally confessed to having broken the thighbone. "I did it. I couldn't resist. I thought the marrow was the best part, and I wanted to taste it." Loki sighed with relief when Thjalfi apparently forgot he had cracked the bone at Loki's urging.

Thor thought the situation over and said, "I will not destroy you or your family, Egil. But I do ask that you give me Thjalfi and Roskva to serve as my squire and handmaiden."

The parents had no choice but to agree.

Thor left his chariot and goats in the care of Egil and his wife so the injured animal's thighbone could set while he, Loki, Thjalfi and Roskva set out on their journey.

Skrymir

After only a short walk they reached the river Ifing and continued upstream until they reached the point where it was deepest and widest. There they found a boat waiting for them. The river seemed peaceful, but once they started across a fierce storm raged up seemingly from nowhere. Their boat tossed about and all except Thor feared that at any moment they would be capsized and drowned. Thor rowed with all his strength, safely bringing them to the opposite bank.

Dark, sky-engulfing mists covered the land and great black rocks rose along the coast. The rocks had been blackened from the wash of the sea and fury of the storms. They traveled inward from this area, passing into the darkness of the immense forest whose trees towered so high the sun was frequently blocked from view.

They traveled through the forest until nightfall with Thor leading the way followed by Loki and Roskva. Thjalfi, laden down with provisions, brought up the rear. It had been a hard journey all day and they were tired and grateful when they saw an enormous building in front of them. It was constructed rather strangely with one great center room which branched off into five other long halls. It was vacant inside lacking both hearth and furniture. And it certainly was odd to find a hall so large and so devoid of occupancy. Outside they looked around but could find no signs anyone had ever lived there. It was a puzzle as to why anyone would want to build such an enormous hall and then abandon it without ever using it. But they were all too weary to think too much about that. After all, here was a nice safe place to spend the night. After eating they wearily laid down on the floor, which turned out to be rather soft, and almost immediately sleep engulfed them.

About midnight a rumbling disturbed their slumber. Since none of the halls in the building had any additional supports they feared the roof might cave in. So they moved from the center room to the side room on the right because it seemed to be the shortest of the five long halls. Thor didn't join them. Instead he buckled on Megingardr, his belt of strength, took Mjolnir and went outside to stand guard before the entranceway. When it became light enough to see he ventured forth to find out what was causing all the noise. He didn't have to travel far before he saw an enormous jotun stretched out and fast asleep. His snoring was making the trees blow almost down to the ground one way, and then the opposite way when he inhaled. The very earth shook with every breath .

Thor stood staring at him. Then the jotun sat up with a start. "Yo, who are you down there? Since when do ants wear clothing and carry hammers?"

Thor braced himself against a tree to prevent being blown over by the jotun's breath. He was amazed to see the jotun had light blue eyes, something rare for that race. "What's your name?"

The jotun responded, "It's Skrymir. What have you done with my glove?" Skrymir bent over and picked it up shaking out Loki, Thjalfi, and Roskva who had been crouching in its thumb. He continued, "And now I know who you are. I was right, ants don't carry hammers, but Thor, the mighty thundergod, does. Might I travel with you a bit? It gets lonely walking through this forest without anyone to talk with."

Thor accepted the offer on behalf of the others, who were a bit chary of having the jotun walking with them. One misstep and they could all be crushed. But, what else could they do?

Skrymir untied his sack and began to eat his breakfast. The others followed his example, sitting a distance away from him, eating theirs. After breakfast while they were preparing to start on the day's journey Skrymir suggested they put their food together. "Since I'm so much larger than all of you I can more easily carry it. That way we'll all make faster progress, and I don't mind helping you out in the least."

The four discussed the offer amongst themselves. Loki, ever distrustful, spoke against the idea, "If he decides to suddenly leave our company then we'll be without provisions. I don't want to be dependent on a stranger."

Although Roskva and Thjalfi didn't have much say in the matter they agreed with Loki, even though having Skrymir carry the sack of food would make things easier for Thjalfi, since he was the one now burdened with the task.

But Thor overruled them all, "Loki, you think everyone is going to act how you act. Not everyone cheats others of their property and then steals away in the night with it." The thundergod tossed their sack of food in Skrymir's sack, who closed it and then flung it over his shoulder saying, "Now let's get on with our journey. We have a long distance to cover today. Let me know if I walk too fast for you."

The path they followed led along a wide lake. Skrymir started off taking seven rost strides, covering acres of land with each step. Before Thor, Loki, Roskva, and Thjalfi knew it he was far in the distance. They ran all day to catch up with him. Occasionally he'd stop to rest and just as they caught up with him and prepared to rest too, he started off again, usually yelling to them, "I hope this little walk isn't proving too much for all of you? We must not dally about if we want to get where we're going."

And so it went all day. They traveled late into the evening, much later than the four would normally have traveled in such a strange land. But Skrymir seemed to know where he was going so they followed along scrambling from footstep to footstep. Finally they saw in the distance that Skrymir had stopped by a great oak. When they caught up to him they were surprised to find he didn't start off again. Instead he tossed down the sack saying, "You may get some food. As for me, I'm going to get some sleep." He immediately went

off to a hillside to sleep. As he departed he added, "Be certain not to break the bonds when you untie the sack."

The four were grateful to finally have a chance to rest. Roskva set to preparing dinner. But almost immediately she ran into a problem. No matter how hard she tried the sack could not be untied. Next Thjalfi tried, then Loki. Finally Thor tried, thinking though the others had failed it would be a simple task for him. But try as he might he couldn't loosen the cords. In fact it seemed to him the harder he tried the tighter the cords knotted. He became angry and heedless of the jotun's warning not to break the bonds, he cut and hacked at the leather with a sword. But without success. Thor stalked off to the jotun who by now was fast asleep, and threw Mjolnir at him, bashing him in the head. The jotun slowly awoke from his sleep and seeing Thor standing there remarked to him, "I think we're going to have an early fall. A leaf just fell on my head to awaken me." Thor didn't reply so Skrymir continued, "Have all of you finished your dinner yet, or been to sleep?" Seeing Thor was not going to reply to the questions, he rolled over and went back to sleep.

Unable to open the sack the four had to settle down to sleep on empty stomachs. At least it was early evening and they could look forward to a nice long rest before morning. They sought shelter under the roots of the oak tree. It was difficult getting to sleep. Growling stomachs can be loud, hunger can be distracting. But eventually they all managed. Then about midnight Skrymir's snoring became so loud the forest itself began to vibrate. Thor didn't take kindly to what was happening to him. First he had had to run all day to follow this foolish jotun; second he had had to go to sleep on an empty stomach; and finally, his hard won sleep was being disturbed by snoring. He headed towards Skrymir, swung Mjolnir three times over his head and let it loose against the unsuspecting jotun. His aim was true and Mjolnir found its mark and sank up to the handle in the center of Skrymir's head, then pulled free and returned to Thor.

Skrymir awoke, sat up, and asked, "Has an acorn fallen on my head? Thor, how nice to see you. How are you?"

Thor replied, "I'm just walking about to stretch my legs. We have only a few more hours of sleep left."

Skrymir nodded in acknowledgement, laid back and was soon asleep, snoring as loudly as ever. Thor tried to go to sleep. But it was soon morning and he still had not closed his eyes. Skrymir's snores were coming at regular intervals. Thor got up and hurled Mjolnir over his head and threw the hammer as hard as he ever had. As it sailed through the air towards Skrymir, cutting a wide path through the trees in its way. It reached its target and sank deeply into the jotun's forehead and again returned to Thor's hand.

This time upon being hit Skrymir jumped to his feet and seeing Thor there exclaimed to him, "Thor, are there any birds in the oak tree I've been sleeping under? I think one has just soiled on me." Thor said nothing so Skrymir continued, "I think we'd better get ready to leave. We want to reach Utgardr before nightfall. Wait till you see that city. If you think I'm large you'll be surprised to see some of the jotuns there. They tower over me. But if that frightens you, you and your friends are free to turn back."

Thor took exception to the remark and replied, "Don't boast so much. We can take care of ourselves. As to turning back. Not until we've set foot in Utgardr."

So again they set off with Skrymir far in the distance and Thor, Loki, Roskva and Thjalfi running as hard as they could to keep up.

Later that afternoon when Skrymir had finally stopped for a rest he spoke to the others, "I think it would be best if we parted here. I'm going to take the north road to Utgardr. You can get there just as well if you take the road over there to the east." He pointed in the direction of a road which was much smoother than the one he was taking. On the horizon they could see Utgardr. Skrymir threw their sack of provisions over his shoulder and started off. To the others his path appeared quite gloomy. The towering black mountains he would have to cross were separated from each other by vast yawning chasms. The mountains' icy snow-covered tops seemed to form an impenetrable barrier to Utgardr.

Skrymir was soon out of sight. The four were glad to be rid of his company. They could continue their journey at less than the breakneck pace set by Skrymir, and on a far smoother path than the one Skrymir had chosen.

The Journey

Utgardr didn't look very far away and they thought they were fairly close to the city, only a field or two away, and it would only take a little while to reach it, perhaps even by midmorning. However, the nearer they got the further away it seemed. For every step they took they slipped back two. After a time they were nearly exhausted but had finally reached a point where the path led through the rocks towards the gates of the great city. Their hopes of reaching Utgardr by midmorning had long since passed.

It was now early evening and darkness had fallen. They continued on, going ever deeper down. They heard the sound of roaring rivers. As they turned the point of a rock, through the darkness they saw what seemed to be a lighted candle. But on closer inspection they found it to be only a dying firebrand near the entrance to a large cave. Barring their way was a strong iron gate. Thor picked up the glowing stick and pried against the closures of the gate. It took surprisingly little effort before the gate flew open, letting loose a noisy gust of stale air. Thor entered first while the other three reluctantly followed behind. Their footsteps echoed in the silence. There was no light now. The road wound downward through fractured rocks of granite so narrow they could travel only in a single file. As they went deeper, more and more the smell of newly-turned earth filled their senses.

Eventually the pathway opened into a large cavern. Hanging along the walls were ghostly corpses swinging from side to side in their own macabre dance; their lifeless eyes staring at the unwanted intruders who glowed with life and the freedom of movement now denied them. The only light in the hall proceeded from two funeral tapers stuck inside the rib cages of a like number of skeletons.

Two thrones made up of skulls and human bones stood at the end of the cavern. Seated before them were two ghastly spectres, one male, one female, who both rose as Thor and the others approached. They wore blue armor over which was wound white sepulchral sheets. In their hands they held maces made from dead men's bones. One of the grey, bloodless faces turned to Thor and spoke. As Thor saw the front of the face he recognized it as Hela, Loki's daughter.

"Why do you come here while you are still quick with blood and have many days amongst the living before you?" The voice sounded like a groan of agony, which caused Roskva and Thjalfi to huddle closer behind Thor for protection. The wail continued,

"You may yet die in battle instead of a cowardly straw death, so why have you come to the domain of Hela?"

Thor replied, "We've been mislead by the jotun Skrymir. He pointed us in this direction as a way of reaching Utgardr. Instead his cruel joke has brought us here to Helheimr in Niflhel." Then turning to speak to Loki he continued, "You must certainly be a proud parent to see how fine your daughter has turned out."

Loki took umbrage at the remark and turned to leave. But Thor still continued his taunting, "Watch which way you go. You wouldn't want to get lost and have to have an even longer visit with Hela. But I can't say I blame you for wanting to leave. Even Odin couldn't stand looking at Hela. She's like her father, only fit to rule over cowards."

Loki realized he couldn't find his way without the others, so ignoring Thor's remarks he said, "We have a long journey ahead of us and shouldn't be standing here wasting our time in silly conservation if we want to reach Utgardr any time in the near future."

Thor turned to Hela and asked for directions. Though angered by the insults thrown at her and her father by Thor, there was nothing she could do. Her power was only over those who had suffered a cowardly death, and the four before her were still very much alive. She directed them, pointing westward with a bony skeletal finger, glad to be rid of the intruders, not wanting any further reminders of life in the other worlds. As the four left the cavern she called out to Roskva and Thjalfi, "Are you certain you don't want to tarry a while longer with me? Let me embrace you and welcome you." But the two knew such an embrace would be death for them. Roskva and Thjalfi were beside themselves with fear at the remark and never were more than a few paces from Thor's side for the rest of the journey to Utgardr.

Utgardr

Outside the cave the four continued their journey, traveling until they reached the north side of the mountain. They didn't stop to sleep that night, but continued eastward until noon the next day, at which time there arose before them a great city spread out over a vast plain. It took them till evening to reach the front gate. The walls surrounding the city, and indeed the buildings themselves, were made of great blocks of ice. The structures were so high the four had to lean backwards in order to see the tops of them.

A filigreed iron gate towered over them. Thor tried to open it but couldn't. The gate was secured with massive chains. Keeping watch nearby were several jotuns whose spears were made from tall pines, while their shields were fashioned from great slabs of granite. Thor yelled up to them to open the gates so they might enter. The jotuns ignored him.

Thor pulled at the bars, but the gate didn't budge. He threw Mjolnir against the chains, but it returned to him, nicked a little on the edge. Thor stalked back and forth frustrated.

Loki was the first to discover he was small enough to fit sideways through the bars. And so that was the ignoble method used by the four to gain entry to Utgardr. The guards made no moves against the intruders thinking them too insignificant to bother about. Or, perhaps, they hadn't even seen them.

Thor, Loki, Thjalfi, and Roskva walked on for awhile until they came to a towering palace constructed of great blocks of blue ice with huge glimmering icicles for pillars holding up a crystal clear sheet of ice for a roof. The front doors were open so they entered and found themselves in an immense hall. Lining each side of the hall were long benches with matching trestle-tables. Seated the length of these tables were jotuns. Higher-up on a dais facing them at the other end of the hall was another table and bench. Seated here was Utgardr-Loki, and next to him were jotuns who, as Skrymir had promised, were much larger than he. Standing behind guarding Utgardr-Loki was a triple ring of jotuns in full armor. The sight was impressive.

Thor walked down the center of the hall towards Utgardr-Loki and saluted him. But Utgardr-Loki sat at his table picking his teeth and then spitting, ignoring Thor. Finally he reached over and struck his shield three times with a steel mace. Immediately the hall began to shake. Flames burst forth from the ground in front of Thor.

Then Utgardr Loki spoke to Thor, "You had better be gone or the roof will also fall in on you."

Thor looked up and saw a huge boulder tottering ready to fall from the rafters. It tottered back and forth, finally sliding forward and falling, hitting the ground with such force it burst into thousands of fragments. Part of the floor had caved in to reveal a cavern filled with treasures. A suffocating vapor wafted upwards from the treasure-room engulfing Thor and the three others in its poisonous mist. Then just as suddenly as these events occurred things were back like they had been. The floor was clean and whole, the mist gone.

Thor had stood unmoved during the demonstration. He spoke again, "I salute you and this is how you answer it? Do you know who I am?"

Utgardr-Loki turned to the other jotuns in the room and pointing towards Thor said, "You see before you Thor, the mighty thundergod of the Æsir." Then addressing his remarks once again to Thor he continued, "Tell us Thor, what feats of strength can you perform for us? And what talents do the three cowering members of your company possess? None may stay in Utgardr unless they can do something that is very difficult."

Loki since recovered from his fright, spoke with his usual bravado. Speaking up even before Thor had a chance to reply, "I can perform one thing better than any other. I can eat more and faster than anyone alive. But be warned it won't be a fair contest since I'm famished and haven't eaten a decent meal since we stopped at a peasant's house several days ago. Bring forth whomever you choose and I'll show you my talent."

Utgardr-Loki spoke, "That indeed would be a mighty feat, that is if you really can accomplish it. Let's see if you can eat enough at one meal to last you eight days. I think it would only be appropriate that your opponent be my cook, Logi. Don't worry about it not being a fair match since you haven't eaten in awhile. Logi's been so busy cooking for our guests he also hasn't eaten in quite some time, though I'm not certain how long."

A long trough was set in the center of the hall. Meat, breads, and all manner of food was heaped on it till it sagged low from the weight. Then Logi was summoned to a place at one end of the trough. He was lean and gaunt with caved in ashy cheeks. He had long jagged iron teeth set in double rows in a monstrously wide constantly grinning mouth. The nails on his bony hands gripped the edge of the trough like vulture's claws, while his

coal-black eyes stared intently at only one area of the hall, the table. His armor glowed white and red. Sparks like flints being struck jumped forth from the joints in his armor as he swayed back and forth in anticipation of the feast set before him.

At a signal the two, one at each end of the trough, began to eat voraciously. They both reached the middle of the trough at the exact same moment. But Logi was declared the winner while Loki admitted defeat. For while Loki had eaten only the meat and breads, Logi had devoured bones, trough, eating utensils, plates and everything else that happened to be in his path. Loki departed to wait outside the hall.

Utgardr-Loki turned to Thjalfi, "What special feat can you perform?"

Thjalfi thought for a moment then answered, "I'm very swift and can out race anyone, whether it be on foot, skis, or snowshoes."

Utgardr-Loki replied, "That certainly would be enough to allow you to visit us. Let's put you to the test and see if what you say is true. Over there near the door is my page, Hugi. He shall be your opponent."

They went outside to a large raceground, a vast plain covered with snow. Everyone gathered in the stands ready to enjoy the spectacle. But it didn't take too long to complete and was over pretty much before anyone realized it.

Hugi and Thjalfi set their stance, twitching, waiting for the race to begin.

Utgardr-Loki raised his hand. A jotun stepped forward and struck a shield setting the two off.

Hugi was so swift he made it to the end of the course, turned around and came back in time to meet Thjalfi who was just crossing the starting line.

Utgardr-Loki spoke, "You'll have to go faster than that in order to win. Yet I've never seen anyone race faster against Hugi."

The two went back to the starting post for a second race. The shield was struck and the two were off once more.

This time Hugi reached the end of the course and on his way back met Thjalfi at the quarter mark. The third race was only slightly better. This time Thjalfi made it to the halfway mark before being met by a returning Hugi. Thjalfi admitted defeat. Everyone except Loki and Thjalfi returned to the great hall where all attention was now directed at Thor.

Utgardr-Loki asked him about his special talent, "I've often heard tales of your awesome strength. But your reputation alone will not suffice here. I wish you would give us actual proof of it."

Thor replied, "I have come here in peace, not to fight you. Therefore, instead of a show of strength I would prefer my talent should be something different. I can out drink anyone in Utgardr. Choose whomever you will as my opponent, and bring forth great horns of hydromel, since that is my favorite drink."

One of the jotuns left and soon returned with a great horn of wrought gold with runes of old carved on its rim. Its mouth was narrow rather than wide, which didn't matter, because it was still bigger than any drinking horn Thor had ever used. The horn was so long its end stretched out of the hall far off into the distance. Thor couldn't see where it ended.

Utgardr-Loki explained its properties to Thor, "This is known as the Cup of Penance. We use it as a means of punishment. For whomever has committed an act against our law has to drink from this cup until it's empty. If you can drink as well as you say then this should prove a minor effort for you. Some of the jotuns here can empty it in two gulps. Only those here who are less than manly would need three gulps or more."

Thor was very thirsty. He put the horn to his lips and began to drink, and continued drinking until he felt certain the horn was empty. At last his breath gave out so he set the horn down. When he looked into it he saw not only wasn't it empty, but the level had barely moved. It was still nearly full.

Utgardr-Loki taunted Thor a bit, "I compliment you. You've done as well as many other jotuns. Although you didn't finish it with your first gulp, it will certainly be honor enough if you drain it dry with your second."

Thor didn't respond, though his face twitched in anger. He picked up the horn and began drinking again. He drank longer and deeper than ever. Eventually, he stopped for a breath and noticed the level still had not changed appreciably.

Utgardr-Loki delighted in Thor's lack of progress, "Are you sure you're Thor? Maybe you're just being polite. But do not let modesty stop you. Finish it off with your third gulp."

Thor seized the horn and drank and drank. He felt he was bursting, but still he drank more. When he set the horn down for the third time the level had only been lowered about an inch. Thor spoke, "I don't know by what means you caused this to happen, but I will drink no more from this enchanted horn."

Utgardr-Loki replied, "I'm surprised the reputation you carry with you is so vast when the amount you drink is so small."

Thor was furious, "We in Asgardr would not call such drinking small. And although I'm smaller than you I think I have more strength. Give me some task by which I can impress you with my strength."

Utgardr-Loki thought for a moment, then replied, "I'll give you one more chance to prove you're worthy enough to stand amongst us. This is a task even my youngest children can do. I wouldn't have even thought to ask you to do something so simple before, but now it seems more appropriate. It's such an easy task. All you have to do is lift a cat from the floor."

Thor turned, looking around the room and asked, "Where is the cat?"

Utgardr-Loki called out and a long lean grey cat came from around the corner of the hall. He stretched first the front half of his body, then paws down in front of him, raised up his back half in a long slow stretch. Lazily he walked over near Thor, rubbed up against the jotun's table, and then laid down to rest some more.

Thor tightened Megingardr, his girdle of strength, about his waist and walked over to the cat which hissed a little at the stranger's approach. Thor put a hand under the cat and tried to lift it. The cat arched his back as high as Thor could stretch his arms. Yet still Thor strained and managed to lift one of the cat's forepaws off the floor.

"Is that the best you can do?" spoke Utgardr-Loki.

Thor whirled around staring at everyone in the hall. "I challenge anyone in the hall to wrestle me. What about you Utgardr-Loki?"

Utgardr-Loki seemed amused, "I don't think it would be a fair match. However, if you are insistent about wrestling someone how about over there on that bench?" Thor's eyes followed to where Utgardr-Loki was pointing. "She seems a worthy opponent for

you. She is Elli, my old nurse. But don't be deceived by her frail looks, mighty Thor. She has bested others whose strength, I would say, was as great as yours, or possibly greater judging by what you've displayed so far."

The old woman slowly rose from her seat, her bent form leaning on a knotted crutch. Slowly she approached Thor with an aged shuffle. After each step she stopped momentarily to steady herself. Her skin was coarse like an old leather bag. Her hair was matted in clumps of grey atop her head. Dark sunken eyes stared out at Thor. Her receding chin lowered as her lips parted revealing a toothless grin. A brief coughing spell overcame her causing the spittle to run down her chin onto her ragged dress.

Thor was shocked, "You expect me to wrestle this old hag? Why she can barely make it the length of the hall. No doubt a sudden gust of wind will knock her over. Send me a mighty jotun to test my strength against."

Utgardr-Loki replied, "There are none who will condescend to fight you. However, if you beat my old nurse then I will fight you myself."

The old woman reached out and took Thor's wrists in her bony tremoring hands. Thor winced because suddenly they became like iron bands gripping him. He sank down to one knee in pain and was struggling to keep from falling over entirely when Utgardr-Loki called off the match. Elli shuffling slowly, made her way back to her seat, collapsed into it and promptly fell asleep.

Utgardr-Loki spoke, "It's now well into the evening, so let's put a halt to these contests. We'll hold no grudges against you and your friends since we have nothing to fear from you. I offer you and your friends our hospitality.

Thor, Loki, Roskva and Thjalfi stayed on for two days and nights feasting and resting up for their long journey home.

The morning of their departure came. Utgardr-Loki had a trestle-table full of meat prepared as a parting meal. After the feast he drank a last cup of mead with them, and accompanied the four past the gates of Utgardr. When they had gone a fair distance he asked Thor about the journey, "Well, what do you think of Utgardr now?"

Thor answered in low spirits, "I fear I've dishonored the name of the Æsir. Hereafter we'll have much to fear from the jotuns, for you will think I am weak."

Utgardr-Loki laughed, "You've all been tricked. For what you've seen the last few days have been an illusion. If I'd known you would do as well at our tests I never would have let you enter Utgardr. Your strength brought us to within an inch of destruction. Here is how it really was."

Thor and the others looked on in disbelief as Utgardr-Loki's form changed into Skrymir.

Utgardr-Loki/Skrymir continued, "I was Skrymir in the forest. The reason you couldn't open the provision bag was because it was tied with a tough magical iron wire in such a way that when you thought you were untying it you were really tightening it. It was really adamantine wire made by the dokkalfar. I tied the sack such that you would be unable to retrieve your provisions and perhaps starve or become discouraged and turn back. At the least I thought the lack of food would weaken you, and the quick pace would exhaust you. The three hammer blows you gave me, Thor, were fearsome indeed. Any one of the three would have killed me had they hit. But in each instance I put a mountain between myself and the hammer. Do you remember on your journey seeing a mountain range with three valleys running through them, with the last valley running deep enough to reach the domain of the dokkalfar? Those valleys were caused by your hammer blows. Your power frightened me so much I sought to mislead you with wrong directions so you'd wind up in Helheimr, where I hoped you'd stay, rather than having you reach Utgardr."

Thor was becoming angrier and angrier. But Utgardr-Loki/Skrymir continued his story, "Loki, when you were eating the food you truly scared us. But not even you can beat wildfire, which is what you were up against. And Thjalfi you were quick, but not as quick as Hugi who is my thought. Now we come to Thor who did the most to cause us to tremble. When you get to Midgardr you will see the results of your drinking. For the horn you drank from had its end in the oceans. You drank so much the seas has sunk back a quarter of a mile from the shore all along Midgardr. You've caused the tides to now ebb and flow.

Thor raised his hammer to strike against Utgardr-Loki/Skrymir, but the jotun continued speaking, "When you tried to lift the cat you succeeded in lifting one foot from the floor. The cat was Midgardrsormr, who encircles all of Midgardr. You held him up so high you nearly pulled him out of the sea. The old hag you wrestled was none other than old age herself who eventually brings everyone to their knees. But such was your strength that you stood firm and she was only able to bring you down to one knee. So now that you know the truth I bid you farewell and hope we never meet you again, for you have tested yourselves against our greatest warriors and might well have won if we hadn't used trickery."

Thor whirled Mjolnir over his head and let it loose at Utgardr-Loki/Skrymir. But before the hammer reached its mark Utgardr-Loki/Skrymir had vanished. Mjolnir returned to Thor. The four turned towards the city of Utgardr in time to see it vanish, too. They found themselves standing in a meadow. Off in the distance they could see a mountain range with three valleys running through it, with the furthest valley deeper than the rest. They didn't know quite where they were but started travelling westward away from Jotunheimr. In a short while they saw a cottage on the horizon which Roskva and Thjalfi recognized as their home. The two children darted off towards it to see who could reach it first.

Egil was surprised to see his children, and almost didn't recognize them since they had changed so much. "You're both taller by a head than when you left. And yet, it has only been one month."

In a short while Thor and Loki arrived. Thor was pleased to see his goats running around. Tanngrisnir was fully recovered. Once again that night Thor prepared them for dinner. This time all of the bones were returned to the skins unbroken, and the next morning when Thor brought them back to life they were whole and perfect. Soon after Thor, Loki, Roskva and Thjalfi departed heading back to Asgardr. Egil and his wife waved goodbye to their two children, realizing they would probably never see them again but honored their children were now working for Thor and would be living in Asgardr.

Back in Asgardr Roskva was sent to Freyja's household to learn how to be a proper serving maid. Thereafter she and Thjalfi stayed with Thor as part of his household.

Chapter 9

The Stealing of Idunn's Apples

In order to gain the Precious Mead for the Æsir, Odin, in the guise of a handsome jotun had slept for three nights with Gunnlod, the imprisoned daughter of the jotun Suttungr. As a result of these embraces, she later gave birth to a son whom she named Bragi. At first she thought him stillborn since he showed no signs of life. Yet his color remained good, so she patiently waited for him to quicken with life. But she never saw this happen.

Shortly after his birth some dvergar came to the cave where mother and son were held and stole the child away. They dressed him in white, a color he wore ever after, and placed him on one of their boats. Near him they placed a magic golden harp and sent the boat off into the world. The vessel drifted on streams that carried it ever downward until it passed by Nain, the home of the dvergar of death. Time passed and Bragi aged and grew as he slept. He reached manhood in this state and his beard began growing and became long and flowing.

Bragi slept on until one day he suddenly sat up and began playing the golden harp and singing mighty songs celebrating life, love, renewal, and noble deeds. He sang of victorious battles and mighty heroes. His eloquent songs were carried on the winds up to Asgardr, as well as throughout the Worlds of the Tree, down to the depths of Niflheimr. His songs raised the spirits of those in Asgardr. The einherjar practiced their battle arts even harder upon hearing the stirring songs of their past and future glories.

In Midgardr Bragi's songs woke up the land. Many there imitated his songs and were called Braga-men and Braga-women. When his songs were sung over the fields the soil became fertile and produced greater quantities of whatever was sown in it. But his songs of joy and hope produced deep despair when they were heard by those doomed in the depths of Helheimr.

Bragi sang on as his boat floated down the river with his goodness coming through in his songs. Eventually his boat touched shore at the edge of a great forest. The trees were still barren from the harsh winter that had just concluded. But as Bragi began walking through the forest, singing and playing as he went, buds appeared and matured into leaves, filling out the foliage on the trees. Birds seemed to appear out of nowhere to begin nesting in their trees and singing their songs of summer. Grass grew under foot as he walked, and everywhere flowers burst forth in full bloom.

He walked on through the forrest and came upon a beautiful young woman wearing a long flowing white garment similar to his, and a crown woven from flowers and leaves on her head. She was Idunn, the daughter of the ljosalfar Ivaldi.

Bragi saw Idunn and his heart immediately went out to her. He was in love, at first sight. He wooed her with songs of intensely felt passion which won her over so that soon she was in love with him. They were married and made their way to Asgardr. There Odin claimed Bragi as his son and carved magic runes on the minstrel's tongue so his songs would be even greater.

Odin commanded him to do various duties in Asgardr, "You are to write and sing songs praising the Æsir and the mighty einherjar of Valhalla. And you will stand with Hermodr, Tyr, and Vidarr and welcome the heroes arriving at Valhalla.

Even more valuable than Bragi's songs were Idunn's overlooked gift. She brought with her a golden ashwood casket containing eleven golden apples. The casket was pretty and golden, but hardly up to the standards of most of the caskets in Asgardr. The apples were barely noticed. They were only apples, even though of gold. Decorative and pleasing to the eye, but there were far better golden objects in Asgardr. And there were only eleven. They would soon be gone. Thor could eat them in one gulp.

As Idunn and Bragi stood before Odin she asked leave to speak and it was granted. "Here are the eleven golden apples of Idunn. And I give their use to those in Asgardr."

Odin nodded, "Yes they are very pretty. I'm sure they'll make a fine pie a few can eat."

Idunn smiled, "They're far too valuable to use in a pie. They have an interesting property. Perhaps you'll recognize them by their other names: epli ellifu or epli elliyfs. Yes, these are the apples of old-age medicine. A bite of one of these apples will restore your youth. The apples also restore themselves at night. The eleven apple cores browned with age renew into bright red luscious apples by the morning. And have no worry that there are only eleven for all of the Æsir. You need not take a bite each day. Just a bite every few years, or when you feel your joints stiffening and old age catching up with you. One bite and you will immediately be renewed."

The Æsir agreed, Idunn's Apples were the most valuable gift brought to Asgardr. For they were not immortal. Over time even the healthiest of the Æsir were brought to their knees by old age. And with old age came the ebbing of their strength and powers. Even now many of the Æsir were not as quick as they had been when they first built Asgardr. Their skin was wrinkled, their bones creaked, their vision had dimmed, and their ears deafened.

The Æsir gathered around Idunn grabbing at the apples. She instructed them to take just one bite. "Just one bite is all that's needed. Afterwards pass it on to the next Æsir."

One by one they took their bites. And that single bite renewed them to their prime years. The fog of age cleared, their health was restored, scars disappeared. The blurred horizon sharpened. And they could hear a sword being unsheathed two rooms away. Some had aged more than others so they took an extra bite or two. The more of the apple they ate, the younger they became. Their youth and vigor returned. However, Idunn's apples were not a cure for old age, and immediately the aging process began again.

The Æsir looked around and marveled at each other. Paunches had been replaced by abs. Stooped shoulders were straight. Gnarly twisted fingers could pinch an arrow in place. They had their youth again.

Now the Æsir were all rejuvenated. In the future there would be no regular ceremony for renewing their years. If an Asa or Asynje felt old they only had to go to Idunn and request a bite. Those who had harsher lives and battled more went to her more frequently. Those with less stressful lives needed the apples less. Some left full of youth on long journeys but returned aged and bent with the knowledge a bite or two would restore their youth.

The other magic in the apples was that no matter how many of the Æsir were served, her casket always remained full with eleven apples.

Idunn and Bragi were welcomed into Asgardr and made their home in the groves of Brunnakr, near Odin's hall, Gladsheimr, and the gold-thatched hall, Gimle. She brought the apple orchard to life and tended it while Bragi sat singing songs to her. Oftimes he'd go off a-minstrelling through the worlds. They were both so happy together.

The apples in the Grove weren't as wondrous as the eleven in her casket, but they did give energy to any who ate them and tasted better than regular apples. The warriors in Valhalla frequently insisted on pies made from the Brunnakr Grove apples.

The Jotun Thjassi

But such were the value of Idunn's apples that many plotted for them. This was the case once when Odin, Loki, and Hœnir were off on a quest.

The three were journeying along hacking their way through a virgin forest. They had been at it for several days, making very slow progress, and in that time had eaten no food. They continued hacking until they came to a clearing in a valley. Suddenly, standing before them was a herd of oxen grazing contentedly in a field. They rushed upon the herd and easily captured and killed a laggardly ox. Then the three set about to boil it. They prepared the fire and set a huge cauldron filled with water over the crackling flames. They skinned and placed the ox in the pot and waited patiently for their dinner to cook. The water was taking a long time to come to a boil, so they set about occupying their time exploring the area. Upon their return they found the water still had not come to a boil. Since the pot was so huge they figured the water hadn't had sufficient time to heat up, so they again went off clearing paths in the forest.

However, when they returned a second time to find the water appeared no closer to boiling than before Loki voiced his suspicions. "It has been long enough for the water to boil. But, look, I can stick my hand in the water and not be burned. Surely someone has cast a spell on our meal?"

Hœnir disagreed, "That's absurd. Our stomachs have caused us to think our dinner should be ready by now. Let's continue our exploring. It'll only make us hungrier to stand here staring at the pot."

Upon their return for a third time, they found the water was still no closer to reaching a boil and the meat was just as raw as before. They all began looking around for a cause. While they were looking they heard a voice coming from a nearby oak tree, "I can make your water boil, and I'll do it very quickly if you'll give me a share of the food in exchange for my services." The three looked up and saw a giant eagle.

At first the three refused and abruptly turned their attention to tending the fire. In a rage the eagle flew down, flapped his wings swiftly and put out the fire. The three Æsir then realized why their water had failed to come to a boil.

Loki spoke to the eagle, "It's clear if we don't deal with you, you'll cause us enough mischief so that our food will take forever to cook. Since we're all hungry and don't wish to prolong the wait for our food much longer, we'll agree to your terms. If you'll help us cook the meal you may have a fair portion of it."

Immediately upon hearing these words the eagle flew down and flapped his wings more slowly. This fanning caused the flames to flare up and burn steadily under the pot. It was only a short time until the water came to a boil and the ox was cooked. Loki and Hœnir lifted the ox from the pot and began to divide it into pieces so they could all share it. The eagle swooped down and eventually making several trips, took the loins, four legs, the hams, and the shoulders for his share. In a moment he was back up in the tree picking away at his meal.

The three Æsir looked at him in amazement. Soon their astonishment turned to anger at the measly portion he had left them. Loki grabbed a pole, ran to the tree, and started beating at the eagle. But much to Loki's surprise when the pole struck the talons of the eagle it stuck. And when Loki tried to let go of the pole he found it held fast to his hands. The eagle flew off with Loki holding onto the pole. When the eagle dove down Loki was bashed against the rocks and dragged along the ground. His arms felt as if they were being torn from their sockets. It didn't take long before Loki was begging for mercy. Out of earshot of Odin and Hœnir he promised anything and everything he could think of, even betraying those in Asgardr.

"I know now you're no mere eagle. Let me loose and I'll give you whatever you want. I'll even bring you a drop of the Precious Mead, Thor's hammer, mountains of gold, whatever you want. Only please stop bashing me against these rocks."

The eagle paused in his abuse of Loki and said, "You're correct. I'm only wearing orne-ham, my eagle-guise. My true name and nature is Thjassi, and I'm a storm jotun. My mother is Greip, Gjalp's sister and the daughter of the noble jotun Geirrodr. My brother was that master mason who built the mighty walls which now surround Asgardr and whom you cheated out of his love for Freyja and his longing for the sun, and moon. As for your offers, what do I want with a drop of the Precious Mead? Might is better than brains any day. If I started thinking while I was fighting someone, I might waste time and lose the battle. Thor's hammer is useless to me when I have my fists. As for mountains of gold? I already have them. When my father Olvaldi gave my brothers and me our inheritances he measured out the gold in mouthfuls. There is only one prize the Æsir has that I'm interested in. Promise me you'll bring me Idunn's golden apples and I'll give you back your freedom. Otherwise, I'll play with you a while longer and then fly to my home in Jotunheimr, and when we are up so high that the river Ifing looks like a spilled glass of water, then I'll give you the freedom you so desire. What do you have to say to that?"

Loki hesitated in answering. Thjassi bashed him against a rock again and Loki readily agreed to the terms. "I give you my solemn oath I'll bring Idunn's golden apples to you if you'll only let me go."

Immediately after Loki said these words his hands slipped from the pole and he fell a short distance to the ground. Before flying off Thjassi yelled down to Loki, "I don't know how valuable the solemn oath of a liar and cheat is. But, it'll have to do. Don't cross me."

Thjassi flew westward to his home. Loki made his way back to Asgardr.

Odin and Hœnir had already been back for some time and had told everyone how funny Loki looked dangling high in the air from a pole. Loki walked passed the crowd, whispering under his breath, "We'll see how long they laugh at me. Soon those strong boisterous laughs will be infirm whispers rasping out in wheezy exhortations from feeble old men and women."

Tricking Idunn

Loki thought long and hard on how to steal the apples. He was presented with a problem concerning their magical properties. They remained whole and good only if they were personally given out by Idunn. If they were just taken from her basket or picked off the trees of Brunnakr Grove they shriveled up and rotted. Loki certainly knew Idunn would never freely give the apples to Thjassi. So, he had to figure out a way to trick her into volunteering to come with him.

He waited until Bragi had gone off on a trip to Midgardr, knowing his task would be a lot easier if he didn't also have to contend with a doting lovestruck husband. He walked to Brunnakr Grove, and spoke to Idunn as he casually walked by, "Your apples look very beautiful today. In fact they look almost as beautiful as the apples I saw the other day on one of my journeys."

Idunn smiled and responded, not really catching the insult Loki had just paid to her apples, "Do you want a taste of one? After that frightful time you had with the eagle I'm sure my apples can heal your bruises and restore your strength."

Loki grinned and answered. He knew he had her. "No, my bruises are all healed. The apples I ate the other day seemed to have not only restored my strength, but given me more strength than I had before, something extra which your apples don't provide."

Idunn could no longer misunderstand Loki's words or intent. She realized Loki had found some apples he thought even better than hers. She had to see them. "Where are these apples? May I go see them? It's difficult for me to think there are apples as fine, or better, than mine."

Loki smiled, thinking it had been easier than he thought it would be. "I'd be happy to take you to them. They're just outside Asgardr's gate in a crystal bowl, sparkling in the sun with its precious contents – much prettier than your old wooden casket. It will only take a moment for us to get there." Then as an afterthought he added, "Why don't you bring your apples along so you can compare them."

They were soon outside the protection of Asgardr. Idunn, looking around but couldn't see any apple trees. She opened her mouth to speak, but whatever words came out were blown away by a great gust of wind preceding the approach of Thjassi in orne-ham, an eagle-guise, who swooped down, caught hold of Idunn, and carried her off to his icy castle on top of a mountain in Thrymheimr, the kingdom of the winds. There he kept her prisoner, and tried to persuade her to give him a taste of one of her apples. She refused. Still he implored. "My youth is spent, I am now old and gnarled with age. With just one bite

I could be returned to the robust health of my youth. If you would have your freedom, that is the price I demand from you."

Still she refused. At one point, in desperation, he seized an apple from the wooden casket. It immediately withered and died in his hands. He threw it down in disgust. Idunn picked it up and returned it to the casket where it regained its red ripe lusciousness.

Seeing he was getting nowhere in obtaining a bite of the apples he shut Idunn up securely in the highest tower in his castle and left on a journey to pillage and plunder Midgardr and Jotunheimr in order to calm his nerves. At least he had the pleasure of knowing the Æsir were no better off than he was.

The storms raged outside Thjassi's castle, pounding against the walls and roof of the tower where Idunn was being held prisoner. After awhile she became nervous and ill at ease from the storm's constant battering. She longed for the peacefulness of Brunnakr Grove. Who would rescue her? Who even knew where she was?

Meanwhile, Back in Asgardr

At first the Æsir thought nothing of Idunn's absence from them. They assumed she had traveled to Midgardr with Bragi on one of his journeys. Time passed and they aged. They grew stiff, their features became drawn and haggard. They looked tired. Soon their hair was white, their eyesight dimmed, and their hearing lessened. Odin's vision had blurred to the point he couldn't see clearly when he looked into all the Worlds of the Tree as he sat in his watchtower on his throne Hlidskjalf in his hall, Valaskjalf, trying to find Idunn while keeping watch over the doings of the jotuns and all the others who sought to work evil against the Æsir and their friends. He called a Thing at Urdarbrunnr Well to discuss the matter. He set it for some days hence, so everyone now slowed down by age, would have time enough to make their way there.

Heimdallr was late to the meeting since he had not heard the call the first time it was sounded. Just as the Thing started Bragi returned from Midgardr. He found it very disconcerting to arrive and find them discussing his wife's disappearance. The Æsir were upset to learn she wasn't with him.

The decision was made. Odin's ravens, Huginn and Muninn, were to fly off in search of Idunn and not return until they had discovered her whereabouts or knowledge about her. Off they went. And who knows when they'd return?

While they were on their journey the situation grew worse in Asgardr. Bragi stopped singing his songs of hope and courage. Instead he sang of despair and sadness and lost loves. Life in Asgardr continued on its downward spiral. Life darkened.

But one day Heimdallr, squinting his eyes trying to make out the blurred images approaching, saw two ravens winging their way towards Asgardr. At least that's what he interpreted he saw. He called a Thing.

All the Æsir were gathered at Urdarbrunnr Well by the time Huginn and Muninn arrived. The two ravens alit on Odin's shoulders and whispered the news they had discovered into his ears. Odin's face was grave as he spoke, "They have not found Idunn's whereabouts. But they have managed to find out she had last been seen outside Asgardr's gates with Loki. While talking to that mischief-maker a great eagle flew down and carried her away."

There was a murmuring in the crowd as everyone looked around trying to find where Loki was standing. Usually he could be found near the center of things trying to create discord. But today he was nowhere to be seen. Odin signaled and Hœnir and Thor left to find Loki.

They soon returned dragging Loki along with them. At first Loki denied the accusations against him. This enraged Thor so much he grabbed Loki and threw him up in the air several times. Each time he was flung higher and higher until eventually his heels touched the moon.

Thor spoke, "If you don't tell us where Idunn is I'll throw you passed the moon. Then you'll have to travel far into the heavens before your feet again touch something solid."

Loki was very cowardly by nature and hated torture. Usually even the threat of torture was enough to frighten him. So, trembling, he pleaded, "Please don't harm me any more and I'll find Idunn for you…" The Æsir looked suspiciously at him, and he added rather quickly, "…even though I had nothing to do with her disappearance." His words convinced no one.

Loki turned to Freyja and asked, "I'll have need of valshamr, your falcon-guise. Where I'm going will be much easier by flight than on foot."

Freyja sent her servant Fulla to fetch it. Thor turned his thoughts to other matters, "We're still growing old and have no assurance Loki can accomplish his task. Therefore, I think we should attack and kill those in Jotunheimr before our powers ebb any further. Right now we have barely enough strength amongst us to win. By tomorrow we'll be that much weaker."

The other Æsir overruled him.

Soon Fulla returned with the magical garment which Loki assumed and flew off glad to be away from the Thing.

The Thing ended with each of the Æsir returning to Asgardr to worry about the future to come. It didn't look good.

Loki Abducts Idunn

As Loki approached Thrymheimr, he could see he was going to have problems trying to abduct Idunn by normal means. Thjassi's castle was high atop a mountain. Indeed part of it was carved out of the face of the mountain. Sea broke against two sides of the mountain. The landward side comprised a steep descent. Loki couldn't imagine fleeing down the side of the mountain with Idunn in tow with Thjassi in hot pursuit. His hope was Thjassi would be off journeying when he arrived.

As he approached the castle, flight became more difficult. His wings beat against the storms raging around the fortress. The icy wind cut through his feathers as he sought a means of entry. He could feel his wings becoming heavier with ice. His view was obscured by the blinding rain beating down on him. He peered into the windows of the castle as best he could, searching for Idunn. Finally he flew up to the highest bower window where he found Idunn inside. He flew in, changed back into his regular form and tried to warm up.

"Come Idunn, we must flee here before Thjassi returns."

Idunn was quite surprised and a bit angered at the identity of her rescuer. She spoke to him harshly, "I don't trust you, Loki. You're the reason I'm here. I don't think I should go willingly with one such as you. Anyway, our escape is impossible. Although Thjassi has been away, he returned just last night. Now he is out in the northern seas fishing for whales for his supper and will soon return to try to persuade me to give him an apple to eat. But I think I would rather stay here than trust you."

Loki responded, "I don't have time to argue with you. I thought Thjassi was still away. It'll be bad for both of us if he finds me here." What Loki actually meant was that it would be bad for him if Thjassi found him there.

He grabbed the casket of golden apples, shoved it in her arms and immediately changed her into a nut, changed himself back into a falcon, picked up the nut and flew off towards Asgardr.

Thjassi returned shortly after their escape. Sensing something was wrong he tossed the whales onto the rocks and made his way up to the castle where he was met by one of his ellewomen servants. Thjassi was always uneasy around them. They were constantly smiling, but it was a joyless smile. They had no heart and pitied no one. When they turned to walk away one could not help but notice their backs were hollow.

Continuously grinning, as if there were something funny about her story, she told him of a falcon who had flown into Idunn's window. Thjassi immediately knew it had to have been Loki and mumbled to himself, "I knew I should also have gotten a promise that after delivering Idunn to me he would not attempt to rescue her. He's kept his vow and still been able to steal Idunn away."

Thjassi put on orne-ham, his eagle-guise, and flew off towards Asgardr. He was much more practiced in flight and his larger wings carried him faster than Loki's did. Soon he could see Loki off in the distance. At the sight he beat his wings harder. Loki, too, flew as fast as he could, urged on by Thjassi's pursuit.

They flew on for five days and five nights. On the dawn of the sixth day Loki could see Asgardr's walls. He only hoped he could make it to the safety of that land before Thjassi caught up with him. He was more tired than Thjassi since he had not had a chance to rest before heading back to Asgardr.

Heimdallr, squinting, looking towards the horizon, was the first to spot Loki. He pointed at a spot near the horizon, exclaiming, "There he is carrying Idunn in the form of a nut in his claws. But I also see another form chasing him and gaining very rapidly."

The Æsir, remembering how they had built a fire to protect Odin when he had returned carrying the Precious Mead being pursued by the jotun Suttungr, prepared kindling and wood atop the walls of Asgardr. Hœnir called out, "We are all old and infirm and too weak to fight him once he gets here. Let the flames do what we in youth could do. Then we'll feast on the apples and our strength will be returned to us."

Loki's wings ached. He didn't have enough strength left to clear the height of the walls. Instead he swept through the gate as the kindling above was lit. The sky darkened as the giant eagle approached. His wings seemed to reach from one side of the sky to the other. His shadow was thrown across the land. His beating wings stoked the flames even higher. As he reached the wall his wings dipped in flight and touched the kindling. First his left wing began to smoke, then his right. Soon they both burst into a bright orange flame which lit up the sky with their radiance. Thjassi lost control and spiraled down from the sky burnt and dying. Some of the Æsir rushed at him and beat him to hasten his death.

Loki discarded valshamr and returned it to Freyja who looked at its worn condition. Loki never was one to respect other's property.

After Idunn was changed back to her regular form she rushed to embrace Bragi who had already started singing a happy song in praise of his wife. She handed around apples to everyone. Youth and joy soon returned to Asgardr.

Odin walked over to the form of Thjassi. Orne-ham, the eagle-guise, had burnt up and now only Thjassi in his normal countenance remained. Odin reached down and plucked the jotun's eyes from his face and cast them skyward into the heavens, "I'll make his eyes constellations in the heavens so he can watch over his own land in Thrymheimr. With this gesture I hope the jotuns will forgive what we had to do to Thjassi in order to save Idunn and her apples."

Skadi Comes to Asgardr and Finds a Husband

But their problems were not solved that easily, for striding into Asgardr the very next day was Thjassi's daughter Skadi, accompanied by one of her sled dogs. She was dressed all in white, wearing a hunting dress, fur leggings, and snowshoes. Her shiny silver armor glinted from miles away. As she came nearer the Æsir could see she was armed with a bow and many sharp-pointed arrows, as well as a very long pointed spear which she waved menacingly as she approached.

She strode through the gates of Asgardr with no fear, despite what had happened to her father, announcing loudly, "I'm Skadi, daughter of the jotun Thjassi. I demand weregild for your cowardly acts against my father. If you don't grant it I'll call upon my two uncles Idi and Gang, Thjassi's brothers, to help me seek my vengeance. They each have the strength of my father. And when we fight you we will not be burnt or injured as Thjassi was."

Odin stepped forward and spoke, "We don't wish to fight you or your uncles. We wish to live in peace. Therefore, name how much gold you demand for weregild so we might buy your friendship?"

Skadi replied, "I have more gold than you could possibly offer me, even if you stripped the walls of Asgardr bare. Olvaldi, the father of Thjassi, Idi, and Gang, my grandfather, died leaving us the wealth of his plunder. The greatest scales in all the Worlds of the Tree would not even be able to measure a portion of it. My father and uncles had to measure it out in mouthfuls. Think of some other offer. And because of the insult of this offer I also demand you make me laugh."

Odin and the other Æsir talked amongst themselves. They thought of many ideas, but none seemed particularly appealing. Thor was growing impatient at the entire matter and spoke his mind, "I think we should rush her and give her the same weregild we gave her ugly father."

Odin tried to calm his eldest son. "No. Must I remind you yet again, we live on sacred soil. We've already committed one wrong act. Let's leave it at that and hope the Norns won't judge us too harshly for it."

Loki spoke up with a gleam in his eyes, "I have an idea. Why not offer her a husband from amongst the Æsir. That way she would be an ally of ours by marriage."

All but Thor thought this a brilliant idea. He was always suspicious of everything Loki said, did, or supported. Nothing he suggested ever turned out the way everyone thought it would. But he was outvoted.

The discussion turned to how she would choose her husband. Finally, they came up with a method and informed her of their decision.

Skadi heard their offer and immediately responded, "I accept. I pick Baldr for my husband." She started walking towards Odin's handsome youngest son.

Odin stepped towards her. "That's not quite what we had in mind. Baldr is the fairest and kindest of us all. Any woman would want him over everyone else. However, in order to give the other Æsir an equal chance for your favors and the happiness you could bring them, we have decided to make a contest of it. All of the Æsir will stand behind a screen. You will choose your future husband by his feet."

Skadi quickly glanced at Baldr's feet trying to memorize their appearance.

All of the Æsir removed their boots and sandals and positioned themselves behind the screen. Loki smiled smugly. He knew no woman in her right mind would ever choose his ugly hoof-like feet. There was no chance he'd have to worry about returning Skadi's tender embraces on a regular basis.

Skadi examined all the feet very carefully and found one pair that was by far the best looking of any lined up. She smiled, certain she was choosing Baldr. "This is the member of the Æsir who will be my husband. Lift the screen and let Baldr come forward."

However, when the screen was lifted the person standing before her wasn't Baldr. He wasn't even originally of the Æsir. Standing before her was Njordr, the hostage from the Vanir. He spent a great deal of his time in the sea making his feet the cleanest and smoothest of all the Æsir.

Njordr's hall, Noatun, which meant enclosure of ships, was by the sea. He had power over the oceans and could smooth out the most raging sea into a glass-like calm. Njordr was tall and very good looking. His tunic was green to match the sea, and atop his head he wore a hat made of shells out of which sprung a heron's plume. His two children, Freyr and Freyja, blessed his union with Skadi.

Loki Does Something Extreme to Make Skadi Laugh

Skadi kept staring at Njordr, the disappointment showing on her face. Seeing this Loki came forward and said, "Now I'll keep the rest of our bargain with you. I'll make you laugh harder than you've ever laughed before. So hard, in fact, you'll forget all about your disappointment at loosing Baldr. Let us all prepare a wedding celebration at which I will provide the entertainment."

A huge wedding feast was arranged for Skadi and Njordr. There was plenty of food and revelry. Towards the end of the meal Loki had a long-horned goat brought into the hall. Everyone watched, wondering what Loki was up to. A servant tied a rope to the beard of the goat. The other end was handed to Loki. One of those assembled yelled out, "Loki is going to entertain us with a tug-o'-war. But how will that make us laugh?"

Loki surprised everyone with his next move. After removing his lower garments he reached down and tied the rope to his testicles. The goat then started leaping from side to side causing Loki a great deal of pain. Thor was the first to burst out in laughter. Soon the others followed suit. All except Skadi. The goat ran around in circles with Loki following as fast as he could howling ever louder in pain. Finally they were both exhausted and collapsed at Skadi's feet. Loki put his head on Skadi's knee and looked up at her. Then the goat mocked Loki's movement by putting its head on the other knee. Loki spoke in a very high-pitched voice, "Are you sure I can't make you laugh."

Once she heard Loki's soprano voice Skadi could no longer contain herself and burst out laughing. "Oh, Loki, your voice is so high. Do you think you'll ever go down to normal.?"

Loki winked at her and whispered, "Perhaps I can visit you this evening to show you that everything's down to normal? Or, up, as the case may be?"

Skadi whispered back, "Perhaps the pulling and tugging by the goat has made you longer? We shall see. But you'll have to wait till tomorrow. Tonight's my wedding night."

Even though the means had been unusual the Æsir had kept all of their promises to Skadi and recovered the honor they had lost killing Thjassi.

At the conclusion of the party Odin pointed out the stars that had once been Thjassi's eyes and gave her added honor. "Because of your prowess with the bow and arrow you will rule the hunt. Those in Midgardr will call upon you to improve their skills and aid in their luck. In the winter you will be called upon by those riding in sleighs, and those wearing snowshoes or skis. You'll be known as the andr-dis."

Skadi seemed pleased with her treatment and the honor given her and her father. She decided to try living in Asgardr with Njordr at his residence. But try as she might after a few days she could no longer stand it. So she and Njordr reached an agreement. They would spend three days in Noatun, his residence in Asgardr, and nine days at her residence in Thrymheimr. This worked for awhile. But soon their different likes and dislikes became too much to overcome. Njordr loved to watch the swooping and diving of seagulls. He could sit entranced all day watching the beautiful swans in the lake near his house. These birds, sacred to him, never failed to cheer him up if he was down. When he really wanted to relax he'd sit in the sun and relax on one of the rocky shores near his home, laying side by side with the seals he loved so much.

Skadi, however, hated the ebb and flow of the tides. Leaping fish filled her with disgust. And the screeching of the seagulls, and the barking and groaning of the seals deafened her. What she liked was the brisk cold of the high mountains; the winds whistling through the pines; the deafening roar of avalanches. The barking of wolves, the howling of bears, and the bellowing of buffaloes were music to her ears. These sounds merely frightened Njordr. Worse yet, he had trouble knowing whether his trembling came about from the cold or from fear. He just couldn't get warm in her castle in Thrymheimr, and was continually walking around slapping at his arms trying to warm up. No matter what the reason, he wasn't happy. Nor was she.

Over the years they grew more and more distant. Things finally came to an end when Njordr came upon Skadi and Loki together. He was incensed that Loki and Skadi had become lovers, and yelled at her, "What is this? Sleeping with the slayer of your father?" He then blurted out the history of Loki's involvement with her father's death. Until that moment Skadi had been unaware of Loki's part in her father's death. After Njordr told her the story she turned on Loki and became his bitterest enemy.

Njordr banished Skadi from his home which pleased her greatly. She went to Thrymheimr to live, only visiting Asgardr on occasion to see Odin, whom she also had as a lover. Eventually she married Ullr, who was sometimes known as the skjaldar ass. He was the illegitimate son of Sif and Aurvandill. He too was called upon by those in Midgardr during the winter for the help he could give them. He and Skadi were happy with each other and known as the ondurgud and ondurdis.

Chapter 10

The Jotun Hrungr

Odin was in his watchtower, seated on his throne Hlidskjalf, in his hall, Valaskjalf, surveying all the Worlds of the Tree. Things seemed fairly calm. Off in the distance he could see Thor journeying eastward, on his way to see his mistress Jarnsaxa, who lived in the Myrkvyrdr Forest deep in Jotunheimr, occasionally stopping to slay a jotun or two. Other of the Æsir seemed to be out adventuring, too.

As Odin looked about, the urge to travel came over him. He decided to visit the biggest of all jotuns, the rock jotun Hrungr. He sent his servant to saddle Sleipnir and prepare his needs for the journey. Dressed in a mantle of blue and wearing shining armor and a golden helmet he rode off towards Jotunheimr. Obviously, he wasn't making a secret journey.

Sleipnir's eight legs carried Odin quickly to the outsized land. He had no trouble finding Hrungr at his mountainous home, Grjotanagardr. Hrungr recognized Odin and marveled at Sleipnir, "Truly, that is a magnificent horse. I'll wager it's very swift."

Odin was flattered by the compliments to his horse and responded, "Yes, he's the fastest horse there is. In fact there's not a single horse in all the Worlds of the Tree, including Jotunheimr with its outsized beasts, that is a tenth as fast. I'll wager my head he could beat any horse anywhere."

There had been a good deal of graciousness in Hrungr's compliment about Sleipnir. For what he had said wasn't truly how he felt. Indeed, Hrungr really felt just about any horse in Jotunheimr would be able to easily beat any horse of the Æsir, including Sleipnir. The fact Odin accepted the compliment literally, and in remark had insulted the horses of Jotunheimr angered the jotun. In a moment he leapt on his horse, Gullfaxi, and said, "I'll take you up on your wager. Shall we race?"

In an instant they were off. The wind whistled behind them, unable to catch up. The trees in the forest bent nearly to the ground as they swooshed by. But Sleipnir led the entire race. Occasionally Gullfaxi closed in, but Sleipnir easily pulled away again, as if he were toying with the horse and rider who had dared challenge him. So intent was Hrungr on winning he never noticed when they rode through Valgrindr Gate, the gate of the slain,

in Asgardr. Finally Odin reined in at the golden Glasir Grove. Looking around, Hrungr realized where he was and knew he was at the mercy of the Æsir. He expected to be killed at any moment. Instead Odin offered him hospitality and yelled out for a banquet to be prepared for their guest.

Hrungr was a bit suspicious. "So, now you've tricked me into entering this place. I hope you aren't planning a banquet such as the one you gave Thjassi? Remember, we are on sacred ground where no blood can be shed."

Odin tried to reassure him, "Be calm, it truly is a banquet, not a funeral feast. We offer you peace and friendship. To know each other is the only way to trust each other. I realized you'd never have come here if I had given you an invitation, so I tricked you into our hospitality."

Hrungr mumbled, "What sort of friendship can develop from a trick?"

But Odin didn't hear and those who did, did not answer.

Eventually the tensions eased as Hrungr watched the great feast being prepared in Odin's hall, Valaskjalf. Everyone in Asgardr attended. Hrungr was flattered because the Æsir seemed very interested in him and spent the evening quizzing him about Jotunheimr. Not all of the Æsir went on adventures. Many seldom left Asgardr. So this was the first time many had spoken face-to-face with a jotun, or even met one. Hrungr answered all their questions as best he could, exaggerating many of his answers to impress everyone.

"I've been talking all evening and have a great thirst, these little goblets hold barely a drop of mead. Don't you have anything fit for a mighty jotun?" Hrungr turned to Odin, who signaled for a servant to bring the large tankards usually reserved for Thor. They were filled with mead and given to Hrungr. He took just a gulp to drain each one. They were refilled, and just as easily finished off again. It was then the mead began to have its effect. Hrungr's boasting started to get out of hand, eventually becoming quite insulting.

"It's lucky for the Æsir I was not too angered by being tricked into coming here. If we weren't friends you wouldn't have a chance against me. I could easily pick up Valhalla with all the supposed warriors still inside and carry it back to Jotunheimr with me. I still might. Maybe I'll tear down the mighty walls of Asgardr stone by stone. But right now I need more mead." He slammed his cup down insistently on the table.

Odin turned to Freyja who walked over to Hrungr and filled his tankard. Sif came over and filled the other tankards set before him. He looked at both the Asynjur and continued his boasting, "Maybe I'll leave Valhalla here for you. Instead I'll take Freyja and Sif with me. Finally they'll have someone big enough to satisfy them. The puny Æsir can't be compared to the greatness and prowess of a jotun." He reached out and put his arms around their waists.

The abuse and threats went on for three days and nights. Finally the Æsir wearied of their guest and his remarks. They sent for Thor who had just returned from Jotunheimr. Thor hadn't been told the name of the jotun who was causing all the trouble, just that there was a jotun who was insulting the Æsir. A jotun was a jotun to Thor. He'd bash the jotun's head in soon enough. He hurried over to Valaskjalf.

Immediately on seeing Hrungr he went into a rage. At first Hrungr didn't notice Thor and continued his boasting. Soon he realized a great quiet had settled on the hall, except in the corner behind him. He turned to see the burning eyes of Thor staring at him.

Thor walked into the hall and yelled to the other Æsir, "You have let scum into our sacred land. Do you not know this is Hrungr, the same jotun who raped my daughter, Hlora? He comes here and threatens us, our homes, Freyja and Sif. Why has he been allowed here? Who gives him safe passage here so he stays and drinks without fear?"

Before anyone could answer, Hrungr stood up to face Thor, "I came here as the guest of your father, Odin. You can't harm me since I am under his protection and on sacred soil. Also, I'm unarmed. Surely the mighty Thor wouldn't attack someone who was unarmed, and an invited guest?"

As he talked on the mead boosted his courage. He continued, "I could easily beat you in battle. But that cannot be since I'm without shield or whetstone. I don't have a servant to aid me as you do. So go sit down and drink from the small goblets, since I have use of your tankards. And even those are not large enough to quench my thirst. Indeed, there are many kinds of thirst which I haven't yet quenched." He eyed Sif.

Thor surprised him with his reply, "All of your objections to a fight can be overcome. After our feast we will travel to your land. There you can have your servant, shield, whetstone, or whatever else you need for the holmgang. We will no longer be on sacred ground so our battle can easily take place."

Hrungr started at Thor's offer. He was also still filled with the courage of the mead and did what few jotuns had ever willingly done. He accepted Thor's challenge.

That evening he journeyed ahead to Jotunheimr to prepare for the upcoming battle. All the way home he boasted of how he was going to crush Thor. But as his journey wore on and the mead wore off he began to wonder how he had gotten himself into such a predicament. By the time he reached Grjotanagardr he was trembling with fear.

Soon other jotuns arrived from far and wide to witness the great battle. They looked at Hrungr with admiration for his courage. Yet they soon noticed he was no longer boasting. Indeed, he seemed to be taking his time with his preparations; putting off sharpening his weapons and sending his servant off on long trips to try to find obscure objects he absolutely needed before the battle could take place. If one didn't know better, one would think he was stalling.

While Hrungr delayed in his preparations other jotuns set up the holmgang field. Four hosler poles made of hazel were pounded into the ground to mark off a boundary. A rope, called a vebond, was tied from one pole to the next so that a circular area was marked off. The fight would take place there. Only Hrungr and Thor and their seconds would be allowed in this area after the ground was hallowed.

Some of the jotuns realizing Hrungr was a coward decided to bolster his courage by building him a clay jotun. The clay figure also solved the problem of who was going to act as Hrungr's second. So far no one had volunteered, knowing if Hrungr darted and ran, then the battle against Thor would fall to his second.

Their finished creation was nine rosts high and three rosts broad across the chest. They had fashioned a vicious looking face for him. His eyes stared fixedly forward under closely knit scowling brows. His lips were drawn back in a terrible snarl to reveal several rows of jagged teeth. They stood him up in such a way that his shadow fell the length of the battlefield. Just the sight of him would fill Thor with terror – or, so they hoped. They named their creation Mokkurkalfi, cloud calf.

He was indeed terrifying and monstrous to look at. But he had one fault. The jotuns had been unable to find a heart large enough for him, so instead of a human heart they had substituted a mare's heart. The name of the heart was Giottunagard.

Hrungr's heart was a bit sturdier. He had a triangle-shaped heart of stone. Because of its shape the rune ᛉ was called Hrungr's Heart, and was carved on randarr iss, his shield, as well as on all his weapons.

Finally, Hrungr could stall no longer. He positioned himself next to Mokkurkalfi and waited for Thor's arrival. The longer he waited the more he boasted to others around him, until almost all of his courage had returned. Proudly and confidently he stood with randarr iss in his left hand. Flung over his shoulder as a weapon was a giant whetstone of the type that was usually used to sharpen the other jotuns' scythes.

One of the other jotuns yelled out, "How do you intend to beat Thor the mighty thundergod?"

Hrungr's strategy had been formed by a head made of the same material as his heart. He had come up with what he thought was a brilliant, yet simple, way to beat Thor. "I'll defend myself with this shield. Then while he's off guard I'll hurl this flintstone at him. That will finish him off." He smugly rocked back and forth on his feet.

One of the other jotuns yelled back, "What if you miss?"

This remark startled Hrungr. What if he missed? He hadn't thought of that. His trembling started again. Just then Thjalfi, Thor's servant, ran up to Hrungr. "Your shield is useless against Thor. He knows you've been watching the sky for his appearance. Therefore he has decided to attack you from underground. Maybe he's beneath your feet at this very instant."

Hrungr flung down his shield, jumping on it for protection. He grasped the flintstone in both hands and held it high above his head ready to hurl it down onto Thor the minute he came through the ground.

The others started laughing at the sight Hrungr presented. Just then the sky darkened; lightning flashed across the horizon followed by peals of thunder rolling ever closer to Hrungr. Then Thor appeared striding from one cloud to another swinging Mjolnir overhead.

Mokkurkalfi shook violently. His mare's heart beat almost loud enough to drown out the thunder, proving it's not the size of an opponent but their heart that matters. As Thor came closer Mokkurkalfi could no longer contain his functions and wet all over himself. All of the other jotuns gathered around were too frightened themselves to laugh at the sight.

Thor loosed Mjolnir towards Hrungr. Hrungr shifted his stance and flung his whetstone at Thor. Both objects crashed into each other in midair. A flash of lightning sparked forth as Mjolnir and whetstone met. The flintstone shattered into hundreds of pieces which flew into Midgardr. One piece fell forming a mountain range. The other small pieces landed far and wide throughout Midgardr, forming all of the veins of whetstone and flint in the land.

Only one piece of flintstone continued forward to hit Thor. It struck him so hard he fell to the ground face first. Mjolnir continued forward and struck Hrungr in the center of his forehead crushing his skull to powder. He fell backwards as Thor fell forwards. Hrungr's leg landed across Thor's throat.

While this was going on Thjalfi ran at Mokkurkalfi with a spade spreading the now wet feet of clay and the rest of him all over the landscape. The battle had taken only a few moments, and now it was over.

The battlefield remained quiet with no movement. Then Thor tried to get up, but was unable to move because Hrungr's foot was pinning him down. Thjalfi ran over to help his master. But even though he strained with all his might he was unable to budge the jotun's foot. One by one the other Æsir came and tried to free Thor, but all to no avail. The jotuns stood back pleased with the small victory Hrungr had had over Thor, even though it had cost him his life.

Suddenly in the distance from the east the Æsir saw a young child striding purposely towards the battlefield. He walked up to Thor, bent over and easily picked up Hrungr's leg and dropped it over the jotun's other leg, giving him a very relaxed appearance. Thor sat up and patted the child on his head. He turned to the assembled Æsir and made a startling announcement, "I've been in the Myrkvyrdr Forest with Jarnsaxa, and this is our son, Magni. His strength is greater than any of the Æsir even though he is but three days old.

Magni interrupted his father, "It's too bad I didn't arrive here sooner. I could have toppled him with one blow and saved you the trouble."

Thor was most impressed with his son. He walked over, took Gullfaxi's bridle and led the horse to Magni. "Here, this is your reward for helping your father when no one else could." His son took the bridle, smiling broadly.

Odin glared at Thor and spoke, forgetting that Thor's son also had the blood of the Æsir, even his own blood, flowing through his veins, "It is wrong for you to give that steed to the son of an evil jotun. You should have presented it to your own father." Odin stalked off back to Asgardr. Even though he wanted the horse, Magni was allowed to keep it.

Gradually the crowd broke up leaving only Thor, Sif, his servant Thjalfi, and Thor's two sons, Magni and Modr, and his two daughters by Sif, Thrudr, Thor's eldest child, and Hlora. Suddenly Thor reeled backwards. His family noticed the flintstone in his forehead and suggested he let them attend to it. However, try as they might, they couldn't remove it. Magni pointed to the underside of the stone. On it was carved Hrungr's runic symbol.

Thor realized what this meant and told them, "This flint has an enchantment on it and can only be removed by sorcery."

They helped Thor was back to Thrudvangr and sent for the volva Groa. Her first husband Svolnir had died and she had only recently married the brave Aurvandil, a friend of Thor's, and lover of Sif's. She had the power to move rocks and divert the courses of floods using her magic spells.

Thor grasped his head and spoke to Groa, "I have need of you Groa. No one has been able to remove this flintstone which is causing me such great pain. I can't defend Asgardr as long as this stone is in my head. I can't concentrate on anything except the stabbing pain in my head. Please help me."

Groa stood bending over Thor chanting spells over the stone and carving secret runes on it as well as on the floor in front of Thor's forehead . At first it seemed just as firm as ever. But gradually it shifted. She continued to pass her hands back and forth over Thor's forehead. Thor felt the stone shift. He was delighted at the lessening of the pain and decided to entertain Groa with a story about Aurvandil while she worked over the stone.

"Not long ago I was in Jotunheimr slaying jotuns. At one village I rescued your husband. He hid in a basket which I carried off slung over my shoulder. We came from the north wading down the river Elivagar. Unfortunately while we were being pursued by jotuns a rock was thrown at the basket and tore a hole in the bottom. Aurvandil's toe poked through at the opening. I glanced down and saw it had turned blue and then white, and then black from frostbite. So that it wouldn't cause him further pain I reached down and broke it off. If you'll look up in the sky you can see where I threw it. The star up there to the north is now known as Aurvandil's Toe."

Groa was delighted with the story. But the best was yet to come. Thor continued, "I have good news for you, Groa. When we parted, Aurvandil told me he had just a few places to visit and then he would be coming home to you."

At these words Groa stopped her spell in mid-incantation. She was so excited that she couldn't remember the rest of it. She ran back to her hall to await Aurvandil's return.

Although Thor's pain had been greatly reduced no one was ever able to remove the stone. The only time Thor suffered any headaches was whenever a honing stone was thrown across the floor in Midgardr. Word of this was spread throughout Midgardr and it was forbidden to throw a flintstone across the floor lest Thor suffer in Asgardr.

Chapter II

Geirrodr and Agnar

King Hrauding was a powerful king on Midgardr who ruled the land known as Reid-Gothland, defined by the river Vistula and the gulf of Finland. He had two sons, Agnar, ten-years-old, and Geirrodr, eight-years-old, who were as different from each other as the night was from the day. Geirrodr was determined to always get the better of his elder brother. Many who saw the two together had doubts Agnar would ever be king, even though he was the elder and the rightful heir. They all said Agnar was just too kind and trusting.

Despite their rivalry they frequently got along and engaged in the ordinary pursuits of boys their ages. One day Geirrodr suggested they go fishing. "I'm certain I can catch more fish than you. I'll wager whatever you want, and give you the odds you choose, so certain am I that I'll win."

Agnar didn't want to bet, "Why must we make a contest of everything? Why can't we just fish. What does it matter who catches the most? We're both going to share eating them. It doesn't matter to me if you catch more fish than I do."

Geirrodr answered, "Good, then let's fish, I'll catch more, and you prove it doesn't matter to you. But, whomever loses has to clean all the fish today, tomorrow, and all week."

Geirrodr knew Agnar hated cleaning fish. So, reluctantly he agreed to the contest.

They pushed off from the shore into a swift current and were soon carried far out to sea. Geirrodr was the first to cast his line in the water, and was immediately rewarded with a bite. He began boasting of his skill as a fisherman, "See, the fish are eager to bite at my line. They're gathering around to see who'll be next."

But Geirrodr's boasting was cut short when Agnar cast his line and it too immediately became taunt as a fish chomped onto the bait.

All day they fished, each one as successful as the other. Oftimes it seemed as if the fish were just waiting to jump into the boat. Soon the entire bottom of the boat was covered with fish.

Geirrodr looked around and began laughing. Agnar couldn't understand why.

Geirrodr explained, "Don't you see? We have no way of knowing who caught what. We were so busy pulling fish out and tossing them down so we could drop our lines again we didn't mark them. I have no idea how many I caught, or which ones I caught. You can't tell which ones you caught, either."

Agnar laughed too, "You're right. I guess we've both won."

They agreed to call off the wager.

Agnar looked around. They were out in the open sea, no longer in sight of the shore. "It's late and I'm tired. I think we should make our way back to shore."

Geirrodr disagreed, "No. Even though we've caught enough fish to feed the entire village tomorrow, there's always the day after, and the day after that. You can't be tired. I know I'm not tired. We can always use as much fish as we can haul. Let's keep at it."

Agnar looked up at the thunderclouds rolling in quickly from the east. "Clouds seem to be gathering and I'm afraid we might be caught in a storm. I really think we should go back."

Geirrodr disregarded his brother's entreaty, "You're always afraid of something. Sometimes it's your horse running too fast, or the wolves in the forest. Now it's storm clouds. You'll be safe enough since I'm here to protect you. There isn't going to be a storm."

But Geirrodr was wrong. Soon the rain was pelting down upon them. The white caps of the ocean caused their small vessel to toss and roll. Many of their fish were returned to the sea, revived and swum off grateful at the second chance they had received.

The boat was not meant to be used this far out and was proving impossible to steer in the raging sea. Geirrodr and Agnar gave up trying. Geirrodr yelled over to Agnar, "It's no use. Let go and just hold on for dear life."

It took all their strength to keep from being washed overboard. The winds batted and tossed them around. Agnar motioned for Geirrodr to follow what he was doing. He grabbed a rounded pile of rope, passed an end through the loop of an iron bar fastened to the deck and tied double and even triple knots to secure it. And then tied the other end around him. Geirrodr was doing the same. This was what saved them from being thrown into the sea.

There was nothing more to be done but wait until the storm subsided and then try to figure out where they were and sail home. But they didn't wait patiently. They were both flung back and forth across the deck as the boat tipped this way and that. Waves washed over them throwing them overboard. But held fast by their ropes they were thrown back on deck and thrown off the other side. At times they feared the boat would capsize and drag them down to the depths with it, both tied securely to the deck.

The storm raged long into the night. But slowly there was a perceptible change in the sounds they heard. In the distance they could hear the crashing of breakers against rocks which meant they were near the shore.

At first they were comforted by the sound. Then as it became louder and louder they both realized their boat was going to be dashed against the rocks and them with it. They braced themselves as best they could. Then with one mighty wave they were carried out of the sea and smashed into a cliff framing the beach. The boat was smashed to bits, but they were thrown clear.

Agnar looked over at Geirrodr. He moaned which meant he was alive. Both were too exhausted and battered to move. They laid on the beach exhausted until morning.

The sun rose and its friendly warmth revived them. Geirrodr immediately took charge of the situation. "Let's explore the area and see what we can find. Maybe someone lives around here and will able to help us." He looked along the beach, "I'm hungry and it seems Ægir and Ran have called all the fish back to them. Not even one of our catch was thrown upon the beach with us. Let's see if we can find something to eat."

Both climbed up a ridge, Geirrodr the stronger and more agile, ahead of Agnar. They surveyed as much of the area as they could. Agnar was the first to see the smoke coming out of the chimney of a cottage off in the distance. "Look, over there. It's a farmhouse. Maybe they'll help us."

"They had better, if they know what's good for them." Geirrodr hurried off ahead of Agnar.

As they neared the cottage they came upon one of its inhabitants, an old man with a long grey beard. He tugged at his blue broad-brimmed hat in order to pull it down to conceal the area over his missing right eye. "What can I do for you two strangers? I heard a boat break up against the rocks last night and was just going out to investigate. By the looks of you two, I'd say you were on that ship. Come with me and I'll have my wife tend to your cuts and bruises. She knows how to use herbs and will have you both as good as new in no time. By the way, my name is Grimnir."

They followed him back to the cottage. His wife greeted them by name. "Hello, Geirrodr. Hello Agnar. Would you like something to eat? You must be hungry after your journey?" They were surprised to see she had already set the table for four. How had she known they'd be coming? How did she know their names? But they were too hungry to dwell on these questions.

They ate and ate and the food kept coming. Geirrodr and Agnar were used to stately feasts and had been raised on meals prepared by the most skilled chefs in the world. But never had they had a meal like this. It was by far the best they'd ever eaten. Course after course appeared before them made up of delicacies they'd never seen before. Some foods they recognized as exotic dishes from far off lands. How could a simple farm wife prepare a feast like this? Where did she get the ingredients?

Grimnir's wife smiled at them and asked about their adventures, "Tell us how you've arrived here. We don't get many visitors since we live so out of the way."

The two related their story in great detail. Geirrodr started it. "We've had a great fishing adventure. The fish almost jumped into the boat by themselves, so anxious were they to be caught by us. I've never had so much fun in my life."

Agnar was a bit more reserved, "We should have turned around before it got so late. Then the storm wouldn't have carried us so far from home. I hope you can help us get back."

Grimnir answered, "It's the beginning of winter and the seas are too treacherous to sail safely at this time of year. I'm afraid you'll probably have to stay here until summer."

Agnar was slightly upset at this news. But Geirrodr looked upon it as another adventure. "Will you teach us how to live out here? I saw your nets as we came in, and they are certainly the finest I've ever seen. Can you teach me to make nets like those?"

Grimnir smiled at Geirrodr whom he found he liked better than Agnar. The two went into the other room while Agnar helped Grimnir's wife clear the table and clean up after the meal. She took a great liking to him. He was so polite.

Soon their stay settled into a routine. Grimnir went out every morning with Geirrodr and gave him lessons, filling the young lad's head with stories of the glory of fighting and righteousness of war. He spoke of great battles that had happened long ago, and of fierce warriors who had conquered nations. It was almost as if he were telling stories of his own triumphs.

Over the weeks he instructed him in warrior skills such as how to fight with sword, spear, hammer, and ax. Together they chose a branch from a young yew tree and fashioned it into one of the finest bows Geirrodr had ever seen. Then they made arrows which flew swift and true when fired from the bow. Even the strongest of winds would not carry the arrows off course away from their intended targets.

Grimnir taught Geirrodr how to unseat an opponent from his horse with a minimum amount of effort. And sometimes late in the evening Grimnir talked of Asgardr and the Æsir themselves, as if he had actually been there. He explained the mysteries of all the Worlds of the Tree to Geirrodr who was impressed and tried to emulate Grimnir in all things, including the most difficult task of all, being polite to his brother.

While Geirrodr was out with Grimnir, Agnar remained at the cottage with Grimnir's wife. His education was quite different. She taught him to understand the language of birds, and pointed out herbs which could be used to cure various ills and heal even the most stubborn of wounds. Other more practical skills included how to farm land so it would yield several crops per season, when to stop planting in a field, or even how to reclaim a field that no longer brought forth viable crops. In its own way his education was just as extensive as his brother's, and just as valuable, maybe moreso.

The winter passed quickly. Both boys had grown and changed. Grimnir and Geirrodr built a new boat, while Agnar and Grimnir's wife set up a store of provisions for the long journey back. Soon everything was ready and the two set sail. As their boat receded from the shore Grimnir yelled out to Geirrodr, "Remember all I've taught you. Be a warrior in all things, but be fair."

Once away from Grimnir's influence Geirrodr's old traits began to reappear. His disdain for his brother was now greater than ever since the gulf between them was now immense. They had many arguments during their journey, usually ending with Geirrodr accusing Agnar of cowardliness and being like a woman.

The closer they got to their home the more an idea that had taken root in Geirrodr's mind began to grow. Once back in their land he would be a second son again, the spare. His brother, being older, was the heir. He thought, "What happens to second sons when a father dies?" Then answering his own question, "First sons inherit everything, no matter how undeserving they are. Second sons are left out and have to seek their glory elsewhere if they can." He looked over at Agnar who was busy twittering away with a dove that had landed on the prow of the ship. Geirrodr's thoughts continued, "Am I to be servant to a mad brother who twitters to birds?"

Geirrodr decided on his course of action. As their ship touched the shore Geirrodr struck his brother on the head with an oar, grabbed the other oar and threw them both overboard, leapt out of the boat and with a powerful heave pushed the boat back into the current yelling after it, "Go where the trolls can get you. If I had a torch with me, this would be a funeral pyre." Agnar lay unconscious on the deck as the boat continued on its journey unaware of his brother's betrayal.

Geirrodr hurried down the familiar paths that took him to the castle. There he was surprised to find his father had taken ill during their disappearance and was on his deathbed. He hastily went to his father who was astonished to see his son, "Today I am blessed because my sons have returned. Please send in your brother Agnar so I might pass my kingdom to him and be on my way to Valhalla."

Geirrodr just stared at his father. King Hrauding continued, "And you must promise me to serve your brother wisely."

This was too much for Geirrodr and he almost delighted in telling him about Agnar, "I am sorry to have to tell you Agnar drowned during the storm. I am your only son."

King Hrauding sighed, "Then it must be as the Norns have commanded. My last act as king will be to pass my crown to you and proclaim you as my successor." Geirrodr could hear the disappointment in his father's voice.

King Hrauding motioned for the amanuensis who was always nearby, "Take down my words. Know it amongst all in my kingdom that my son Geirrodr is to succeed me, and have all my lands and property. He is the rightful king and any of his issue will be the rightful heirs."

He turned to Geirrodr, "If Agnar is dead, then it is up to you to be king, marry, fight battles, and bring further glory to our family name. But, even as I say this, I feel uneasy about Agnar's death. I would feel better if we had a body."

Geirrodr felt it was time to change the subject. As he spoke, hoping to bolster his image in his father's mind, his father signed the proclamation making him king, "I have learned many warrior skills while I've been away. I won't let you down. I promise I won't let you down."

King Hraudrung spoke one last time, "I hope you'll try to be as good a king as your brother Agnar would have been. I…"

The old king looked at his son and tried to continue speaking, but an exhale of breath was all that came from his mouth. A death gasp. And he was gone without ever giving his son the gift of his blessing. His last words had been of Agnar. And Geirrodr all too painfully knew that.

Despite the wobbly start to his reign Geirrodr proved to be a very effective king. He ruled harshly, but usually justly. He taught his armies the battle techniques he had learned from Grimnir. He led them to victory after victory as he conquered many lands and expanded his kingdom many fold.

In the meanwhile the boat carrying Agnar had drifted to a far off land. It was many days before Agnar regained consciousness. Unfortunately his thoughts were hazy and he never regained the knowledge that he had been born to be a king. Eventually he settled in that land, married a jotun and lived a long life raising many children. His farm was the best in the district. The other farmers were amazed at the food he could coax from his small plot of land.

The years passed and both sons were successful in their own way. Agnar didn't remember his past, and Geirrodr had forgotten the evil deed upon which his reign was based. But the Norns and those in Asgardr never forget acts of dishonor.

One day Odin and Frigg were seated on their thrones in the watchtower of Odin's hall, Valaskjalf. Odin caught sight of Agnar and pointed him out to Frigg, "Look there, to the east, Agnar sits siring half-breeds while he wiles away his time raising corn. See how he has turned out using the knowledge you gave him. He sits there with the longest ears of corn in the land. Surely that is a worthy feat for one of royal blood?"

Frigg was upset at the fate that had befallen her favorite. She pointed to Midgardr, "Look what has become of the inheritance thief Geirrodr, the unlawful king. The noble thoughts you imparted to him have been all but forgotten. Guests arrive at his castle never to leave again. Instead they're put through the most horrendous torture, just for Geirrodr's pleasure. What about the generosity you taught him to show his guests? Instead they grow thin from the meagre table he sets. And if he entertains them long enough they die of starvation from his hospitality. Is that something you're proud of?"

Odin disputed Frigg's statements, "I can't believe any warrior I've trained would treat his guests so callously."

Frigg smiled and said, "Then perhaps you should go and see for yourself. Be certain you eat a few big meals first. They're the last ones you'll enjoy."

Odin decided to leave the next day in disguise. That evening Frigg sent for her messenger Fulla and gave her instructions, "Rush quickly and reach Geirrodr's before my husband does. Tell Geirrodr a dangerous sorcerer is on his way to try and trick him." She gave a few further instructions and sent her off. Fulla arrived at Geirrodr's the next day, just as Odin was leaving Asgardr in disguise.

Geirrodr was not really as bad as Frigg had made him out to be. He welcomed Fulla to his hall. She stood before his throne and gave him Frigg's warning. "Beware of a tall man wearing a mantle of blue and slouched hat over his left eye. You'll be surprised because he will sneak up on you. He is a wizard, and from him your death will ensue."

Geirrodr laughed at this, "Do you expect me to believe what you say? All entrances to my hall are guarded. No one sneaks in. And he'll be a wizard? How can I be sure you aren't some sort of wizard yourself?"

Fulla continued her message, "You can believe it or not, but I suggest it won't harm you if you heed my warnings. One way you'll know I speak the truth is that your dogs will not bark at him. Even those dogs that might be frothing at the mouth with illness and madness will not bark at this man. If you don't think that odd, then don't listen to me." She turned and left the hall.

Geirrodr sent a guard to stop her so he could hear more. But the guard returned telling Geirrodr the woman had disappeared just as she rounded the corner of the passageway.

That evening Odin arrived. He entered the hall noiselessly and surprised the king and his assemblage at dinner. Geirrodr started remembering Fulla's words, "You'll be surprised because he will sneak up on you."

Instead of welcoming the visitor, Geirrodr yelled at him, "How did you get in here?" Then turning to one of his men he added, "Send for the guards on duty."

But that was unnecessary as a guard came running in after the stranger whom he was surprised to see had made it to the base of Geirrodr's throne. The guard was questioned closely, "How did this man get in here unannounced? Have you been sleeping on duty?"

Trembling the guard answered, "No, sire. I've been as alert as ever."

Geirrodr continued, "Why didn't the dogs outside the castle bark at his approach and attack him? I don't understand how he could have gotten past them without at least a couple of them taking a nip out of him." As he spoke he remembered more of Fullla's warnings from that afternoon.

The guard continued with his report, "It was a strange sight to see. The dogs ran out to him, but instead of barking and attacking they suddenly slunk down low and crawled back against the walls with their tails between their legs. Not one of them yelped."

Geirrodr looked at the stranger, horrified.

The stranger had waited long enough to speak, "I don't want to trouble you for much. I only want lodging for the night. On the morrow I will leave you in peace and continue on my journey."

Geirrodr turned to one of his attendants and gave him some instructions. Then he began questioning the stranger closely. "Who are you? Where do you come from? Where are you going? Why are you here?" He was most insistent on the last question. But the stranger refused to answer any of the questions.

"I'm sorry, but those answers are not for you to know. All I want is lodging for the night and then I'll be on my way at the break of day tomorrow, and leave you in peace and with goodwill. As Nott's chariot disappears on the horizon I will disappear too. I'll begin my journey before you've awakened."

Somehow in Geirrodr's fear he interpreted the phrase to mean he would never awaken. Before he could speak, the people in the hall turned to the entranceway as a commotion from without interrupted the proceedings. A servant appeared with two vicious dogs in tow. He unhooked their leashes and set them on the stranger. The dogs ran up to the blue form, slavver dripping from their mouths, anticipating the fun they would have tearing him to bits. But the same thing happened that had happened before. When they got within a few feet of him they both stopped and began backing away with their tails between their legs.

Geirrodr yelled out for the stranger to be taken. "Seize him and bind him tightly with our strongest chains. He means me great harm."

After this was done attendants lit two fires, one on each side of the guest. Geirrodr gave him one more chance to speak, "I have commanded more and more wood be piled on the fires. Gradually the fires will grow and eventually the flames will be dancing at your feet. The flames will approach closer and closer to your cloak, and then they will engulf you. All you need do to prevent this is tell me the answers to the questions I've asked."

The stranger turned away without answering the king. More wood was piled on the fires and their flames shot ever higher. This continued for eight days and nights. The only person who dared approach the stranger or show him any kindness was Geirrodr's ten-year-old son, Agnar, named after the king's long lost brother.

By the eighth day fires were licking at the stranger's cloak. But Agnar was not frightened and took him a full horn of mead and spoke to the stranger, "Although he is king and my father, I do not agree with how he is treating you. You've done harm to

no one, and have only asked for shelter for the night. This is not the shelter that should be given to one who is blameless. Sometimes my father can be very cruel." Odin was impressed with the young child.

Geirrodr was again sitting on his throne trying to question the stranger, "I'm giving you one last chance. The fires will soon be about you and it'll be too late. Answer my questions."

The stranger remained silent. Then the mantle caught fire and the stranger yelled out, "Great gifts will I give the one who rescues me. The blessings of Ullr will be upon the one who brings me relief." Then as if in a trance he sang mystical songs of battles from long ago, and those that seemed yet to be. His songs were of Asgardr and the Æsir who dwelled there. Those who heard were frightened because they felt he must have been to Asgardr, or else he never would have been able to sing about the land and the Æsir so convincingly. He continued, his melodies carrying the knowledge of the dead in their words. Suddenly he stood and the chains fell from him, broken. The flames engulfed him yet he did not burn. Then they subsided and he stood there, radiant like one of the Æsir.

Geirrodr was lost in thought sitting on his throne with his half-drawn sword in his lap. Where had he heard such stories before? His thoughts went back to the winter long ago when he and his brother had been shipwrecked on the island where he had been taught warrior skills by Grimnir. He now recognized the stranger as the foster-father he had loved.

The stranger continued, "You want to know my name? Very well, I'll tell you. But it'll take some time since I'm known by many names in many lands. These are the names I'll answer to if they are called out: Bjorn was I called when I rode Blakkr, and Bjarr when I rode Kertr. Then I was known as Skilfing, Sadr, Harbardr, Nikudr, Herfodr, Elgr, Bolverkr, Sigdir, Blindr, Gizur, Gautr, Hroptr, Jafnhar, Oski, Rafnhud, Hottr, Hnikarr, Grimr. Many have feared me as Jormunr, Kjalarr, Langbardr, Nikarr, Fengr, Biflindi, Sidskegg, Bjarki, Ulvrung, Hraudgrani, Opnir, Herblindi, Sigtyr, Thudr, Herjan, Hjalmberi, Sigautr, Havi, Fjorgyn, Omi, Grimnir, and Mistarblini. Others have worshiped me as Jol, Fjolsvidr, Sanngetall, Har, Bileygr, Galgatyr, Tveggi, Njotr, Jolnir, Hangatyr, Udr, Farmagud, Hnikudr, Fimbultyr, Hangi, Sidgrani, Gautatyr, Sidhottr, Galdrsfadir, Tviblindi, Vecka, Farmatyr, Valfadir, Thundr, Sigmundr. In far off lands I am known as Heiteitr, Jalkr, Thridi, Gondlir, Audi, Sigfadir, Hrossharsgrani, Baleygr, Atridr, Svidrir, Gangleir, Vegtamr Valtamssonr, Thror, Vakr, Hroptatyr, Sigrhofundr, Helblindi, Yggr, Hrafnass, Veratyr, Arnhofi, Thekkr, Vafudr, Glapsvidr, Hrafngud, Gangraaf, Sigtryggr, Herfajodr, Vidrir, Svigdir, Herteitr, Svipall, Gladsvidr, Hangi, Vidurr, Seidmadr, Haptagud, Fjolnir, Hangagud and Svafnir. You, Geirrodr, knew me as Grimnir. But my sons know me as Odin."

Geirrodr was terrified. Trembling, he grabbed his sword and ran at the old man hoping to break any chains that were unbroken and scatter the flames from his feet so he'd be free.

Odin calmly said to him, "The Æsir are angry with you. The disir have departed."

Geirrodr realized his fate was sealed. Trembling he dropped his sword as he ran down the steps from his throne, stopped, picked it up, tripped and fell upon it. It cut through his heart, killing him instantly as he fell dead at Odin's feet.

The assembly was quiet, wondering what would happen next, and whether or not they would all be punished. Odin signaled to Agnar to take the throne. He passed his hand in blessing upon the young king and then disappeared.

Agnar ruled long and wisely and righted the wrongs of his father. He was much loved of his people. Odin kept watch on him from Hlidskjalf, and what he saw made him proud.

Chapter 12

Thor Goes Fishing for Midgardrsormr

Ran and Ægir, who was sometimes known as Hler, ruled the sea. In addition to being married they were also brother and sister and were descended from Ymir. Ægir was the eldest, while Ran was the youngest in the family. There were two other brothers. Logi, whose name meant fire, was the second oldest. He lived in Utgardr and worked for Utgardr-Loki as his cook, and had won an eating contest against Loki. Kari, whose name meant flame, was the other brother. Many of the sea jotuns such as Mimir, Gymir and Grendel were descended from these three brothers. Kari's most famous descendents included the hrymthursar Frosti, sometimes known as Jokull whose name meant iceberg, Snor whose name meant snow, Fonn whose name meant dense snow, as well as Thrym, Thjassi, and Beli. The Æsir didn't believe in brother/sister marriages, but accepted Ægir and Ran because they were good hosts and very powerful. It was better to have them as friends than as enemies. They were frequent visitors to Asgardr.

Ægir had a long flowing white beard and green hair. He was tall and gaunt with long thin grasping fingers. His hands convulsively opened and closed hoping to catch whatever came in their path. Atop his head he wore a helmet called Ægishjalmr which frightened anyone who looked on it.

He and Ran delighted in inviting sailors to their hall, whether they wanted to visit or not. Ægir overturned vessels and using mighty currents the sailors would be carried over for a visit, which usually turned out to be a quite lengthy stay.

Ran had her methods, too. She'd hide behind a rock and lure a vessel to its fate. Then she'd gather up the sailors in her net and pull them to the hall. Many sailors of Midgardr carried gold with them to propitiate the couple should their vessel run into rough seas and be overturned. The gold they carried in their pockets might be enough to buy their way out of the fate that usually awaited those capsized into the sea.

Ægir and Ran lived on an island in the Kattegat, also known as Hlessey. Their hall was a golden cave built within a cave. The walls were decorated with shells whose color seemed to change depending on the angle at which they were viewed. Multicolored coral

pillars placed unevenly throughout the hall held up the roof. The banquet room, lit by the brilliant golden walls and floors, rather than by fire, lay further inward. There were many driftwood tables and seats softened with cushions of seaweed awaiting those who feasted as Ægir and Ran's guests.

Serving and humming sweet music to the drowned sailors who came to the hall were Ægir and Ran's nine wavemaiden daughters. Their names were Angeyja, Bara, Drofn, Beylgja, Hefring, Blodughadda, Dufa, Himinglœfa and Kolga. Their skin was snow-white, and all nine had blue eyes. Their blond hair billowed down their backs in long waves while they gracefully carried golden goblets of mead and seashells filled with the finest food, prepared by Eldir, Ægir's cook, to the sailors. When they weren't serving at the feast they loved to play on the seashore, usually in groups of triplets. With their long transparent veils, some of which were blue with white edging while others were solid green, trailing behind them they ran in and out amongst the rocks on the coast. They swam out to ships and guided them to safety and away from perilous obstacles. Although most times their play was all in good fun, sometimes they were sullen and moody. It was then they drove each other into an almost mad frenzy as they hurled themselves against the rocks on the shore. Then the ships avoided the nine for fear of the harm they would meet.

During one particularly long feast in Asgardr, which Ægir and Ran had attended, the drinking had been so great that the ale gave out. Thor, whose tongue had been loosened by drink blamed Ægir for the lack of further drink. "It seems every time you give us the pleasure of your company, when you leave we are left with a dry cellar. You drink as if we had an ocean of ale to spare. When are you going to repay our hospitality by having the Æsir over for a feast?"

Ægir laughed at Thor, "My hall is nothing compared to the great mansions in Asgardr. However, that's not what's preventing me from offering the Æsir my hospitality. Although I could never provide you with a feast to compare with the ones you have here, I could come close. No, my problem is the kettle I use for brewing ale is much too small to provide the Æsir with the drink they require. It has taken us several days of constant drinking for you in Asgardr to run out. At my hall we would barely have enough for one round. What kind of host would I be if I ended up serving the noble Æsir milk? But Thor, if you'll find me a kettle large enough, then I here and now extend an invitation to the Æsir for a monstrous celebration on my island in the Kattegat at the end of the flax harvest."

The discussion turned to how they might obtain a kettle large enough to meet Ægir's needs.

Tyr had been listening to the problem and spoke up, "I know a place where Thor might get a kettle large enough. My foster-father Hymir lives in the north, east of the rivers of Elivagar. He has a kettle that is at least a mile deep and a mile across. I believe it will serve our purposes quite adequately." Though Odin was Tyr's father, his mother, Griseldis, also one of the Æsir, lived in Jotunheimr with Hymir and his nine-hundred-headed mother, Gmir.

Thor was always interested in going to Jotunheimr and bashing in a few heads, and the thought they could also steal a kettle in which to brew more drink for him added to his delight. "How can we get this kettle?"

Tyr answered, "Hymir is usually not a very reasonable fellow. Also, despite the fact he has a huge head, he is not very smart. So, first I suggest we just try force. If that doesn't work then we can use some strategy to trick him."

Thor and Tyr put on the guises of two young men of Midgardr. Thor adopted the name Veorr for the journey. Then they set out eastward in Thor's goat-drawn chariot. When they got to the river Ifing they decided to leave the chariot behind for fear Thor's famous goats would be recognized and their disguises given away. They left the chariot and goats with Egil and his wife at their cottage near the river Ifing. They were the parents of Thor's servants Roskva and Thjalfi, who were permitted to stay and visit their parents while Thor and Tyr continued on to Hymir's.

As they traveled northward the land became colder and colder. Soon the river Ifing was frozen over enough for the two to cross. Fortunately the ice wasn't thick enough to support the weight of a jotun. Eventually they came to a huge stone hall that had been hewn out of the side of a mountain. When they entered the hall they first came upon Gmir. The nine-hundred-headed hag had fiery eyes that grew out of heads that covered her body. It was hard to tell which end was up, or where exactly she was looking. She just stared at the two young men with her eighteen-hundred eyes, making them very uncomfortable. Each face was as horrible as the one next to it. You would think with all those heads one of them would have been pleasing to look at.

Griseldis heard the commotion in the hallway and went to see what was going on. Tyr watched as Griseldis entered the room and was amazed at how beautiful his mother was. She was dressed in a gold tunic with long golden hair falling on her shoulders. Being one of the Æsir she saw through their disguises at once and ran up to embrace her son.

She gave them refreshments and asked Tyr all about Asgardr. He talked relating many adventures the Æsir had had. Finally she noticed it was getting dark out, "Hymir will be home soon. If he hasn't caught a lot of fish he'll be in a bad mood. And you know how he doesn't like to be surprised by visitors. You and Thor should wait over behind that stone pillar under the staircase while I break the news of your visit to him. His baleful look might just cut through both of you."

Thor was about to remark that no mere look could harm him when the hall began to shake. "Hurry, behind the pillar. He's home." Tyr's mother looked toward the entranceway and motioned the two Æsir towards the pillar. Thor and Tyr didn't argue and ran behind the pillar.

Hymir entered the hall. His beard was frozen white with icicles, which clanked together as he moved about. He carried no catch of fish with him. Griseldis could tell he was in a bad mood. Before he could say anything his nine-hundred-headed mother burst out with a cacophony of echoes telling her son the news of their visitors, "Over there, Hymir." "Look out." "Behind the pillar." "Watch out." Hymir clasped his hands to his ears to shut out the awful noise. He was used to his mother yelling at him, but he was in no mood for it tonight. All he could think of was the constant nagging he had heard from her when he was growing up. Nine-hundred mouths telling him what to do, how to dress, where to go, what to eat, when to sleep, when to get up. Finally she calmed down and spoke with one loud voice as she gazed towards the pillar, "Behind the pillar under the staircase you'll find your measly foster-son come to visit with an obnoxious friend."

Hymir turned and gave the pillar an icy glance, whereupon it split in half and toppled over. The pillar was supporting a cross beam from which eight large cauldrons had been hung. As the beam sagged the cauldrons slid to the ground, one against the next, cracking and ruining all but one pot. Tyr and Thor, brushing dust and splinters off themselves, stepped out of the rubble.

Hymir didn't particularly like Tyr, and certainly didn't like the intruder he'd brought with him. But since they had come on such a long journey to see him, and because Tyr was his foster-son he couldn't refuse them hospitality. Besides Tyr's visits were few and far between. The sooner he was entertained and sent on his way the longer it would be before he'd visit again.

"You're welcome to rest here for the night. I'll have my servants prepare dinner for all of us. Introduce me to your friend, Tyr." He motioned for them to follow him into the main hall.

Tyr responded as he followed his foster-father, "This is Veorr, a friend of mine from Midgardr."

Hymir laughed, "Then they're growing them bigger in Midgardr than when I was last there. If I'm not mistaken you must be one of the Æsir. But which one?"

Before Thor could answer, the servants informed Hymir the tables were set. Thor, Tyr, Hymir and Griseldis sat at one table. A separate, much larger table was set for Gmir. There were very few who could stand to watch the disgusting way she ate. Some of her mouths slurped at mead while she forced as much food as possible into other mouths. Food and mead dribbled down her chins to the tops of other heads. Some heads reached over to lick food from these heads. And their spittle and some of the food fell down even further into the mouths of upturned heads hoping for whatever dregs they could get. All of this made quite a mess. Dirty matted food encrusted hair was everywhere.

Three roasted oxen were set at the main table along with huge tankards of sweet-tasting home-brewed mead. Thor was so famished he immediately finished off two of the oxen and drank most of the mead. Hymir was surprised at his guest's gluttony and guessed his true identity, "If I'm not mistaken, Thor is the only one of the Æsir known for his prowess in eating. You must be Thor?"

Thor acknowledged that he was. Hymir began insulting him, although Thor was too busy eating to realize it. Finally Hymir said, "Tomorrow I'll be going out fishing again, so we can have fish tomorrow for supper. I hope there's enough fish in the sea to satisfy the mighty Thor."

Thor just answered between mouthfuls, "Perhaps I should accompany you on your expedition. I'm an excellent fisherman."

Hymir accepted the offer, "I never knew you fished. You're so small looking, I would think you'd have trouble landing the catch I fish for. I also have a tendency to row far out to sea where the largest catch is. Usually I am beyond the sight of land. This might frighten you. However, no matter what your ability or lack of ability is, I would be glad to have your company."

Finally Thor realized Hymir had been making fun of him all evening, "It will not be me who first suggests we put back to land." He turned back to his plate and continued eating.

Soon they all finished. And with Thor's ominous prediction still in their thoughts everyone retired for the night so they could rise at dawn to get an early start.

Hymir was up first and out by the shore preparing the rowboat. During the night he had come to the conclusion Thor would be more of a hindrance than a help and had decided to leave without him. Just as he was ready to shove off Thor arrived.

"I see you have everything ready." Glancing into the boat Thor saw there was only one pole and just enough bait for Hymir. "Can you tell me where I can get some bait to use?"

Hymir grunted and pointed to his field of grazing oxen. "The oxen over there have left plenty of bait laying around on the ground for your use. Look, the ox over by the trough is dropping some fresh bait just for you."

Thor's eyes burned red from the insult. "Very well, you have offered me your oxen to use. One of them will make excellent bait." With that Thor stalked over to the field and grabbed Hymir's most prized ox, his coal black bull Himinhrjodr, which meant heaven springer, and twisted off its head with a single movement. He carried the head and carcass back and flung them both into the boat.

Hymir was too shocked to realize what this would eventually mean to the quality of his herd. Instead he concentrated on Thor's other problem. "What are you going to use for a pole? I know of no wood or line strong enough to hold both your bait and the fish it might catch."

Thor sat in the stern seat, grabbed two oars and began rowing, "I have a few ideas about that."

Hymir sat forward and also rowed. But it seemed to him it made no difference what he did. The boat shot over the water as if propelled by magic. Even if he tried pulling in the opposite direction the boat wouldn't slow down. Finally they reached the spot where Hymir did most of his fishing.

"Pull in your oars, Thor. Here is the best fishing spot. I've been able to fill this boat with fish from here in just a short time. After awhile the fish just give up and start jumping into the boat by themselves." Hymir decided maybe a little jocularity might improve the situation.

But Thor paid no heed to Hymir's words. "We have many rosts further to travel before we get to where the fishing is best."

Thor rowed on without speaking. Finally Hymir began to get really worried. "Please stop, Thor. If we go any farther we'll be over the mighty serpent Midgardrsormr."

Thor answered, "Hah, so you are the first to suggest we turn back."

Thor continued to row. Then he came to a stop at a place where there was no land in sight. "We're here. Make your first cast in the water and see what you come up with."

Hymir was too scared to move. He held tightly to the sides of the boat watching Thor.

"Very well then, if you won't try to fish, I will." With that Thor picked up the ox's head. He reached over and grabbed the iron kedge to use as a hook and spitted the ox's head on it. He tied one end of a rope to the anchor and the other end to Megingardr, his belt of strength. His belt seemed to have magical properties. Although it was tied twice around Thor's waist it still stretched enough to sink deep into the ocean once the anchor was cast over the side of the boat.

Slowly Hymir's courage returned. He baited his hook and cast it into the ocean. No sooner was this done than two whales both seized the bait. He easily hauled them in. So far the trip was proving to be extremely successful. He forgot his trepidation. With luck he might catch enough from the sea to last all winter.

Suddenly Thor felt something tug at his bait. He knew it was Midgardrsormr and braced himself against the boat while the serpent struggled and strained to free himself. Thor pulled on his line so much that his feet went through the bottom of the boat causing him to almost lose his grip. But he steadied himself by standing on the ocean floor.

Thor and Midgardrsormr struggled against each other. The water churned about causing giant waves to pound against all the shores of Midgardr. Storms broke around Thor as thunder and lightning flashed overhead. The serpent pulled to and fro so that Thor's knuckles were scraped back and forth across the boat's gunn'l causing more lightning to fly about which threatened to set the boat afire. Thor tightened his grip around his belt until his knuckles shone white.

Meanwhile Hymir clung desperately to the boat afraid he'd be tossed overboard and drowned. The whales were tossed about like flat-fish. But the worst was still in store for poor Hymir. As he looked about he saw rising up out of the sea the terrifying face of Midgardrsormr whom Thor had managed to pull from the ocean's floor. The serpent spat out a stream of poisonous venom at the boat, which luckily missed.

Thor and Midgardrsormr stared at each other. They seemed evenly matched. Suddenly Midgardrsormr sank back pulling the boat down with him hoping to drown the fishermen. Hymir, now fearful of not only drowning but of being eaten if he fell into the sea, pulled out his magical knife which had been forged in Svartalfheimr and lunged at Thor's belt and started hacking at it, without any success. Runes had been cut into Megingardr at its forging and magical spells chanted as it cooled. The belt was protected from being cut, even by a magical knife forged in Svartalfheimr. Hymir reached his long arm into the ocean and began cutting at the line tied to the belt. It had no magical enchantment protecting it and finally, strand by strand it gave way, giving freedom once more to Midgardrsormr who sank back to the bottom of the ocean.

Thor removed Mjolnir from where it had been folded up and hidden inside his shirt, leaned over the edge of the boat and flung the hammer after the disappearing serpent. Then he turned to Hymir and boxed the jotun's ears for causing him to loose his prize. The force of the blow heaved Hymir over the side of the boat.

Mjolnir had not been flung hard enough to travel through the water with force strong enough to hit Midgardrsormr with any strength. Midgardrsormr halfheartedly snapped at Mjolnir hoping to swallow it. But he was rapidly becoming too drowsy to make much of an effort. The hammer traveled down a rost or two following the sinking serpent, and then returned to Thor's hand without inflicting any damage.

Suddenly the ocean was calm, with no sign that a tremendous battle had ever taken place. The peace was eerie. All of the fish and life of the sea had fled from that part of the ocean never to return.

Hymir hurriedly scrambled back into the boat fearing another appearance of the serpent. He shook his head trying to clear out the ringing in his ears, while attempting to start a conversation. "Well, at least we have the two whales to eat for our efforts." Thor said nothing. He picked up the whales and used them to stop up the footholes he had made, so the boat wouldn't sink. Finding there were only two oars in the boat, the others having been lost during the battle, Thor picked them up and silently rowed back to shore.

By the time they reached land Thor's anger was gone. Hymir, still not knowing Thor's mood, timidly spoke to him, "Which do you want to do, secure the boat or carry in the catch?"

Thor smiled and jumped out of the boat. Before Hymir had time to bail out the bilge water in the boat Thor had hoisted everything and everyone up on his shoulders and carried his cargo up the steep path to Hymir's house and set it down and secured it. Hymir jumped out of the boat with the two whales and took them into the kitchen.

In just a short while Tyr, Griseldis, Hymir and Thor were seated at the breakfast table feasting on their catch. Hymir's mother had a small portion over at her separate table. In fact everyone had a small portion except for Thor who, almost as soon as the whales were placed on the table, began shoveling portions into his plate and gulping them down.

After breakfast they sat around the table talking and drinking mead. Thor brought up the purpose of their visit, "We would like your kettle so we might take it to Ægir's and have a huge feast?"

Hymir thought the matter over for a moment. He wasn't really inclined to help out someone who had given him such a fright as the one he'd had that morning; nor to help out at a feast at which he had not been invited. "You might have rowed exceedingly strong, and fished better than anyone I've ever seen, yet I will only yield up my kettle if you succeed at the task I give you."

Thor agreed.

Hymir signaled for a servant and whispered something in his ear. Immediately the servant ran off. Hymir continued, "I've sent my servant to fetch my most prized possession, a crystal glass goblet. It's so strong it is considered virtually impossible to break. If you can break it I'll give you the cauldron free and clear, otherwise the only way you'll leave with it is if you dishonorably steal it.

The servant entered and placed the goblet in Thor's hands who flipped it from hand to hand thinking something so fragile looking would be easy to smash. He threw it at the wall. Instead of breaking against the wall it just bounced off. Hymir retrieved it and handed it back to Thor for a second try. This time Thor tightened Megingardr about his waist and heaved the goblet at one of the pillars with all his might. The pillar splintered apart. The goblet continued on through the wall behind the pillar, finally landing outside the hall. The whole house had shaken with the blow, yet when the goblet was returned to Thor he saw it had not even been nicked.

All the while Griseldis had been sitting at a spinning wheel, spinning. As Thor walked past her she whispered to him "If you want to break it throw it at the hardest object in the room." Thor looked around to see where she meant. She continued, since Thor hadn't picked up the hint, "Throw it at Hymir's forehead."

Thor whirled around to face Hymir and hurled the goblet straight at his forehead. The action was so quick the expression on Hymir's face didn't have time to change to surprise before the goblet hit him. It shattered into thousands of pieces, although Hymir remained unhurt.

Hymir controlled his anger, "You've won. Take the cauldron off the hearth, that is if you can carry it from the hall for my servants will give you no help."

Tyr went over and tried to lift it. It was too much for his one-handed effort. He tried once more, but with the same result. Thor went over. He tightened Megingardr to the last notch and grabbed the rim of the cauldron and lifted it with such force the floor shattered beneath his feet causing the entire structure of the house to give way. Tyr ran under the cauldron which Thor had heaved over his head and was wearing like a giant hat. The handles dangled loosely hitting against what was left of the floor. As rubble fell down all around them they made their way out of the hall, protected by their helmet. They didn't have to worry about trying to fit the cauldron through the door, since there no longer was one. They just walked through where the wall had been.

The two started off in the direction of Elivagar. After traveling quite a ways they paused to rest. When they took the kettle off and set it down they heard a great roar. Turning to see what was causing the noise they saw Hymir with a hoard of jotuns closing fast on them. There were jotuns of all sorts, rock, frost, multi-headed, multi-limbed. All of them approaching as fast as they could waving clubs and shouting threats and insults at the tops of their lungs.

There was nothing Thor liked better than a good battle. And the best battle was against the jotuns. Again he tightened Megingardr and waited for the assault. He swung Mjolnir overhead hitting out as fiercely as he could. Tyr, filled with courage, joined the battle inflicting his share of damage on the jotuns. Slowly a few of the jotuns realized they were losing. They fled yelling behind them that Hymir would have to fight his own battles.

Eventually Thor and Tyr stood victorious amid the gory remains of bodies. They continued on their way, changing their course to take a different road to reach Egil's farm to lessen the chance of meeting up with more jotuns unexpectedly. Using this route they had to ford Elivagar.

Fortunately they reached a point that seemed quite easy to ford. It was made even easier when they saw an old ferryman and his boat on the far side of the shore. His appearance gave them great doubt he could carry the kettle across the river. He was an old one-eyed man with a long white beard. He wore a broad-brimmed hat pulled down over one eye and a dark blue cloak.

Thor yelled across to him, "Bring the boat over to us so we can make our way to the other side. If you do I'll reward you with the food I have in my pouch. I have herring and oat-cakes to share with you."

The old man replied, "Who are you to shout orders at me without identifying yourself? I am Harbardr. My master is the jotun Hildolf who lives by Rathsey Sound. This is his boat and I don't think he would appreciate it if I brought thieves or poachers onto his land."

Thor replied, "I am not a thief. My name is Thor, and I am Odin's eldest son. My mother is Jordr, also known as Fjorgynn. Meili is my brother."

Harbardr replied, "Hah, you expect me to believe someone as puny as you is the mighty thundergod Thor? Even if you are, I am not impressed, for I could easily best you."

Thor was surprised. "I've battled many great jotuns. I've slain Thrivaldi, a powerful jotun with nine heads, as well as Leiti, Hengjankjapta, and Svivor. I fought with Leikn and broke her leg. Just recently I slew Hrungr. And just now we have come from winning a battle which was mighty and fierce and in which many jotuns lost their lives. Who are you that you think you can beat me?"

Harbardr replied, "Once I traveled to Algrœn Island and spent five winters there. I fought against Fjolvar. After besting him I contended with a battle of another sort. I gained the love of his seven jotun daughters who lived there. Can you match that?"

Before Thor could reply Harbardr boasted of yet another deed, "You have no doubt heard of the jotun Hlebard. He is one of the mightiest of his race. Using my wits I tricked him into giving me his magic wand. Then I betrayed him, forcing him to loose his senses. Then using his wand I was able to lure away the women of his men and woo and win them with love enchantments."

Thor interrupted, "You bested him by questionable methods, returning evil for good. That certainly was a deed that did you proud."

Harbardr disregarded Thor's comment with, "One oak gains from what is peeled from another. His loss was my gain. What other deeds have you accomplished?"

Thor responded, "On the island of Hlesey I slew the wild jotun women who were tempting those in Midgardr to do evil deeds."

Harbardr showed his disgust, "The best you could do was to slay women?"

Thor answered, "They were not ordinary women. They wandered about as wehrwolves, and through enchantments caused my ship to crash into the rocks. They almost killed my servant Thjalfi."

Harbardr shook his head, "Are you sure it wasn't your poor sailing that crashed your ship into the rocks?"

Thor ignored the taunt, "What other deeds can you boast of? Or, have we reached the end of your list?"

"We would be here for many years if I were to list all of my adventures. I can tell you of the time I was in Valland fighting for the men of Midgardr. I believe this must have been while you were trembling in the thumb of Skrymir's glove." Harbardr laughed at this.

Thor was enraged, "If you had the courage to come over here I would show you with Mjolnir how I trembled inside Skrymir's glove. Or, I could show you what I did to the sons of Svarangr, who while I was guarding the river Ifing, pelted me with mountains. I slew them all. Where were you?"

Harbardr seemed bored, "My battles are too numerous and more glorious to trade against your little squabbles. I have grown weary of this conversation. It's strange an old man such as I could delay Thor's journey home with mere words."

Thor answered, "Very well, I'll no longer speak with you or listen to your lies. Tow the ferry across if you dare. For when we meet I intend to teach you a lesson."

Harbardr mocked Thor, "I tremble at your bold words."

Thor yelled, "If you will not ferry me across then give me directions on how to get around Elivagar by another route."

Harbardr pointed to the southwest, "It's a long journey. Don't hurry home too quickly or you'll surprise Sif and also yourself since she is at this moment entertaining a friend. I believe some call him Loptr, others Gammleid or Villi-Eldr. I believe you call him Loki, or some such like that."

Thor made a threatening move towards Harbardr who continued with his directions. "Travel over rock and stone, then veer to the left until you reach Verland. Once there your mother Fjorgynn will show you the rest of the way."

Thor inquired about the trip. "If I start now can I finish today?"

Harbardr answered, "If you travel swift and hard without further tarrying you could make it by sunset." Then suddenly Harbardr's manner changed. The boat sped across the river in a blur. The last thing they heard was Harbardr's oath to Thor, "Go where the trolls can get you."

When the ferry arrived on Thor's side of the shore Harbardr was no where to be found. Thor and Tyr placed the gigantic kettle on the ferry and crossed to the other side. Soon they made their way to Egil's where they retrieved Thor's chariot, his two servants Thjalfi and Roskva, and journeyed back to Asgardr. From there they carried the kettle to Ægir's diamond and gold lit hall. Ægir had Thjalfi and Roskva begin brewing mead so that by the time of the harvest feast there would be enough on hand to easily get all the Æsir roaring drunk.

During the feast everyone was enjoying the revelry. All, that is, except Thor, who sat at his place brooding over the identity of Harbardr. He turned to his father and asked him a question, "Were you on Hlidskjalf when I was trying to cross the river Elivagar? Did you see the ferryman guarding the river? Do you know who he was?"

Odin changed his voice to that of an old man. Indeed, Thor was startled to hear Harbardr's voice emanating from his father. "At the time you were trying to cross Elivagar, I was on the other side trading words with a very boastful son. Now I'm ready for the wrath you promised to give me when we next met."

Thor remembered his boast to smash Harbardr with Mjolnir. He burst out in laughter at the trick his father had played on him. Soon the other Æsir joined in. Great waves of laughter rolled out of Ægir's hall into Midgardr.

The wavemaidens replenished the empty cups. Tyr told of their adventures winning the kettle and of Thor's fishing expedition. Then the other Æsir told of their recent adventures.

Eventually Bragi was called upon to tell a story. He gladly responded, "I'll tell a story about some of Ægir's relatives.

Ægir has a brother named Kari who is the father of many children. This is the story of one of his descendants, Frosti, who is the ruler of a vast kingdom in the north. Many are the times when he has raided his neighbors or journeyed into Midgardr for conquest. One of these journeys took him to Finland in Midgardr where King Snar ruled. There, at the king's court, he saw and fell in love with King Snar's beautiful daughter, Mioll. He asked the king for Mioll's hand. But the king refused and even forbade Frosti to gaze upon her or communicate in any way with his daughter. However, Frosti was able to send a secret message to Mioll telling her he loved her. She replied to the message that she had also seen him and loved him and would go to the seashore at a certain time and wait for him to come so they could go off together. The time came and he went to meet his love. Unfortunately King Snar had found out about the intrigue and had sent his men to ambush the would be lover. An entire squadron of men attacked Frosti, but he was protected by his silver armor and able to kill them all. He and Mioll leaped on his magical storm horse and were borne away across the sea to his lands in the north where they remain happy with each other to this day."

Ægir was pleased with the story and yelled out another invitation to the Æsir, "I'm glad you find my hospitality so acceptable and that I have been able to repay your past generosity. "Thank you Bragi for the story honoring my family. You are all invited next year to attend this feast again, and the year after that, for as long as we have before the great battle."

The feasting lasted well into the night until the mead had made everyone drowsy and one-by-one they all drifted off to sleep.

Chapter 13

Freyja's Lovesickness

Freya was one of the former Vanir hostages living in Asgardr, the daughter of Njordr and sister of Freyr. She was married to the handsome Æsir Odr. They had two daughters, Hnoss and Gersime, names which both meant jewel. But her marriage was not without its problems, which seemed to be the case with her family and their attempts at interpersonal relationships. Whenever Odr went on his frequent long journeys Freyja sought comfort from others. Many facetiously called her the Vanabrudr, the bride of the Vanir, and apparently everyone else as well. One who gave her comfort was Odin. To reward her for their relationship he gave her a portion of the slain for her hall, Sessrumnir, located in her land which was called Folkvangar.

Like her brother, Freyr, she owned a boar that had been fashioned by two dvergues. Her boar also had golden bristles which glowed in the dark. She called him Hilksuin, which meant battleboar. And like her brother, pigs and boars were very sacred to her. Cuckoos and swallows were also to be included amongst her sacred pets. In addition, she owned a cat-drawn chariot. Because of her love of cats she was known as the eigandi fress, owner of cats.

Like the other Vanir she was more interested in the harvest than in battles and the glory of war. She was a practitioner of that ancient witchcraft called seidr. Using the powers of seidr she could change her form. Sometimes she changed into a goat, other times into a cat. As a favor to Odin she had taught him the spells of seidr. But in order to practice the ancient arts Odin had to change his form into that of a woman. He kept this secret from the Æsir, who believed the practice of seidr by a man was a shameful thing.

Loki knew of the special relationship between Freyja and Odin, and was jealous of it. He had tried to seduce the beautiful Freyja many times, without success. So he decided if he couldn't have her then he would have revenge. It wasn't difficult for him to come up with a plan. He knew of four dvergues who were madly in love with Freyja. They were Dvalin, the eldest, and his three brothers, Alfrigg, Berling, and Grerr. Loki went to them and set his plan in motion. All four were assembled to hear what he had to say.

"I've come to you, my good and true friends, Dvalin, Alfrigg, Berling, and Grerr . . ."

Dvalin interrupted Loki, "Just say what you have to say. We're not your good and true friends, unless, of course, you regularly cheat your good and true friends."

Loki turned to go. "All right, if that's the way you want it, I won't tell you how all four of you ugly little men can have beautiful Freyja begging to sleep with each of you and perform whatever pleasures you desire."

The four ran over to Loki. Two of them pulled at his coat to stop him, while the other two tumbled into each other as they ran to block the doorway. Dvalin spoke, "How can you arrange this?" Then he thought of Loki, and asked more practically, "And what will it cost us?"

Loki answered, "Oh, the price will be very inexpensive for what you are purchasing. Others have been willing to spend seasons building walls for her favors. All you have to agree to do is grant me whatever favor I desire at some later time."

The four considered the request amongst themselves and came to the conclusion it was so indefinite they could easily agree to it. "After all," Alfrigg whispered to the others, "we could always pay Loki back like he's paid us so often, by forgetting we have ever made the deal. How will he be able to take back the pleasures we've already enjoyed?"

Berling gave Loki their answer, "We'll gladly agree to your fair terms. Tell us what we must do."

Loki answered, "First you must set up your forge in the mouth of your cave so anyone passing by cannot help but see what you're doing. Second, you must design and make the most beautiful necklace you can imagine. Make certain it's made of gold and silver with lots of glittery jewels to attract Freyja's attention. Her weakness is jewelry. She just can't resist it."

While the four set about this task, Loki hurried off to find Freyja with the news of his discovery. "Freyja, I know how fond you are of jewelry. I have exciting information about a necklace that's being forged at this very moment. Its name is Brisingamen, and when it's finished it will undoubtedly be the most beautiful necklace ever made."

Freyja was very excited by the news. She begged Loki for the whereabouts of the master jewelers and was surprised when he told her the location of their smithy the first time she asked.

She left Asgardr and traveled first through her brother's land of Alfheimr on her way to Midgardr. Then on Midgardr's border, heading ever downward, she came to Svartalfheimr, the land of the dokkalfar.

As she was passing Dvalin's cave she saw the forge glinting red and gold at the mouth of the cave, sparks flying with each hammer blow. She stopped to watch their handiwork gradually moving to the doorway just as they were putting the finishing touches on the necklace. It was made of two chains, one silver, the other gold. Both were intertwined in intricate knots. Fixed the length of the strands were all sorts of precious stones, including diamonds, rubies and emeralds. Set in the center was a beautiful sapphire with a perfect star on its face. The light reflected from facet to facet and gem to gem ever changing with each turn. Rainbows reflected on all the walls of the cave. She was dazzled by the beauty of the necklace and had to have it, no matter what the cost. She stepped into the cave and called out to the dvergues. They held up Brisingamen and admired it amongst themselves, ignoring Freyja.

Finally she stepped forward to make an offer for it, "Please, I must have that necklace. What can I offer you for this wondrous work of art? I can give you mountains of gold or silver. Name your price for I must have that necklace." She stared at it, entranced, while she spoke.

Dvalin answered, "There's not enough silver or gold in the world to purchase this necklace from us. What do we need with your offer when we can find all the gold and silver we want in our cave? We also have mines filled with rare gems. So you would be wasting your breath offering us diamonds, emeralds, rubies, sapphires, or other precious stones."

Freyja asked them their price, "Surely there must be some treasure I can trade for that necklace? I must have it, for now that I have seen it I know I shall never be happy unless it is mine to wear as often as I want." With those words she lost any negotiating advantage she might have had. Never let the other side know you must have something. Always know yourself you can walk away from a deal. If you can't, then you are the mercy of those on the other side.

Dvalin turned to Freya and told her their price, "There is certainly one way you can purchase it. All you have to do is spend a night with each of us, doing whatever we command. Then the necklace will be yours for free." Free was never paid for so dearly.

Freyja, blinded by the beauty of the necklace, forgetting her husband Odr and about her sacredness as a member of the Æsir and Vanir, agreed to their price. "I agree. To own the Brisingamen Necklace I would sleep with all of Midgardr if that were the price."

But that was not necessary. Just the four.

The four dvergues tumbled about in delight and expectation, shaking, unable to contain their lusts.

In four days the Brisingamen was hers. She was tired and tried not to think of the horrid acts she had performed to win it. Her back still hurt.

She returned immediately to Folkvangar in Asgardr. She was reminded of her shame every time she wore the necklace, and so hid it from everyone lest someone ask where she had gotten it and how much it had cost. But when she was alone in her room she knew she was safe from discovery for no one could enter without her permission. And while alone in her room she'd remove the necklace from its case and wear it, staring at and admiring herself in the mirror.

What she didn't see was the dazzling light show visible in her window to anyone looking at her bower. And Loki frequently spied on her.

Freya kept the Brisingamen's existence secret for a long time. Gradually her fear of discovery lessened. The dvergues had told her no one else had ever seen the necklace, which was true, and promised not to tell anyone about it. However, they also implied that no one else knew of its existence, which was not true. So Freyja thought she was safe from Odr finding out what she had done to win the prize. She had no suspicion Loki knew.

Now was the time for Loki's revenge.

Loki went to Odin and told him the story of Freyja's adventures with the four dvergues and her reward. Odin was furious someone living in Asgardr had consorted with dvergues. He sent for Odr and told him the story.

Odr refused to believe it. "Loki is always seeking to create dissension amongst us. This is just another of his plots. He lives to plot. He spends days devising lies. Freyja has spurned his advances, and this is his way of getting even. I don't believe his accusation that my wife has been unfaithful to me. Certainly not with four dvergar. And I certainly don't

believe she owns a necklace called Brisingamen. Why haven't I seen it, since I live in the same hall?" He turned and stared at his wife's accuser.

Loki answered, "There are a lot of things that go on in your house that you don't see." He looked directly at Odin. There were more than four dvergar in Freya's life. Odin was a frequent visitor. Odin stared back at Loki.

Odr, oblivious to the little drama that had just taken place between Loki and Odin, continued, "I'll only believe this lie if Loki can bring me the necklace to examine for myself." Loki hadn't expected this reaction and answered, "That might prove difficult. Freyja keeps the door to her room locked so she'll not be disturbed in the night, as you well know, Odr, and it would be impossible to steal into her hall during the day." Odr stepped towards Loki at the insult, but a look from Odin reminded Odr they stood on sacred soil and he should not throw a blow at Loki.

Loki continued, "You'll just have to take my word Freyja has the necklace."

Odr was angry at Loki's continued accusations against his wife and was determined the charge be either proven or recanted, "You have accused my wife of being unfaithful. If you can't prove this lie then I will have Thor take care of you for spreading your evil rumor. Beware. The first time you step outside Asgardr's protective area Thor will set against you, and I'll be there watching."

Before stalking out of the hall Loki answered Odr's threat, "Just like you to have someone else do your work for you – whether in bed or in battle. Be back here late tonight and I will bring the shameful necklace to you."

Once by himself Loki had in no time formulated a plan to steal the necklace. Late that night when all the household was fast asleep, he went to Folkvangar. He looked up to Freya's window making certain her window was dark and no rainbow of light was dancing around the room. All was quite. Everyone all tucked up.

It was easy to get into Sessrumnir, the main hall. But when he arrived outside Freyja's door he found it completely secured. He tried chants and spells to unlock the door, without success. He changed himself into a fly and flew in through the keyhole and flitted in and out amongst the tumblers and joints of the lock, but could find no space to squeeze through to the other side. He flew back out the lock and up to the top of the door, searching for any crack that might allow him entry. Finally, he found a pinhole that went through to the other side. With a great deal of effort Loki managed to squeeze through the opening.

He was careful as he flew about to make certain Freyja was fast asleep. He hovered over her and saw Brisingamen fastened around her neck, glowing only slightly with each breath she took.

If she had awakened at that moment instead of a fly she would have seen Loki bending over her for he had changed back into his own form. He carefully reached down to take Brisingamen. Unfortunately she was sleeping on her back trapping the clasp under her, making it impossible for him to unfasten it. Time for another transformation.

Loki changed into a flea, flew down and bit her on the cheek. She partially woke up, brushed her hand against her cheek, turned over and then sank back into a deep pleasant sleep. She was dreaming and walking through fields, openly wearing Brisingamen.

As soon as her breathing calmed down and once more became regular, Loki changed back into his own shape. With the light-fingered practiced hands of the thief he was,

Loki unfastened the clasp and gently slid the necklace off. He quietly stepped to the door, unlocked it and left, heading straight to Odin's hall where he found both Odin and Odr waiting for him. He flung the proof of Freyja's betrayal at Odr, and explained how he had stolen it. Odr dropped the necklace, turned and left. He didn't stop to see Freyja, didn't stop at his own hall. He left Asgardr walking down Bifrost and on into Midgardr.

Morning came and Freyja awoke from a very fitful sleep. Her dreams had been guilt-ridden and troubling. She sat up and automatically reached to her chest to touch Brisingamen. It was gone. She noticed the door to her room standing wide open and began weeping bitter tears of red gold. She sent a servant to bring Odr to her so she could confess her wrongs and beg his forgiveness. The servant returned with the news Odr had left Asgardr. Freyja wept even more.

She dressed and left her hall to see Odin. In his hall she confessed what she had done, "I'm so sorry for my actions. You must tell me where Odr is so I can go find him and beg his forgiveness."

Odin shook his head and told her what Odr had told him, "He has decided to leave Asgardr and wander throughout Midgardr. I don't have the power to stop him or call him back."

Freyja answered through her tears, "Then I'll follow after him, and I won't rest or be happy until I've found him and begged his forgiveness."

Odin answered, "As you wish. All in Asgardr will grant you forgiveness for the foolishness you have placed in a silly golden chain. But, so you'll never forget your shame it will be your punishment to wear Brisingamen, and never remove it until you have found Odr and received his forgiveness."

She fastened the necklace around her neck and went back to Sessrumnir where she prepared all day to leave Asgardr to begin her search for Odr. That night she retired early to get plenty of rest before leaving Asgardr the following day.

Heimdallr was standing guard on Bifrost. Towards morning he heard suspicious footsteps approaching Sessrumnir and turned to see who was sneaking into Freyja's hall. Next he briefly saw Loki standing by the entranceway before disappearing. Heimdallr focussed his vision and saw a tiny fly was flying into the palace heading in the direction of Freyja's room. Heimdallr went to Odin's hall to report the strange occurrence.

Meanwhile Loki once more stood at Freyja's bedside. He reached down and unhooked the clasp and stole the necklace for a second time. This time he closed the door behind him in order to allay suspicion.

The next morning Freyja awoke to find the necklace missing once more. She ran to Odin's hall interrupting Heimdallr's meeting with his father.

Odin glanced over at Freyja, and was furious to see she wasn't wearing Brisingamen. "You aren't wearing the necklace you paid such a dear price for, even though I told you that that would be your punishment."

Freyja frantically told Odin her necklace had been stolen, "I don't know who did it or where Brisingamen is."

Odin replied, "Be calm. Heimdallr has just been telling me a very interesting story. It seems Loki is the thief, for a second time." Turning to Heimdallr he continued, "Do you know where Loki is hiding?"

Heimdallr answered, "Yes. He has changed himself into a seal and is hiding by the rocks of Vagasker and Singasteinn."

Odin commanded his son, "Then go and take Brisingamen from him. Bring it here so Freyja can wear her shame once more."

Heimdallr left striding purposefully towards Loki's hideout. He was wearing his seven league boots so it didn't take him very long to reach his destination. He stood atop the rocks and yelled for Loki, "Come forth and return the necklace Freyja gave up so much to win. If you are so fond of the necklace you should have slept with the dvergues yourself to buy it. I'm sure that would have brought you much delight with your reward. I can only imagine the spawn that you would have born from those relations."

But there was no response. He looked around and saw the faintest glow of a rainbow flashing from behind a rock, for Loki was wearing Brisingamen.

Heimdallr found Loki huddled behind some rocks, drew his sword and threatened Loki with beheading if he didn't turn over the necklace. "Removing your head from your shoulders will make it that much easier for me to take the necklace from around your neck."

Heimdallr raised the sword threateningly. As he brought it down Loki changed into a flickering cold-blue flame which the sword passed through without harming it. But Heimdallr was very quick-witted and transformed himself into a cloud of rain in order to put out the fire. But again Loki was quicker and changed himself into a large white polar bear. He reared back his head and opened his mouth wide to catch the rain for a drink. But in a moment Heimdallr had changed himself into another polar bear.

They fought back and fourth, pushing and shoving each other against the rocks. Brisingamen had fallen to the ground when Loki changed himself into the blue flame and was now being kicked back and forth as the bears fought. Finally, when it looked as if Heimdallr was winning, Loki turned back into a seal and dove into the sea. Heimdallr did likewise, diving down after him. Again the battle resumed. Loki darting in and out amongst the rocks trying to hide. Eventually he exhausted himself and Heimdallr was finally able to subdue the evil son of Laufey and Nal. They both took their regular forms and Heimdallr pushed-shoved-carried a reluctant Loki back towards Asgardr.

On their way they stopped at Brunnakr Grove where Idunn handed Heimdallr an apple. He bit into it and his wounds were immediately healed and his strength was replenished. She refused to serve Loki, remembering the imprisonment she had endured as a result of his actions. So Loki had to suffer his bruises and wounds, and let them heal naturally.

Heimdallr carried Loki back to Odin's hall where he was ordered to fasten the necklace back around Freyja's neck. Reluctantly Loki did as he was commanded. Without saying a word Freyja left and began her wanderings throughout the worlds. And everywhere she went she wept tears of red gold which she left to mark where she had searched for Odr. She used many names during her travels, including Forn, Hæn and Syr.

For a long time after that she was absent from Asgardr. Her brother Freyr was upset by her departure and blamed Odin for sending her out on her wanderings. Odin had the power to recall Freyja at any time, yet he would not do so. This made Freyr extremely bitter. But Odin had his reasons. He wanted Freyja to wander through the worlds teaching the men and women of Midgardr the gentle and painful ways of love.

Chapter 14

The Longobards

Once Odin and Frigg were sitting in Odin's hall, Valaskjalf, in Odin's watchtower, Odin seated on Hlidskjalf and Frigg on her throne. Both were gazing out over the nine Worlds of the Tree. Finally, they settled their gazes on the island of Skadan far to the north. Here was the land of the Vinnilers. They were a subject people who had been conquered by the Vandals. Fortunately, until this moment they had been pretty much left alone by their conquerors. But now two dukes of the Vandals, Ambri and Assi, were threatening the Vinnilean people with war if they didn't agree to pay further tribute to them. The Vinnilers, lead by Ibor and Ajo didn't want war, but they also didn't want to pay an unjust tribute. Events had come to the point where both parties were preparing for battle.

Odin watched as the two great Vandal warriors, Ambri and Assi, prayed ardently to him that the victory might be awarded to them. "We promise if our enemies, the Vinnilers, are defeated we will redden our altars with the sacrifices of our enemies and their blood to Odin. It is only just that victory be awarded to us. The Vinnilers are a nation we have conquered, yet they refuse to pay the tribute we would exact of them. With that tribute we could build even greater altars and let the glory we give to Odin be further known throughout all the lands we rule." Odin looked with favor on their efforts and was disposed to award victory to them in the upcoming battle.

Meanwhile Frigg's attention was focussed on the Vinniler camp where their leaders Ibor and Ajor had beseeched their mother Gambara to pray to Frigg on their behalf that victory might be awarded to them. Gambara went to the fields, freshly sown with corn and vegetables, and knelt to pray. She promised Frigg their harvest would be dedicated to her, their lives of peace and prosperity would be a tribute paid to the beneficence of Frigg. Frigg looked with favor upon the gentle Vinnilers.

Frigg turned to Odin and saw he was also interested in these two warring factions. "It seems to me the Vinnilers are the more just and victory should be theirs. They have been set upon by the Vandals who have destroyed their lands, taken their crops, and now they want to exact an unfair tribute. Which group do you prefer?"

Odin disagreed, "All I see is that their most powerful warriors must rely on an old woman to pray for their victory, while Ambri and Assi take matters in their own hands, praying directly to me and promising me magnificent blood sacrifices if they should win. Their victory insures there will be bloody altars telling of my greatness. Their victory will inspire young men to become warriors. What will a victory for the Vinnilers do? The call to ploughs will be heard throughout the land. Young men will take up hoes and rakes and attack the land. It will bleed green with grass. What good will that do me in Valhalla? I want warriors, not farmers. I want blood on my followers hands, not dirt running through their fingers. I am disposed towards the Vandals. They suit my purposes better. They are hard, rough and ready men." Seeing Frigg seemed upset, and not wishing to have a family quarrel at the moment, he modified his decree, "Rather, I suppose it would be fairer that either should be welcome in Valhalla. Thus, I suppose I will give victory to those whom I espy first tomorrow before the battle."

That was enough of that. Odin cast his attention away towards other quarters and was soon lost in something occurring in Jotunheimr.

Frigg decided she would make certain her favored would be the first seen the next morning. She had lived with Odin long enough to see through his slyness. She knew perfectly well Odin's bed lay to the west so upon arising he looked to the east. As it now stood the first sight he would see, even before climbing on Hlidskjalf, would be the Vandals. That evening she made certain Hrist and Mist served Odin a goodly quantity of mead in Valhalla, so that during the night his sleep was deep and not easily disturbed. Gently she had her servants turn his bed to the east so when he arose his gaze would be to the west, to the Vinnilers' direction. Next she sent a messenger to Gambara to instruct her to have the Vinniler women don armor and comb their hair in such a manner that it fell across their faces and down their fronts until the illusion was given they had long flowing beards, noticeable at a distance.

The next morning Odin arose and stretched. Gazing out the window he was surprised to see a group of warriors gathered for battle wearing strange flowing beards of a style he had never seen before. He yelled to Frigg, "What ho, look at the long-beards who approach the battlefield."

Frigg was pleased. Her plan had worked perfectly. Odin was now bound to award the Vinnilers victory since they were the first warriors he had seen that morning. However, to insure victory for them she reminded Odin of his obligation under Northern custom of giving a gift to whomever one has named. "Odin, you have given them a new name and now must give them a name gift. Wouldn't it be just that that gift should be the victory they have prayed for? You see, these warriors are part of the Vinnilean army."

Odin was surprised and realized he had been twice tricked. "Since the Vinnilers have such a cunning champion as you, Frigg, then it is only right they be awarded the victory, and those Vinnilers who are slain shall be awarded to you. I will instruct the Valkyries of my decision. Come, let's prepare for tonight's victory feast in Valhalla. Anyway, it'll be a pleasure to welcome Ambri and Assi to the ranks of our warriors." The two went out to continue their day knowing many would die in battle that morning.

The battle came about as Odin had commanded. Many warriors on both sides met noble deaths and were guided to Valhalla by the Valkyries. The foremost, of course, were Ambri and Assi.

Ibor and Ajo decided to honor Frigg for the victory she had won for them. Ever after the Vinnilers were known as Longobards. Eventually this name evolved into Lombards, by which name they are known today.

Chapter 15

The Jotun Geirrodr

Loki was usually quite mischievous, but this time he even outdid himself. Silently he stole into Sessrumnir, Freyja's hall in Folkvangar. After searching about he found what he wanted and stole valsharmr, her falcon-guise. He had had so much fun cavorting in it when he rescued Idunn that he wanted it for himself. "After all," he reasoned, "Freyja has been gone a lot lately in search of Odr and hardly ever uses it, whereas I can think of hundreds of times I would have found it useful to fly into the sky at a moment's notice; times when I wanted to escape, or peer into windows."

Thus justified by his own specious logic, he put on valsharmr and flew out of Folkvangar heading northeast. Soon he looked down and saw a great hall which was far larger than any other residence on the landscape. He was looking at Geirrodr's Garth, the home of the hrymthursar Geirrodr. It was shaped in the form of a mountain with a massive chimney rising from the center of the structure. As it happened it was about dinnertime and smoke was pouring forth from the chimney. Loki hadn't eaten all day, so he decided maybe an uninvited visit would be in order. "Surely there's some mischief I can get into here. Maybe I'll get a good meal out of it."

He flew down and perched on one of the windowsills. As luck would have it he found himself staring into the dining room where Geirrodr and two of his daughters, Gjalp and Greip, were just sitting down to the dinner table. Geirrodr was old and grey-headed. His two withered daughters were knobby and ugly, they took after their father. Loki still remembered the trouble he had gotten into helping steal Idunn's apples for the jotun Thjassi, Greip's son. Perhaps he could get even with the family in some way.

Their appearance contrasted greatly with the room they were in. It shone with gold. The table and chairs were made of solid gold, the walls gilded and encrusted with jewels.

At that moment Geirrodr happened to be glancing in a mirror opposite the window when he saw the reflection of the falcon perched on the windowsill. He noticed it was very unusual in that it had human eyes, and realized it must be someone wearing a wehr-costume. But why would anyone want to spy on him?

Geirrodr yelled for Glapp, his servant, on the pretense his meat was too well done, "Do you expect me to eat this piece of leather? Come take this away and bring me a piece of meat drenched in blood."

Glapp was confused because the meet was blood red. But, not his station in life to argue. He went over to take the plate from Geirrodr at which point Geirrodr whispered to him, "This meat is fine, but over on the windowsill is some meat that's even finer. I want that falcon captured and brought to me. I feel like fowl for dinner tonight and that bird is most foul if I am right in my guess."

The servant took the plate and left the room. However, instead of gong to the kitchen he put the plate on a sideboard and went outside. He started clammering up the mountainlike castle. Loki saw Glapp. It made him laugh to think the puny servant even had hopes of catching one so clever as he. Loki waited on the sill until the servant was just within an arm's length of grasping him. Then Loki stretched his wings and flapped to take off and elude capture. But to his surprise he found his feet were stuck fast to the sill. Glapp smiled as he grabbed the falcon which was flapping its wings furiously, and carried him off to Geirrodr.

As Glapp brought Loki through the front gates of the hall the two guard dogs barked and strained at their leashes trying to nip at the bird being carried past them. Once through the main entryway Loki discovered the gold dining room was the only elegant area of the castle. All the other rooms were large cavernous areas, dark, dank, and clammy. Mold covered the walls, and the floors were filled with adders and other venomous reptiles that crawled through their own filth. The servants held close to the wall as they darted in and out of the rooms. Loki felt the place was very unpleasant. The stench was unbelievable.

Geirrodr commanded Loki to speak, "Tell me who you are?"

Loki responded, "Chirp."

Again the jotun gave an order to speak. Loki chirped again. Then for a third time he was commanded to speak. "Your eyes give you away. You're no bird, but someone wearing a falcon-guise, so speak." He put a ring around Loki's claw and placed him on a perch.

This time Loki didn't respond at all. He merely cocked his head from side to side staring at the jotun. Occasionally he plucked at some feathers, grooming himself. And being Loki he couldn't help preening a bit. He puffed himself up, gave a little shake and settled down on his perch and stared.

"Very well," said Geirrodr who reached over grabbed Loki and placed him in a stone chest, "we'll see how long it takes before you cry out for food."

Loki was trapped. For three months he held his tongue. Locked in the stone chest he rested and waited in his own excrement. Finally, faint with hunger he cried out, "I am Loki of the Æsir, what must I do to regain my freedom?"

Geirrodr leaped up from the chair he had patiently been waiting in and opened the chest. Loki tried to fly out, but weakness had slowed his actions and Geirrodr was able to catch the dull and ragged-coated falcon. "So you would escape from me? How about another three months in the chest?"

He moved to close the lid again, but Loki spoke once more, "I'll not try to escape again. I give you my oath to that. But tell me what I must do to regain my freedom?"

Geirrodr responded, "Very well. You must swear a solemn vow to me that you'll persuade Thor to journey here of his own accord."

Loki interrupted, "That will be easy enough. Let me go."

Geirrodr continued, "Don't interrupt. I wasn't finished. Of course Thor would gladly come here, delighted at the opportunity of bashing in my head and destroying my household. So you must persuade him to come here without Mjolnir, his hammer, the gloves he wears when he wields Mjolnir, or Megingardr, his girdle of strength, also known as asmegen."

Loki didn't know how he could possibly persuade Thor to come unarmed, but wanting his freedom he made solemn vows and promises. Loki reasoned it's easier to make a promise in desperation than keep it in freedom. He would agree to anything to get to fly out the window.

Geirrodr went to the window and threw Loki high into the sky. Loki dropped a bit before his wings started flapping since they were stiff from disuse. Then he flew directly back to Asgardr.

Once in Asgardr Loki thought, "Why not lure Thor to Geirrodr's. It's a challenge to get him to go there unarmed. I'm certain I can do it."

Loki quickly sought out Thor and suggested an adventure for them, "I have just come from the most marvelous mansion. My host was the kindest, most generous person I have ever met. He is the hrymthursar Geirrodr. His food and entertainment were so compelling I could not tear myself away from there for these last three months. He's an enormous admirer of yours, Thor, and would really like to meet you. He sets the finest, and largest table, I've ever seen. And the mead is delicious. I drank enough to fill every lake in Midgardr."

Thor had just returned from a journey eastward bashing in jotun heads and wasn't particularly anxious to leave again. And, too, there was Loki's gaunt appearance which did not suggest someone who had been feasting for three months. "If you've been eating so well how come you look so awful? You look as thin as one of your daughter's dead servants in Helheimr."

Loki was ready with a reply, "I'm so thin because I spent all of my energy eating, drinking and loving. The more food I ate, the more appeared. Food from all the Worlds of the Tree. Delicacies you've never seen before. And although I've eaten mountains of food in the last three months, I've expended so much energy making love to Geirrodr's beautiful daughters I've been left thin by the exertion. Two at once can take its toll."

This appealed to Thor, as well as the thought of heaping quantities of food and mead. Thor was never invited back for second visits, so traumatic to his hosts were his first visits. He usually ate and drank everything in sight, eating an entire winter's supply of food at one sitting and drinking the entire mead cellar throughout the evening, becoming more raucous as the drink took effect. And a raucous thundergod with lightning shooting out everywhere could cause quite a bit of damage. People were deafened by the rolls of thunder accompanying his laughter. Yes, a new place to visit appealed to him, "Very well, let's get started now. If we take my chariot we can be there before the evening meal."

Loki raised his hand to stop Thor who had hurried towards the door, "There's one thing. He's very afraid of you. Your reputation as a jotun slayer has preceded you.

Although he is delighted you would be his guest, he requests you leave Mjolnir, your gloves, and Megingardr in Asgardr."

The clouds darkened and the sky rumbled a little as Thor furrowed his brow. "That's absolutely out of the question. I never travel anywhere unarmed. What if we should be called to the great battle and I'm off somewhere without my weapons? And if I come upon a jotun invading a village in Midgardr, what then? No, I think the meal is not as attractive to me as it once was."

But Loki implored Thor to come with him, mentioning more delicacies and telling how beautiful Geirrodr's daughters were. Thor seemed tempted. Loki continued, "Surely you were the mighty Thor before you ever won Mjolnir, or your gloves or girdle of strength? They only enhance your natural abilities. They don't make you what you are. I'm sure every battle you've ever fought with your weapons, you could easily have won with your bare hands."

The flattery touched Thor, "Of course, you're right in that respect, and I am ravenously hungry. All right, I'll leave my weapons in Odin's safekeeping and we can leave immediately. While I'm at Odin's hall you fetch Thjalfi and have him prepare my chariot for our journey. He will accompany us."

Soon they were travelling eastward towards Jotunheimr. The journey was taking longer than Loki had anticipated. Thor was getting very hungry, with apparently no prospect of Geirrodr's Garth or its food in sight. "It appears you're wrong about how long it will take us to travel to Geirrodr's Garth. I hope, for your sake, that that's the only thing you're wrong about."

They went on further, and yet they still seemed no closer to Geirrodr's than they had been before.

"Are you sure we're headed in the right direction?" asked Thor.

Loki looked around trying to find some familiar landmark. "I don't know. The last time I came this way I was a falcon and everything looked different, bigger."

It was obvious Loki wasn't going to be much help, so Thor decided they should rest for the night, "I think we should give it up for tonight and find some lodging. We're now in the Jarnvid Forest and strange things could happen to us if we tried to travel through this magical place at night. One of my father's mistresses lives near here. She is Gridr, the mother of my half-brother Vidarr the silent. She'll give us a place to rest for the night."

They found her grinding corn on a quern stone for dinner.

"Welcome Thor and Loki. Please stay the night and tell me everything that has been happening in Asgardr. Start now. Tell me everything while I start dinner. How's Freyja."

Freyja was not a subject Loki wanted to talk about, so he started telling her stories about Valhalla and her son Vidarr the silent.

During dinner they talked about Thor's adventures and about where he was off to now.

Thor told her about Loki's visit to Geirrodr, "And such was his repast that I've been persuaded to go there unarmed so I will not frighten him out of his hospitality."

Gridr started at the mention of Geirrodr's name. "You mean Geirrodr the Troll King?"

Loki didn't answer and started to speak to change the subject. But, Thor cut him off, "Why, yes, that's exactly who we're going to see."

Gridr told Thor the truth, "You haven't been told the truth about that deceitful jotun. He's vicious and cruel to everyone who crosses his path."

Thor turned and glared at Loki before speaking, "Then I've been tricked. I think I'll still pay him a visit. This time to teach him a lesson."

Loki sank down in his seat and said nothing. This trip wasn't turning out to be as fun as he had hoped.

Thor turned to Gridr and asked her a favor, "Will you lend me your girdle of strength and iron gloves? I know you don't have a mighty hammer like Mjolnir, but you do have a magic staff called gridarvolr which I would like to borrow. I'll bring them back to you undamaged."

Gridr readily agreed, "I would certainly like to see someone pay him back in kind for the blows he has given to others."

The rest of the night went quite peacefully. They passed the evening in deep sleep and were well-rested by the break of day. Thor and Loki ate and left early that morning following directions Gridr had given them that would take them the fastest way to Geirrodr's Garth.

They had only traveled a short distance when they came to the river Vimur, which was called Hemra by some. Instead of a calm river what confronted them was a raging torrent. This was odd because it wasn't the time of year for it to be flooding.

Thor drew the notches on Gridr's girdle of strength tightly about his waist. Supporting himself with gridarvolr he started wading across the river with Thjalfi hanging to the straps of his shield and Loki clinging to his belt. Just as they reached the middle a sudden rush of water caused the river level to rise up to Thor's shoulders. He yelled at the river, "Stop this nonsense. You aren't acting as a river should." Thinking there might be some sort of enchantment on the area Thor glanced down and up the river. When he glanced upstream he saw the cause of his problems.

An enchantment was not causing his troubles. What he saw standing upstream was Geirrodr's ugly daughter Gjalp. She was straddling the river relieving herself. It was also her time of the month and blood was flowing down the insides of her thighs.

Thor was disgusted by her pollution and grabbed a boulder from the riverbed and hurled it at her yelling, "A stream should be dammed at its source."

The boulder hit her just as Thor, Thjalfi and Loki reached the far side of the river. Gjalp collapsed forward, smacking into the river. A giant wave rushed downstream and swept Thor off his feet. Thor reached out and grabbed a rowan tree growing out from the side of the bank. He clung to it, while Thjalfi and Loki clung to him, until the wave had passed. Thor struggled to regain his footing. From that time on because the rowan tree had saved Thor it was known as "Thor's deliverance," and those who used it met with magical results.

Finally, Thor managed to pull himself and the others up onto the bank. Thjalfi and Loki were all but drowned. Soon they regained their breath and the three continued on their journey. They had gone but a few paces before a group of trolls met them and led them the rest of the way to the castle.

They were shown to a stone-covered room next to the mountain hall. There was a roaring fire in the fireplace, but just a single stool next to a it. Their accommodations were an insult. They had been shown to the goat house.

Thor sat on the stool waiting to be summoned by Geirrodr when suddenly the stool began to rise towards the ceiling. Thor quickly thrust gridarvolr up to the ceiling forcing his full weight against it. There were a couple of shrieks as the stool fell to the ground. Geirrodr's two homely jotun daughters had been hiding under the stool hoping to crush Thor against the ceiling when they stood up. Now they were sprawling on the floor with their backs broken.

Geirrodr sent a servant to fetch Thor on the pretense of challenging the thundergod to some games. Thor didn't refuse the challenge.

There was a great hearth fire in a trough running down the middle of the hall. As Thor entered, Geirrodr reached into the fire with a pair of tongs and pulled out a white hot piece of iron and flung it at Thor. Thor was wearing Gridr's iron gloves and easily caught the iron bar without injury. While Thor's head was turned Geirrodr ran behind a pillar to hide. But Thjalfi grabbed valsharmr from Loki, donned it, and flew around the pillars to find the jotun. He started pecking at him and caused such a commotion that Thor knew where to hurl the iron bar.

The iron bar crashed through the pillar, through the breastplate of Geirrodr's armor, through Geirrodr, on through the wall, and continued on into Midgardr where it landed and formed a mountain of iron.

Thor took gridarvolr and as he left the hall he flailed the staff from side to side killing all the trolls caught in his way. Outside he strode up to Geirrodr's lifeless body and struck it with Gridr's spear, whereupon it turned to stone. Thor set the jotun up on the side of the mountain to serve as a monument to his strength and a reminder of his victory over Geirrodr.

On their return journey Thor, Thjalfi and Loki were easily able to cross the now receded Vimur and headed back to Gridr's house. She was pleased after hearing about Thor's victory over Geirrodr and glad no damage had been done to her gloves, belt, or spear.

Then the three returned to Asgardr and boasted of their great adventure and victory over the jotuns.

King Gormr of Denmark Searches for Geirrodr's Garth

Tales of the stone monument to Thor's courage spread throughout Midgardr. The stories were told for centuries until finally King Gormr of Denmark decided to organize an expedition in search of Geirrodr's Garth.

His party consisted of three ships, with a crew of a hundred each. He chose Thorkill to captain the expedition, an explorer known for his travels to distant lands. If anyone would be able to find Geirrodr's Garth, he would.

They set sail towards the river Vimur, which seemed as wide as most oceans. The wind was calm throughout most of their journey so their progress was slow. They had traveled a long time without spotting land and their stores of food and water were almost depleted. Everyone was hungry and thirsty. Their tempers were short and soon arguing broke out amongst the crew. But when all seemed lost, and small fights were turning into violent confrontations, suddenly someone spotted land.

The ships headed for the shore. Much to their surprise they could see enormous herds of cattle roaming the land. Trees, whose branches bent almost to the ground laden

with fruit, were seen in the distance. Everyone's spirits rose with the excitement of their discovery.

Thorkill gave instructions to the landing party warning them to use restraint in their foraging expedition ashore, "Kill only enough cattle to take care of our immediate needs. If we're greedy the landvættnir will be angered at us and curse the rest of our expedition."

But the sailors had other ideas. Hungry men seldom exercise restraint when searching for food. The sailors had come close to starving to death and weren't going to trust to luck that they would find more food in a few days. They killed and roasted cattle for the evening meal. And unbeknownst to Thorkill they slaughtered a good deal of the rest of the herd and stored the meat in one of the ships.

That night, exhausted from the slaughtering, well-fed and slightly drunk, everyone drifted off to sleep. But their sleep was far from uneventful. During the night a band of trolls led by an ugly bergrisar laid siege to the three ships. The next morning as the sailors tried to aweigh anchor they found the kedges held fast to the bottom of the river, stuck by the use of magical spells. Their strength was no use against enchantments.

When they found whom their captors were and that they were held fast through magic, they had no choice but to deal with the trolls on the troll's terms.

The bergrisar leader spoke to Thorkill, "I wouldn't have minded your taking one or two of my cattle, but you have helped yourself to most of my herd. I demand as payment three sailors, one from each of your ships. If you don't agree then you, your men, and your ships will stay where they are until you all starve."

Thorkill had to agree to the demand, even though some of his men started yelling they should fight the trolls and jotuns. Thorkill rejected their urgings to battle, "I warned you not to take advantage of your good fortune in finding food. But since you have we must now suffer from your actions and pay the price for your gluttony. Better we should lose just three through this solution than lose more in a solution whose outcome is less certain."

Three men were chosen by lot and handed over to the trolls who carried them back to the island. The ships were released and they went on their way trying not to think too much about what happened to their three shipmates on the island.

They continued sailing across the river Vimur. The air became colder and colder and the once smooth sea was now broken up by ice flows and glaciers. They were in a part of Jotunheimr called Glæsisvellir, which means Glittering Plains, a name derived from the sun reflecting off the glaciers and ice flows. They were nearing the land which Thorkill sought; a land deprived of the lightness of life, and over whose mountains and valleys darkness brooded.

Thorkill spoke to all of the men, "We're nearing Geirrodr's Garth, and are not welcome in this land. To avoid misunderstandings let me do all of the talking since I'm more familiar with their speech and customs. I'm not likely to accidentally offend anyone as some of you might."

At dusk that evening a jotun waded out to the ships as if he were walking in a shallow pond. King Gormr and his men were too frightened to speak. Thorkill whispered to King Gormr, "That is Gudmundr, Geirrodr's brother. He'll offer to show us around, but instruct your men to say nothing to him, touch nothing and no one, and refrain from eating whatever is offered no matter how tempting it might be. If anyone thinks he might be hungry, then take some food from our hard-won supply to eat, but stay away from their meals." His instructions were passed along to everyone on the three ships.

Gudmundr invited them to his hall, which was called Grund, for dinner.

After the men reached the shore and while they were walking to the hall, Gudmundr noticed no one was speaking. The jotun turned to King Gormr and asked him why, "King Gormr, I haven't heard you or your men utter a single sound. Have I come upon a ship of mutes? Perhaps you and your men are under a spell which I can break?"

King Gormr shook his head and nodded towards Thorkill, who spoke, "There is a reason for their silence. They're ashamed of their inability to speak your language without making mistakes. I'm only the one who knows it well enough to dare carry on a conversation with you."

They reached the hall where they found a festive banquet set before them. The tables bent under the weight of the food presented to them. They all took their places at the table. King Gormr and Thorkill sat with Gudmundr, his twelve sons, and many of his daughters. And though the temptation was great and their host urged them on, none ate the repast set before them.

Gudmundr spoke, "Why do you not partake of my hospitality? Have I done something to offend you?"

Thorkill replied, "It's only out of thoughts for our stomachs we ignore your plenty. We've been at sea for many months, eating only the bland provisions stored aboard our ships. Just meals of crackers, really. If we were suddenly to gorge ourselves on your marvelous food, I'm afraid we would suffer for it later. Such food as this takes getting used to."

Gudmundr looked at his guests suspiciously, not entirely accepting the explanation offered by Thorkill. He thought of another ploy to enthrall his guests. He yelled out to all, "Since I can't feed your stomachs allow me to feed the other hunger men have. I offer you the hospitality of my virgin daughters. Your men can teach them the ways of love." Surely, he thought, this would tempt them, for his daughters were exceedingly beautiful. Yet not one of the sailors responded to the offer. Gudmundr gave a puzzled look to Thorkill and said, "Could it be your ships have sailors who prefer the company of other sailors? I have heard of such ships."

Thorkill answered, "I'm afraid we are all married men, and it is the custom in Denmark that a married man cannot be disloyal to his wife by engaging in play with another woman, even so much as a little kiss, no matter how great her beauty or how innocent the kiss. And are there any innocent kisses, anyway?"

Yet as Thorkill spoke three of the sailors could not resist the offer. They kissed three of Gudmundr's daughters. But their momentary pleasure was lost in a lifetime of madness. They never again gained the reason of their minds. The results of their disobedience were so sudden it frightened the other men who were even more determined to follow Thorkill's orders, now having the direct proof of disobedience before them.

Gudmundr smiled at his conquest of three of the men. He offered further hospitality to everyone, "Please, you are welcome to visit my garden and pick any fruit you might wish to take back to your ship for your long journey home. And, again, if the fruits of my daughters tempt you, you are welcome to pluck them too."

Thorkill stepped forward lest the temptation become too great for some of the sailors, "I'm afraid we have stayed here too long already. We don't have the time to see your gardens, even though I have heard the world over how beautiful they are and how tempting the fragrances from the flowers are. Perhaps the next time we are near here we can stop, but now we must hasten on our journey."

Gudmundr realized Thorkill had bested him in their contest, and tried no further tricks on the company. Instead he pointed them in the direction of Geirrodr's Garth, knowing what awaited them there would be more than enough punishment for them.

They didn't have to travel far before they came to a strange city of troll houses. Trolls took on many of the professions of dvergar, but with considerably less skill and no magical enchantments on what they made. Treasures forged by them were rather ordinary and not very valuable. Many of the trolls lacked even enough skill to eke out a poor living as an artisan, and were forced to work as servants to jotuns. Trolls weren't very clean and their city smelled.

Thorkill had heard of such places as this troll city, but had never seen one before. Each house was a stony mound which by very ingenious construction could be raised upon red pillars in order to let light inside. That is, whenever light was wanted inside, which was seldom. The air was dark and smoky over the central part of the city, where most of their smithy work was done. Here and there they saw heads impaled upon pikes stuck in the ground, a grim reminder of the deadly pleasures trolls occasionally engaged in. As the explorers made their way through the city they could feel the bulbous eyes of the trolls watching them. And occasionally, if they turned around fast enough, they caught sight of ugly heads darting back behind curtains.

After they passed through the troll city they could see Geirrodr's Garth off in the distance. As they neared it they were set upon by several emaciated dogs guarding the way. The dogs stood fast growling at King Gormr and the others. Their teeth shone through their ferocious grins. Slavver dripped from their mouths in expectation of a fight. However, Thorkill had foreseen this occurrence and from his pouch drew several bones smeared with fat. He threw them far away. The dogs ran after them, choosing an easy licking over a hard one.

It was but a short distance further to the other walls of the castle. As they approached they could hear shrieks of agony coming from the other side of the wall. The screams were so horrible the men stopped dead in their tracks, a little reluctant to proceed. And if that wasn't enough to discourage them they smelled a foul stench which was also coming from beyond the castle walls.

Thorkill saw the hesitation on the part of his men. He urged them on. "There's no danger. If you follow what I say, and do what I do. And if you're tempted to disobey just remember the three witless friends we have amongst us. Inside we'll see some wondrous sights. There will be more plunder than you've ever seen before; armor of pure gold, silver enough to ensure a lifetime of ease, and precious gems in blinding quantity. Our feet will tread on these jewels, and the temptation will be great to perhaps pick one up. After all, no one will notice. But I warn you to touch nothing. Want for none of the things we'll see, for a terrible fate awaits you if you heed not my warnings. And it is a fate which can never be undone."

With those words of warning still echoing in their thoughts, they entered through the front gate of the castle. The men were surprised by what they saw. The entryway was encrusted with soot and filth. Lifetimes had come and gone without any effort of maintenance on the property. They expected to see beautiful maidens on the benches. Instead there were ugly serpents and monsters. The jewels they were warned about were no where underfoot. What they stepped on were snakes who formed a mat under their feet. The snakes were content to stay where they had been for ages. They hadn't moved except to eat, and that was usually the snake laying on either side, or back or front – unless they were eaten. They spent their lives in one area settled on their own excrement. Their lives had been totally useless, and being stepped on by a group of explorers was still not reason enough to move. They were resigned to their miserableness and longed for a footfall to end it.

The sailors found none of this tempting and looked doubtfully at Thorkill. King Gormr ordered his men into groups of four. They entered the castle's main hall in this manner. Still they were disappointed at what they saw. The inside was even filthier than the outside. Vines and grass had grown up and was covering or entwined about everything. The growth in turn was covered with soot. The reason for this was quite simple, as the explorers immediately saw for themselves. There was a great fire burning in the center of the hall. Unfortunately the chimney was partially closed with soot, so great deal of the smoke found its way to the ceiling, the walls, and the floor. Seated at tables were dirty old starved trolls. Crawling in and out of everything were even more snakes. As their eyes followed the benches down to the end of the hall they found what they had hoped for. A broken pillar was behind the table and in the distance they could see a path that followed the trail of the iron bar Thor had thrown into Midgardr. They could see Geirrodr balanced as Thor's monument, with a hole in his stone body which the bright blue sky shone through. Near the pillar sat Geirrodr's two ugly daughters, still alive, but now all bent and misshapen with their broken backs that had healed improperly and crookedly. They were covered with open sores. Their looks certainly didn't tempt King Gormr's men. They didn't speak to King Gormr or his men, nor did they even look up.

The party turned to leave the awful place. It was then they saw wondrous treasures glistening off to one side. Never had any of them seen such sights. There were kegs of jewels, each gem larger than the one next to it. Golden belts, silver helmets, bracelets encrusted with gems the likes of which they had never seen before. There was a carved tusk from some unknown animal. The ends of it had been gilded of gold and tipped with emeralds. And laying closest was a stag's horn covered with precious jewels. But even though the temptation was great the group held back in awe. That is except for three. One grabbed at the bracelet and clasped it to his upper arm. Another grabbed the tusk and held it. And the third claimed the stag's horn as his own as he held it over his head. None of the others fought them for their gifts. Startled they watched what happened next.

The arm bracelet turned into a snake and bit the sailor around whom it was entwined. The poison ran out of the wound and down his arm. The pain was so great he hacked off his own arm hoping to stop the spread of the poison into his body. But he was too late and fell over dead. The tusk changed into a sword and plunged itself through the heart of the man holding it. And the stag's horn grew into a serpent and fell to the floor curled around its prey.

The group turned and ran as one out of the hall. But as they neared the exit they passed by the open door of Geirrodr's treasure chamber, where even more wondrous treasures were in sight. It beckoned them and they did not resist. The contents of the room even bedazzled Thorkill who reached out for a beautifully woven cloak. The others, seeing Thorkill had no fear to take something, reached for other objects in the room. But then the room began to tremble and a cry of "Stop, thief!" echoed in the chamber. All at once the previously languid trolls rushed toward the group with their swords drawn in a vicious attack.

Forgetting the plunder the men drew their swords and began to fight. They were greatly outnumbered. One warrior, a famous archer named Buchi, drew and fired arrow after arrow while as many as could made their escape. Then he fled to the shore where he met King Gormr, Thorkill, his brother, and sixteen others. Thus out of the three hundred original crew only twenty survived.

King Gudmundr met them at the shore and ferried them back to his hall for the night. They accepted his hospitality, but were wary of it. They ate only from the plates King Gudmundr sampled. And all seemed well with them. However, later in the evening Buchi fell under the charms of one of Gudmundr's daughters. He asked her to marry him. She accepted and they kissed, whereupon Buchi lost his wits and was never the same again.

The next morning King Gormr, Thorkill, and his remaining men went back to their ships. They now needed only one, and even then they had barely enough of a crew with which to set sail. But somehow they managed. They journeyed down the river Vimur and across the seas back to King Gormr's land. They fought many storms and engaged in many battles with trolls along the way. In comparison to their journey to Geirrodr's Garth, the fights were merely nuisances. Finally they reached Denmark with great tales to tell. But such had been their loss of men and the fright they had endured that not even Thorkill ever dared return to that cursed land.

Chapter 16

Hyndla
is Tricked

Ottar the Simple, the son of Instein, was in a dispute with Angantyr. They both laid claim to a munificent treasure. A Thing was to be held, and the one with the noblest lineage would be awarded the treasure. Unfortunately for Ottar the Simple he lived up to his name and wasn't very bright. For the life of him he couldn't remember more than a couple of his ancestors. But fortunately he had worshiped Freyja faithfully for years. He prepared a great sacrifice to her and knelt down by the fire and asked for her help. He had decided to spend the entire night praying to her.

Freyja had long followed his devotion to her. She was by far his favorite of the Æsir and Vanir. So, when he asked for her help she was moved to intercede on his behalf.

She appeared before him, glowing in white. He was so startled he fell over and caught his sleeve on fire. He beat out the fire. He had prayed for years to her and it had never crossed his mind she would actually appear before him. He didn't know quite what to say or how to act. This had never come up when discussing the Æsir and Vanir with his friends. Though they had prayed for it, they never actually expected to meet any of the Æsir or Vanir. So, he improvised, "Oh great and wonderful Freyja. Um, your beauty exceeds um your, your, um, legend. I am so transfixed that I can't, ah, um, avert mine eyes. You have blessed this um um humble um man with your presence. What can I um do for you?"

Well, he'd managed to get it all wrong. It was what could she do for him? He realized his mistake and began to correct himself, "Or, ah um um what you can do for me er what we can do for each other um or together we can do things um together um or apart as you may want um I am your humble servant um um Ottar. Yes I am Ottar." He thought to himself, "I'm pathetic."

Before he could start up again Freyja raised her hand, "Enough. I know what you're trying to say…"

Ottar broke in, "Of course, you do. You are Frigg the all power um er Freyja, you're Freyja the all powerful."

"Oh, I've called her Frigg. She probably doesn't like that. I should just shut up," he told himself.

Freyja took it all in stride. She knew the affect she had on some of the Æsir, imagine the potency of that effect on a mere man of Midgardr

He bent over so low and so near the fire she was afraid he'd catch himself on fire again. "Arise, Ottar the Simple," aptly named she thought, and continued, "Stand on your feet before me and tell me what it is you want."

He got up and began explaining his situation, "I have claim to a great treasure, but I must prove my lineage is greater than Angatyr's." He was calming down and starting to make more sense.

"Very well, I will help you. But, my aid comes at a price. You must foreswear all other members of the Æsir and Vanir, and all of your love and devotion must be only for me. You must honor me only, and no other Æsir or Vanir." She repeated it so in his simpleness she made certain he understood.

He already did this, except, maybe for a few devotions to Odin. Even he realized it wouldn't do to forget about the leader of the Æsir and Vanir. Yet, it was Freyja standing before him, not Odin. So what would it matter if he decided to worship only her? It was unlikely Odin would even notice he'd stopped with his small offerings. He was nobody. He was too insignificant to be noticed. Yet, a member of the Æsir and Vanir stood before him. He had been noticed. His logic was already a little faulty.

Ottar agreed, "I will worship only you and will do whatever you command me to do. And in exchange you will help me win the treasure I've laid claim to."

Freyja pressed him further just to make certain, "And you agree to built no altars to others, not even Thor, not even Odin."

Had she read his mind. He reassured her, "Yes," he replied. Freyja stared at him waiting. He added, "Yes, I will built altars to no one except Freyja."

With that she immediately changed him into a boar and rode him to Jotunheimr to visit the one person who could help them. He certainly hadn't expected this.

He was exhausted by the time they reached Jotunheimr. He hardly ever walked to the end of the road and back. Now he found himself transmogrified into a boar with Freyja riding on his back as he galloped with neither rest nor food to Jotunheimr. He wasn't prepared for the distance. And he certainly wasn't prepared for Jotunheimr's size. Every time he tried to stop and rest Freyja kicked at his sides. He ran for days. They didn't stop to eat. Nor, did they stop so he could relieve himself. So, he did the only thing he could and relieved himself as he ran. Nothing like this had ever happened to him before. He was beginning to regret his devotion to Freya. Was a treasure really worth all this bother. And he was so tired.

The jotun Hyndla lay sleeping deep within her cave. Her dreams were not peaceful, so in her sleep she rolled about growling and snorting, flailing with her arms trying to get comfortable. No one dared enter when she was in this state lest she accidentally lash out at them, confused between what was in her dreams and what was real. For her the waking and dream worlds overlapped.

Freyja and her boar Ottar stood at the mouth of the cave listening to the rumblings from within. Freyja yelled into the darkness, "Hyndla, Hyndla, arise. It's too late in the day to be sleeping. Come out my friend so we might talk."

The growling changed to a howling sound, like that of a wolf baying at the moon. Hyndla was yawning and stretching as she came awake. She rolled over trying to decide whether to really get up, or simply go back to sleep. She decided to go back to sleep.

Freyja, sensing Hyndla was not making much progress towards leaving the cave, yelled in again, "Wake up Hyndla. Darkness will soon be upon us and we have quite a ways to travel to reach Asgardr. You must come with me so we may sup with Odin tonight in Valhalla, and win his favor. Those who have his kindly attention can expect great rewards. Did he not give a magnificent helmet and war coat to Hermodr? And the bold warrior of Midgardr, Sigmundr, was given a fierce sword with which to win great treasures and kingdoms. So, do not wile away your time in a dank cave. Instead, come with me and wile yourself upon Odin."

Hyndla had sat up at the mention of possible treasures. She listened, weighing how difficult it would be to journey to Valhalla, and what she would expect in return for such an effort.

Freyja knew she had her now. To further lure the jotun out she mentioned what Hyndla loved most. "Gold is one gift in abundance in Asgardr, and Odin hands it out as if the nuggets were mere pebbles. And don't forget Odin can award you glory in battle. Or, he might offer you a drink of the Precious Mead, though I don't think great wisdom has ever been a goal of yours. But perhaps you might like to be so skillful a speaker you could trip up your opponents in flyttings by skill rather than trickery. Other gifts Odin has to offer include fair winds to guide sailors and their ships, and high tides so they might hug to coastlines rather than having to venture out over Midgardrsormr. Skalds and poets are given word skills to use in their stories so no one will fall asleep listening. But the most precious gift Odin gives to warriors is one that can win riches and kingdoms. It is more prized than a magical sword. It is the gift of courage and a brave heart."

Freyja listened and could hear Hyndla moving towards the front of the cave. Then she continued, "If you come with me I will woo Thor on your behalf. Even though he thinks of jotuns as his enemies, he has often looked fondly on jotun women. As you know, Jarnsaxa is a particular favorite of his. You, too, could feel the rumblings of earthquakes and see the flashes of lightning that come with Thor's lovemaking."

Hyndla's head emerged first from the mouth of the cave. She crawled out on all fours, blinking into the late afternoon sun. Although, it was quite late even this much sun hurt her eyes, since jotuns abhorred sunlight. In all the Worlds of the Tree but Jotunheimr the sun could turn them to stone. So they avoided it even in the protective world of Jotunheimr.

Rarely had Hyndla left her cave. So most of her life had been spent bent over crawling from cavern to cavern. She raised up as straight as her gnarled jotun body allowed. She was dressed in coarse burlap and obviously had not bathed in awhile, if ever. She smiled at Freyja, revealing many gaps in her teeth, glad she was going somewhere. So far her life had been consistently dull with each day resembling all the others.

Freyja sized up the jotun and realized her boar wouldn't be able to carry both of them at full speed. "Call one of your wolves out so I might harness it next to Hilksuin. Although my magnificent boar could easily carry both of us back to Asgardr, I wish for us to travel as swiftly as possible. If you ride one of your wolves Hilksuin will not be overtaxed."

Hyndla looked from Hilksuin to Freyja, then back to Hilksuin. She stared at the boar's eyes and laughed at the deception she had discovered. "You expect me to trust you when you deceive me from the start. Your boar Hilksuin could easily carry most of the Æsir fully armored to the last battle at full gallop without even becoming winded. Yet look at this panting, sweaty, beast whose back legs are brown from having soiled himself. No, this is not the famous Hilksuin. It's clear you wish to protect the strength of your lover Ottar, the son of Instein. You have conveniently changed him into a boar, though I cannot guess for what reasons. Its his eyes, they give him away. They are not the red glowing eyes of Hilksuin. They are human eyes."

Freyja scoffed at this. "You have sat in your cave far too long imagining things. This is Hilksuin, my battle-boar. Look at his carefully groomed golden bristles which glow so he can even travel swiftly in the dark. He was made a long time ago by the clever dvergues Dain and Nabbi.

Freyja's denials made Hyndla even more suspicious. She could understand someone turning their lover into a boar, since they were so frequently boring. But why deny it? She smelled Hilksuin. He did not smell like the boars she had known. Though there was that odor about him. She began retreating into the cave.

But Freyja had dealt with dim-witted jotuns most of her life and knew how to manage them. At first she tried threatening Hyndla. But that didn't work. She then resorted to flattery and promises of great wealth. She again sprinkled her conversation with words like gold, emeralds, precious stones, and wealth.

Hyndla agreed to go to Asgardr with Freyja, but in order to save face added, "I suppose if I don't go with you, you'll just stand outside my cave begging me until it's time for the last great battle, and I'll never get any sleep."

Freyja mounted Ottar, while Hyndla sat astride one of the largest wolves Freyja had ever seen. It was almost as large as Fenriswulf himself. Freyja looped a twin harness around the wolf so she could control both animals as they rode along, and to protect Ottar in case the wolf became a bit nippy.

Their journey was quick, and in short order they were at Valgrindr Gate, the outer gate of Valhalla. Hyndla could see the goat Heidrun munching away at Læradr, standing on the roof, with mead flowing to Valhalla and a constant stream of urine flowing to those doomed in Elidner. Heidrun caught sight of Hyndla, became frightened and ducked behind a gable.

The two rode on to the banks of the river Thund. After they dismounted, Freyja secured the two bridles to a tree at water's edge. Hyndla protested, "Why do you lead me away from the meal you promised me inside Valhalla. I have no desire to play on a river bank. I have not eaten in ages and want some food."

Freyja realized Hyndla was probably not exaggerating. It most likely had been ages since she had eaten. What could she have been thinking bringing such a large hungry person to Valhalla. She tried to distract the jotun, "I thought it would be interesting for us to talk about two mighty warriors, noble heroes who fought bravely and won honor and fame. I speak, of course, about Ottar the Young and Angantyr. They were both sons of the Æsir." Well, she rationalized to herself, Ottar the Simple is also young, so calling him that wasn't wrong. Technically it was true.

Hyndla decided to put up a while longer with Freyja's company, The meal she expected to eat would more than make up for this minor wait. Though, she couldn't help but add, "I have never heard of a warrior called Ottar the Young. I have heard of a fool called Ottar the Simple, though."

Ottar the Simple could take no more of this and said, "I'm right in front of your. Show some respect." But to Freyja and Hyndla it just sounded like a series of grunts and wheezes.

Freyja poked at Ottar to quiet him, and continued, "The great warrior Ottar the Young once built an altar to me. And through magic those stones were turned to glass which reflected into the sky. Ottar piled many oxen onto the shards of my altar. Their blood dripped down and caught in the chinks of the glass forming little pools of sacrifice. Soon the glass was reddened with my glory. Ottar the Young never bothered worshipping Odin or Thor. He preferred to sacrifice to women, and chose me above all others. Even above Frigg, Sif, or any of the others in Asgardr. And his devotion to me was greatly rewarded. But show me how smart you are Hyndla. Tell me about the great warrior families. Who are the Skjoldungs, the Skilfings, Othlings and Ylfings? Tell me about those on Midgardr? Tell me the names of those who were firstborn, and those who were high born? Say the names of the most noble on Midgardr."

Hyndla had not asked for this flytting, but saw that she had no choice. She first turned to the tethered boar. Nodding in his direction she spoke, "Ottar the Simple was the son of Instein, who was the son of Alf the Old. Alf was the son of Ulf, the son of Sæfari, the son of Svan the Red."

Ottar, hearing his name turned his head to listen. But nothing he didn't already know was being said, so he swished his tale to bat away a fly that was bothering him and returned to drinking from the river Thund.

Hyndla continued with Ottar's family history. "Ottar the Simple's mother wore red-golden bracelets and other jewelry befitting the princess she was. Her name was Hledis. Her father was Frodi. Her equally noble mother was Friaut whose mother was Hildigun. Hildigun was the daughter of Svava and Sækonung. In your boarish state, can you remember all this, Ottar?" Freyja didn't bother to try to pretend the boar wasn't Ottar anymore.

Ottar began to be caught up in his family history. Freyja was also listening intently. Hyndla continued, "It is odd that one who has such a noble lineage would wind up slurping water out of a river and grazing on grass. But I will remind you of your other illustrious relatives. Hildigun married the noble warrior Ketil, your great-grandfather on your mother's side of the family. Frodi was the father of Kari. Hoalf was born of Hild. Nokkvi's daughter, Nanna, was then born. Her son married your aunt, your father's sister. But these are not the only noble persons in your history. Skurhold was the daughter of Skekil. She married Olmod, and they had two sons, Isulf and Osulf, both great warriors in their own right."

Ottar was exhibiting more interest in what Hyndla was saying.

Hyndla continued, "Your family history contains twelve berserkers who fought with the battle fury of hundreds of warriors. They ran into battle foaming at the mouth and naked, confident their warriors skills would protect them and therefore they did not need armor. The twelve were born on the island of Bolmso, the sons of Arngrim and

Eyfura. Their names included two named Hadding, as well as Hervard, Hjorvard, Hrani, Angantyr, Bui, Brami, Barri, Reifnir, Tind, and Tyrfing.

Hyndla had still more to say, "The noble Jormunrekkr sacrificed all of his sons to the Æsir. He was kinsman to Sigurdr Fafnirsbani, who slew the terrible worm Fafnir. Volsungr and Hjordis of the Hraudungs were his grandparents. Hjordis was the daughter of King Eylimi of the Othlings. Their blood also runs in your veins. But there are more. Hvedna's father was Hjorvard. One of her brothers was the great warrior Haki. Aud the Profound was the daughter of Ivar. She and Hrorek the Ring Giver had a son named Harald War Tooth. Aud the Profound also had a son with Rathbard. His name was Randver."

Suddenly Freyja yelled in triumph. "You have won an inheritance in gold for Ottar the Young. He and Angantyr had a wager concerning their lineage. The winner inherited the entire family treasure, the loser, nothing. Now I will give Ottar this mead of memory to drink so when he meets Angantyr in three days he'll be able to recite his entire family history. The same family history you have just recited. Because of your knowledge, Hyndla, the wealth of Instein will go to its rightful owner.

Hyndla, realizing she had been tricked, grabbed the cup of mead from Freyja and strode over to Ottar the Simple. She bent over him and yelled curses into his ear. Pus oozed from the gaps between her teeth where once teeth had been. Her putrid breath caused Ottar the Simple to shiver. Freyja was a short distance away jumping about in triumph. Hyndla turned her glance and tongue to the Vanir asynje, "You jump and gambol about as if you were Heidrun running around with a herd of goats in heat. But I can bring your happiness to a close. All I need do is pour this mead onto the ground. Your hero can't even remember his own name is Ottar the Simple. Without this mead of memory Angantyr, the more deserving of the two, will win the inheritance. Should you not help a warrior on merit, rather than on how blindly he worships you? Angantyr is by far the more deserving. Yet, he has not raised a sacrifice of glass to you. So you ignore him in favor of a fat simpleton. Have you an answer to my charges?"

Freyja ignored the question and threw her arms up menacingly, "I will cast a ring of fire around you so the only way for you to escape is through it. Hopefully, you'll burn in the process. Give me the cup to save yourself."

Hyndla seemed not to be concerned. She taunted Freyja even more, "And that ring of fire will cause a fine pork roast, too. I'll hold Ottar the Simple and he will not escape the flames. Where is your husband Odr? Why has he left you? Could it have something to do with the dvergues you slept with for a rather gaudy, showy, necklace?"

At these words flames shot up around Hyndla and began closing in on her. Hyndla yelled, "These flames threaten me. But even more threatening is the sun who will soon be showing on the horizon. I am not within the protective lands of Jotunheimr, so the sun's rays will soon turn me to stone. You leave me no choice but to give you this cup. But before I do, I curse it and curse Ottar the Simple who will profit unfairly from my knowledge."

The flames lowered and Freyja took the cup. She set it before Ottar. While he drank she stroked his bristly back. "You give Ottar a curse, I give him my blessing and assurance he will prosper. Time will tell whose words are more potent."

Hyndla did not reply. Instead, she jumped onto her wolf and hurried back to Jotunheimr, lest the rays of the sun catch her and uppr dagr turn her into a new mountain in Asgardr.

Chapter 17

Rogner

One day Odin, Hœnir and Loki were wandering in Midgardr. Towards evening while looking for a place to stay for the night, they happened upon the cottage of a farmer and his family in the Faroe Islands. The three Æsir were wearing their disguises so the farmer didn't recognize his guests as being of the Æsir. He showed them the hospitality he would have shown any stranger, and welcomed them into his house where he and his wife offered to share their evening meal with them. The three accepted.

The farmer and his wife noticed the three ate a great deal. Although it cost them dearly they fed their guests until they were full. After the table was cleared the three moved over by the fire and sat drinking their horns of mead and telling stories. The farmer's wife sat at the hearth mending some coarsely woven clothing. The farmer busied himself over in another corner of their cottage, occasionally turning his face from his guests to weep. Odin noticed the strange behavior of their hosts and asked after their troubles, "Something seems to be bothering both of you. What is it? Since you've been so kind to us in sharing more of your meal than I dare say you have to spare, perhaps we can be of service to you. We aren't without resources to come to the aid of someone who has shown us such friendship as both of you have shown us tonight."

The farmer could contain himself no longer and broke down completely in front of the three. Amid the tears he finally got his story out. "I'm afraid you can't help me, for no one of Midgardr can help me. I've been plagued by a horrible jotun called Skrymali. Tomorrow he's coming here to take away Rogner, my youngest son. Then towards evening he'll make a meal of him. Yet there's nothing I can do to stop him. I've prayed for help from those in Asgardr, but the Æsir have more important things to think about than the problems of a farmer of Midgardr."

Odin thought a moment and then began questioning the farmer about the flaws he saw in the story, "But why has he chosen you? I've had some acquaintance with jotuns and know them certainly to be evil. Usually, though, they don't steal others away without some reason to justify it. Surely you haven't told me all the story?"

His wife spoke up, "That's true. He forgot to mention how he used to boast in the village he could play chess better than anyone. He'd make any wager, and always win. Sometimes it was close but the outcome was always the same. As is the nature of boasting, it carried far and wide and the jotun Skrymali, who fancied himself something of a chess player too, heard of him and came to make a wager for a game. My husband offered the usual wager of a field of corn or forest of wood for the winter. But Skrymali had his own ideas. He said, 'If you're as good as you think, then you won't mind wagering your son. If I win, Rogner will be mine to do with as I please.' My husband had second thoughts about the wager, but could hardly refuse with Skrymali towering over him like that. An angry jotun can easily step on you."

The farmer broke in to continue the story, "If I won Skrymali promised to do whatever I liked for one season. He would have been a great help, so, I accepted the offer. At first I was easily winning. I think he saw this. And when I was within a move or two of beating him he mumbled something. Suddenly I couldn't think straight. My eyesight faded and I was unable to see the pieces. I thought I was moving my queen, but it was only a pawn so I left my king and queen vulnerable to attack. I lost the game. We had already hidden Rogner, just in case I lost. And after I lost I begged the jotun to take our crops for this year. He refused and said he would be back in three days to claim his prize. He'll be here tomorrow to take our son. We've tried to hide Rogner, but have had to hide him right here. None of our neighbors would take him out of fear their property would be torn apart by Skrymali in his efforts to find our son. Skrymali will easily find him, even if he has to tear down our house to do so. What are we going to do? Oh, what are we going to do." The farmer hid his head in his hands.

Odin stood, discarding his disguise in the process, and changed before the frightened eyes of the two peasants. At first they thought maybe they had been tricked by Skrymali in disguise. But the form before them was not at all ugly like a jotun's. Then Hœnir and Loki discarded their disguises. The farmer and his wife fell to their knees trembling before the three. Rogner, who had been hiding behind a panel in the wall, opened it a crack to see what was happening. What he saw frightened him so much he lost his footing, fell against the panel, and tumbled out into the room.

Odin tried to calm the family, "Fear not, we three are of the Æsir and will help you against the evil Skrymali."

Odin went outside and began to chant mysterious words and sayings. He carved runes into the dirt. The corn in the field began to grow for a second time that season. Odin seemed satisfied and went back inside. "Tomorrow at dawn we will hide Rogner in the field. As you know something only has to go two or three stalks deep in order to be completely invisible in a cornfield. And you'll have an extra harvest this year to pay you back for the meal we three ate tonight."

With that everyone retired for the night. Odin, Hœnir and Loki slept peacefully. The farmer, his wife, and Rogner tossed and turned, especially Rogner. The farmer thought, "It's bad enough having a jotun mad at you. Now I have to worry about trying not to offend three of the Æsir. I vow by Leiptr's holy waters I'll never play chess again."

By morning the corn was fully grown and ready for harvesting. Odin took Rogner with him. The farmer still seemed worried. "How will standing him in a field of corn help? Skrymali towers over my house and can easily see out over the field and spot Rogner."

Without replying Odin waved his hand. Suddenly Rogner was transformed to the size of a kernel of corn. Odin went into the field and hid him in an ear of corn and returned to the farmer's house, content Skrymali would have an impossible task in trying to find Rogner.

About mid-morning Skrymali came striding up to the farmer's house. "Where is my dinner? I had hoped to have him for breakfast, but was too hungry to wait until I got here and have already eaten. However, he will make a fine evening meal."

The farmer was shaking so much from fright he blurted out his son's whereabouts, "He's hiding in the cornfield, please don't step on me or my house." His wife looked at him and he added a bit belatedly, "Or my wife. Don't step on my wife, please." Though it seemed to her he was saying, "If you must step on something, step on my wife and not me." She made a mental note, they would have to discuss this later.

Skrymali's words boomed out over his shoulder as he turned and headed for the cornfield, "Then I shall have little difficulty in finding him in time for my evening meal."

The jotun drew his sword and began hacking away at the corn. As he cut each stalk he shook and inspected every section of it before binding it together with others into sheaves of twenty-four. By late afternoon he had come close to harvesting the entire crop. He stopped for a moment to rest and looked at the cleared field behind him. Then he started up again with renewed fury.

Soon his diligence paid off. He gathered up one stalk, cut, and shook it. Some kernels fell in his hand. Pushing them about with his finger he inspected them. As he turned the kernels over in his hand one rolled apart from the others and out fell Rogner. Terrified he called out to Odin for help, which was sent immediately. Before Skrymali could close his fist Odin's raven Huginn flew down and snatched Rogner from the jotun's upturned palm and carried Rogner back to the farmhouse where he was changed back into his normal shape and size.

They heard Skrymali trampling off vowing to return the next day. His shuffling stride overturned the earth in the field so it was prepared for another planting.

Odin turned to the farmer, his wife, and the frightened Rogner, "I've helped you this day and saved you from Skrymali. You have a newly harvested field and an extra crop of corn cut and bound for this year. Ask no more of me."

The three Æsir stayed yet another night with the peasants, which gave a great deal of comfort to Rogner. Morning came, and while they were all breakfasting they heard off in the distance Skrymali's footsteps thundering towards them. Soon the cottage would shake, they would be able to see him. Rogner ran to the secret panel to hide, but was shaking so much he had trouble finding the secret latch to open it. He kept looking around and pulling at the panel. He was shaking and making no headway with the secret latch.

Hœnir stepped forward, offering to help, "Hiding behind that panel certainly won't help you, and it'll only result in your parents' cottage being torn apart. I know a proper place where you can hide. Come with me."

At that moment two beautiful white swans were flying by. Hœnir beckoned out the window for them to come to him. Then he changed Rogner into a tiny feather and placed it on the neck of one of the swans. The two swans resumed their flight to a favorite pond in the nearby woods.

Skrymali approached, not noticing the swans flying overhead away from the cottage. He bellowed out, "Give me the prize I won, and I'll leave you, your wife, and your three friends alone. Otherwise, I'll have to smash all of you, and your home."

The farmer began to tremble again. This time he didn't give away as much as before, but he did give away enough, "Spare us, he's not here. He's hiding in the woods."

Again Skrymali stalked off vowing to find Rogner in time for his evening meal.

He searched the woods all day looking under leaves and rocks, behind waterfalls, in the fur of animals, but still no luck. He tore up a good deal of the forest in his search. Towards evening he came to a pond and thought, "All of this activity has made me thirsty. I shall have a drink here and rest a few moments."

He bent over the edge of the pond, cupped his hands and began drinking. The peaceful water churned violently at his giant gulps. As he scooped out more water to quench his thirst everything floating at the center of the pond was pulled towards him. And amongst the swans swimming in the pond was the one on whose neck Rogner desperately clung.

At first Skrymali paid no attention to the lily pads, frogs or other animals who were interrupting his drink. Some of the smaller creatures he gulped down as he drank.

As the water dribbled through his fingers he peered over his hands and noticed one of the swans, and in particular a feather on its neck. More swiftly than anyone could image a lumbering oaf moving, he grabbed at the swan and yelled out in triumph as he lunged at its neck. "Aha, there you are. I'll make a meal of you right now, along with this delicious swan." He had the swan by the neck and was trying to shake the feather loose.

But it was not to be. Hœnir was hiding behind a tree watching. Just as Skrymali grabbed at the neck of the swan and began shaking, Hœnir conjured up a gust of wind which blew the feather from the swan's neck and back to the farmhouse. Skrymali was startled enough to lose his grip which gave the swan enough time to fly away. Again the jotun had been thwarted, and left vowing to return the next day.

Back at the farmhouse Rogner was changed into his original size and shape. Hœnir told him, "There, I've done what I can for you. Ask no more of me."

The three Æsir decided to stay one more night. Loki sat twitching all night at the prospect of really being able to save the lad and prove who was the most cunning of them all. He'd be able to do what neither Odin nor Hœnir could do. And that would make him the best.

As before, the next morning during breakfast they heard Skrymali approaching. Loki grabbed Rogner by the hand and pulled him down to the seashore where they boarded a small boat. He didn't want Rogner's father to know where his son had been hiding because of his tendency to blurt things out. But the farmer saw his son with Loki as he rowed away.

Loki rowed out beyond the horizon and began fishing. Rogner sat shaking wondering what was in store for him next. He couldn't take much more of this. He was a nervous wreck. He just wanted a calm life back. Farming, eating, sleeping, farming. That's all. He'd be happy. He was through with having jotuns trying to find him. But, tell that to Skrymali, who wasn't through with Rogner.

Rogner soon found out what Loki had planned. Loki caught a flounder, inspected it and then threw it back. Then he caught another and also discarded it. Rogner could only wonder at how this would help him. Then Loki caught a third flounder and smiled, very satisfied for he had caught a female. He made Rogner small enough to hide inside the tiniest egg in the roe of the flounder and then threw the fish overboard.

In the meantime Skrymali had arrived at the farmhouse asking the inevitable question, "Where is my evening meal?" He raised his foot and held it threateningly over the cottage.

The farmer quickly answered to protect himself, "Your evening meal has gone fishing with Loki. Please don't step on my house." He looked over at his wife and added, "Or my wife, or me." He made certain to put her first. They had had a little talk he had found quite unpleasant. He wasn't used to his wife saying such things.

Skrymali answered, "Then I shall also go fishing for my evening meal. Your house is spared for the moment."

At the seashore Skrymali found a boat large enough for him and rowed out beyond the horizon until he came to Loki's boat. He waved to Loki in a friendly manner, "Have you seen the young lad Rogner? I have some business with him."

Loki replied, "I can just guess what that is."

Loki immediately turned his boat, aimed it at Skrymali's vessel and rammed into it. But his plan backfired. Instead of sinking Skrymali's boat he managed to sink his own and fell into the cold sea which had not yet been warmed by the morning sun. Loki thrashed about calling for Skrymali who ignored him and continued preparing his fishing line. Loki finally managed to climb aboard the jotun's boat and sat shivering and cold in the stern.

"Let's row back to land. I'm freezing and I'll surely catch my death of cold if I don't have something to warm me."

Skrymali just glanced at Loki and then cast his line into the water. Within moments the jotun had landed three flounder. Loki recognized the one in which Rogner lay hidden. Loki begged for the fish, "So far I've had a very bad day. I've been nearly drowned in the cold sea and haven't yet had breakfast. Please spare just the smallest fish there for me. I'll reward you greatly when we are back on land if you'll do me this favor."

Skrymali set about his task of cutting up the fish and inspecting them. "You'll have to wait until evening like me for a meal. Just be grateful I'm allowing you to stay in my boat. It would be a long swim for you back to shore in this water."

Skrymali continued inspecting the innards of the fish. He came to the female and began sorting through the eggs until he reached the one in which Rogner lay hidden. Just as he found the egg Loki changed himself into a falcon, for he had not yet returned Freyja's stolen falcon-guise, valsharmr. Again Rogner was snatched from Skrymali's upturned palm before it closed.

When they reached the shore Loki changed Rogner back into his regular shape and gave him instructions on how to act, "Stand fast here until Skrymali actually steps onto the shore. Don't move until that time. Then run as fast as you can, as if your life depended on it, for indeed it does. Run across the beach to that far point and put up this iron pole. But remember, don't start running until Skrymali is actually on the shore. Do you understand what I've said? Should I repeat any of it?" Rogner nodded that he understood.

Skrymali had been rowing with all his might to reach the shore as quickly as possible, lest his prize get away from him for yet a third time. As the land came into view he was puzzled by what he saw. There was Rogner standing, waiting for him. The boat crashed into the shore and the jotun leaped out yelling to the boy, "Oho, you've decided to give

up the game. I can't say I blame you. Don't worry, you're so scrawny I'll finish you in just a gulp or two."

As Skrymali's feet touched the sand Rogner turned and ran to the far end of the beach. The sand seemed to move strangely under his feet. But he had no time to think about that as Skrymali had also started to give chase and it took many steps by Rogner to make up for each step taken by Skrymali. But finally he reached the spot Loki had indicated and plunged the iron pole into it. The sand around the pole hardened and held the pole steady. Looking back towards Skrymali he was surprised to see the jotun sinking in the sand.

Soon Skrymali had sunk to his knees. His anger at being trapped gave him extra strength and he was able to pull one leg out of the mass and take another step. But in so doing he managed to trip himself up. As he fell forward he tried to catch himself with his hands. Instead of breaking his fall his hands plunged through the semi-liquid sand, unable to find anything to hold onto. He managed to pull one hand free and reach upwards with it before he was frozen in place. Rogner ran out of the way as Skrymali fell towards him. The iron pole stood fast as the jotun fell forward. Rogner watched in horror as the pole went right through the top of Skrymali's head and held him pinned to the sand.

Skrymali yelled out charms and runes to try and free himself from the trap. But the injury to his head had unsettled his wits and he was unable to get through the charms coherently. He tried again, more slowly, but his mind was too muddy. The charms he was thinking just didn't come out right when he uttered them. While he continued babbling, Loki came up to him and using Skrymali's own reaping hook cut off the jotun's head as well as one of his legs. However, Skrymali had been able to get some of the runes right and the still talking head was rejoined to the neck and healed immediately as did the leg. Loki cut the head and neck a second time. But before the magic charms could work again Loki cast flint and steel between the two wounds so they couldn't be rejoined. Thus was the magic broken. Skrymali soon died and his body hardened immediately leaving a very grim memorial on the beach. Most of his body was buried in the sand, leaving only his head, an arm, two legs, and some of his back and side protruding.

Loki and Rogner walked back to the cottage. It was not yet mid-morning. The farmer and his wife were relieved to see their son safe and whole. Loki couldn't help boasting of his success, "You've nothing more to fear from that evil jotun. He'll bother you no longer for I, Loki Laufeyjarsonr, have bested him in battle. After we leave here sing my praises and remind everyone Loki succeeded where Odin and Hœnir have failed."

The three Æsir were given one last meal before leaving the grateful family.

Odin and Hœnir had to put up with Loki's boasting all the way back to Asgardr. But this was not the worst of it. Loki actually began to believe he was all powerful; that he was more powerful than all the others in Asgardr as well as those who lived at the other roots of the tree combined. He felt he should be lord of the Æsir. And this inflated view of his self-importance was to lead to a great deal of tragedy.

Chapter 18

Freyr's Lovesickness

Freyja, Freyr's sister, had been gone from Asgardr for a long while. Worried about this Freyr decided the best way to find her quickly and make certain she was alright was to steal his way to Odin's hall, Valaskjalf, and to the watchtower to sit on the throne Hlidskjalf so he could see out into all the Worlds of the Tree. "It'll only take me a few moments to make certain my sister isn't in danger from the jotuns or those who live in Svartalfheimr."

Freyr left his home in Alfheimr and journeyed to Odin's hall and made his way through the hall with no difficulty, until he reached the door leading to the throne room. There he found Odin's two wolves, Geri and Freki, guarding the entryway. They growled as he approached causing him to step back and draw his magical sword Gambanteinn. He let go of the hilt and immediately the sword came to life flailing about of its own accord. The two wolves were frightened and ran off leaving the way into the throne room unguarded.

Freyr cautiously entered, looking around to see what other traps might lay nearby. But there were none. Odin didn't think anyone would ever be able to get this far, so hadn't added any extra security to the room.

Freyr climbed the steps to Hlidskjalf and settled himself onto it and looked out into the worlds. His eyes became transfixed by a light shining out of the far north of Jotunheimr in Gymirsgardr. He saw a house in the midst of a high hedge, causing him to look long and earnestly. The sight became clearer and his eyes began to focus on the details of the scene before him. Then he saw her, Gerdr, the daughter of the hrymthursar Gymir and his wife Angroboda. Angroboda was the same evil witch who had tried to destroy the Æsir with a love of gold, and had been burned for her crimes and reborn twice, first as Gullveig, and then as Heidr. It was her heart Loki had eaten and subsequently become pregnant and born his three monster children, Fenriswulf, Midgardrsormr (Jormungandr), and Hela.

But as Freyr stared at the vision before him he wondered how two ogres such as Gymir and Angroboda could have had such a fair and beautiful daughter as Gerdr?

Gerdr turned to enter her father's ice castle. When she lifted her hand to the door latch a light shone forth. It reflected through the ice crystals and broke into shades and

hues that burst onto the northern sky for the people of Midgardr to see. After the door closed behind her it seemed to Freyr the brightness of the world had gone out. He made his way back to his home in Alfheimr where he refused to eat or sleep out of want for the vision he had seen in Gymirsgardr. A strange punishment had been meted out to him for daring to climb on Hlidskjalf. He had fallen in love with Gerdr, and began pining away for her.

Njordr, Freyr's father, was upset by the decline in his son's health. He went to Skirnir, Freyr's childhood friend and loyal servant, to ask him to do something to bring his son out of his black mood.

Skirnir went to see Freyr. "Freyr, we are old friends. Perhaps there's something I can do to help you. But I have to know what it is that's troubling you."

Freyr broke down to his old friend and told him what he had done; that he had stolen into Odin's hall and been rewarded for his deed with the punishment of love. "If you could but help me win Gerdr, for I will die without her. I'll reward you well."

Skirnir agreed to the task. "But only on condition you give me the sword Gambanteinn. And since this is no ordinary journey, but one wrought with danger, I'll need a horse that's out of the ordinary. I'll need your horse, Blodughofi, that wondrous animal who can understand speech, travel as easily through the night as through the day, and can leap almost as high as eight-legged Sleipnir."

Freyr agreed, "What do these treasures mean to me if I don't have the love of the most beautiful creature alive? Gladly I give you my sword which I have only recently won from Hermodr. Willingly I give you my noble steed to carry you on your journey that I might know happiness from the result." And with that he gave away the treasures that might have saved him at the last great battle.

Freyr went back to his daydreaming. He sat near a brook staring into it thinking of his love. Skirnir, unnoticed stole Freyr's reflection from the brook and cast it into a drinking horn so he might be able to show Gerdr Freyr's good looks and bewitch her with the drink. He took the other gifts and started on his treacherous journey, riding over rolling hills and damp fells to Jotunheimr.

A high wall of flickering flames, known as myrkvan vafrloga, circled Gymirsgardr. Skirnir made his way to the gateway only to find two firehounds tethered there guarding the entrance. He rode on around the wall until he came to a shepherd sitting on a howe striking his harp and singing of the doom of the Æsir and those in Midgardr. When he saw Skirnir his song changed to one about the intruder and his death while seeking Gerdr.

Skirnir spoke to him, "You seem to have nothing better to do all day than sit on the rocks and look out over this land. Perhaps you know it well enough to tell me how I might find Gerdr, the lovely daughter of the jotun Gymir and the evil Angroboda, so that I might speak with her in private about a very important matter?"

The shepherd turned to him and replied, "You must be mad. No mortal can win speech with Gymir's maiden daughter. You'll die first."

Skirnir became angered, "Dangers will not thwart me. The thought of death will not deter me. I'll die when the Norns decree it, not when you sing it." Skirnir turned and went on his way.

That night inside the castle Gerdr heard the pounding of horses' hooves. She summoned her handmaiden to inquire about the noise. The handmaiden informed her there was quite a commotion going on in the courtyard. "A man on a great steed has leapt over the wall into the yard. The dogs ran to attack him, but he let loose a sword that chased them away. Then it returned to its sheath of its own accord. He has turned his horse out to graze and says he will not leave until he has had a chance to talk privately with you."

Gerdr ordered her servant to bring the warrior into the hall, "I'll get clear mead to serve him. I feel uneasy by his presence. I know my meeting him will bring great harm to my brother Beli. But there is nothing I can do but offer him hospitality."

Gerdr, dressed completely in white, entered the main room of the great hall carrying a horn of mead for her guest. She could tell by his manner he wasn't of Midgardr. "You're either of the Æsir, Vanir or alfs? Which is it? My father's castle is guarded by a high wall. How do you come to have a horse fearless enough to leap over it?"

Skirnir replied, "I was not born of the Æsir, Vanir, or alfs, although I'm their friend. I come here as an emissary for Freyr, who is of the Vanir. My task is to persuade you to journey with me to Asgardr and dwell there as Freyr's wife, for he has fallen madly in love with you."

Gerdr turned to leave the room, "I refuse your offer. Finish your mead and then go."

Skirnir brought out eleven golden apples from the folds of his cloak, "I have here the Apples of Idunn. They are priceless, for they promise the owner eternal youth. When you feel age creeping up on you take but a bite and your youth will be restored. The apples also regenerate themselves and always remain at the constant number of eleven. I'll give them to you for the purchase of your favor and your agreement to wed Freyr."

Gerdr refused. "My love cannot be bought with fruit. Freyr will never be my husband. Besides, you offer a false gift. Only Idunn can hand out her apples. If others take them from her, the apples shrivel and dry out. Those are not Idunn's apples."

Skirnir persisted, putting away the apples and taking out an arm ring, "I offer you the magic arm ring Draupnir. It has the unique property of every eight days making nine other rings of equal value. It belongs to Odin, but can soon be yours if only you will say yes to Freyr."

Again Gerdr refused, "I don't need gold. Look around and you'll see my father's house is filled with it. Besides, why should I accept as a gift a piece of jewelry stolen from Odin. He will surely come to take it back, or offer it to me at a price higher than I'm willing to pay."

But still Skirnir persisted, "Such gifts usually come in threes. The first two have been rejected, but hopefully this one will be accepted. I offer you this gift from myself out of my friendship for Freyr. He has given me the priceless magical sword Gambanteinn. I could easily cut off your head with it, but instead I offer it to you as a gift."

Gerdr stared at the sword, momentarily transfixed, before shaking herself loose from its spell, "I'll never be forced into love. You don't frighten me. How would Freyr reward you if you returned to Asgardr with just my head. Better I should be given in marriage to Mimir. Freyr lusts for more than just a portion of me."

Skirnir waved the blade before her again. This time she saw other scenes reflected in its side. "I see the blood of many of my kin who will be slain by the Æsir. Yet I believe my father will protect me from your threats. So leave me in peace."

Skirnir, angered by her refusals, spoke in a loud commanding voice, "Your father is not here now. Your father is doomed to die before this blade." Skirnir brought the blade nearer to Gerdr, "See upon it the magic runes. The first represents Freyr, ᚠ, and the second, ᚦ, will tame your heart. I will scratch three more runes upon the sword which will now no longer be known as Gambanteinn, but as Tamsvondr. And with this now taming wand I'll utter a curse upon you. This blade will pierce your heart, and in death you'll be sent below to the depths of Nagrindr Gate, to the Eagle's Hill near Helheimr, to wife to the loathsome three-headed hrymthursar Hrimgrimnir, which means frost-hooded. That should give you an idea of how cold it is there and how cold you'll be. Cold in every sense because you'll have no desire for you husband who will desire you often. And cold because you'll never feel warmth again. Your heart will be cold, your body will be cold.

Things will not go well for you. You are beautiful now. But your beauty will not last. It will fade to just the opposite. Now you elicit stares of awe at how wonderful you look. At your new home you'll elicit stares that any creature could look as awful as you. You'll feel yourself becoming as ugly as Hrimgrimnir. All manner of boils and sores will grow upon your once beautiful body, and no matter what ointments you use they will never be healed. They will spread until you are one big pustule. You'll begin to hate yourself and suffer the pangs of longing which Freyr is now suffering. But it will not help you then, for there will be no turning back. Odin will be angry with you, as well as Thor. And the love Freyr now holds for you will turn to hatred and contempt. But even that will not be the end of your suffering. Demons and imps will nip and pinch at you for as long as you live there, which will be until the last days of the Æsir. And these same demons will bring to you your sustenance, horns filled with urine from the goat Heidrun. That will be your mead to drink. You'll always weep for what you've lost. I utter a curse of sterility upon you. Though your new husband will enjoy you, perversion will plague you with unbridled, unnatural sexual desires, and his all too frequent touches will bring nothing but repulsion to you. Lechery, loathing and lust will haunt you in this special place in Hela's kingdom reserved for those who insult the Æsir and Vanir. Change your mind and I'll scratch away these runes and you may look forward to a life of worship and tenderness from Freyr."

Gerdr saw the fate reflected before her. All in all it seemed it would be better to accept Freyr's offer. She held up her crystal cup to offer a toast to her future husband, Freyr. But Skirnir handed her instead the cup which contained Freyr's reflection. She looked in it and drank, "I drink to Freyr. I have felt to love one of the Vanir would be wrong for me. But, if by wedding Freyr I can stop the bloodshed I foresee, then it shall be but a small price to pay." She took a sip from the cup and gave it to Skirnir to drink, which he did.

Skirnir spoke, "Tell me more on how we should arrange things before I return to Asgardr with this good news. When and where will you meet with Freyr? Do you swear after I leave here you'll still keep your word?"

Gerdr replied, "I will meet Freyr in the windless wood called Barri, a peaceful place he is no doubt familiar with. I'll meet him there nine nights from now, as is our religious custom. That's where we will be wed. There I promise I will give him my love."

Skirnir leaped upon Blodughofi and hurried back to Asgardr where he met Freyr anxiously waiting for him at the entrance gates. "Skirnir, quickly, before you dismount or even take care of your horse, tell me what happened? What of Gerdr? Will the fair maid love me as I love her?"

Skirnir answered, "Barri is the name of a grove which you know well. In nine nights Gerdr will meet you there and become your wife."

Freyr was ecstatic, "How can I possibly wait for that time to come. One more night without her is torture, two unbearable. A month has often seemed to me shorter than even one of these nine nights of waiting."

But, as time inevitable does, eventually the nine days did pass and Freyr set out for Barri. His journey was not a peaceful one. He was met on the way by Beli, Gerdr's brother, who opposed the wedding, "As long as I'm living you will not marry my sister. I'll kill you first, which will be an easy task since you foolishly gave your magical sword to Skirnir and now travel unarmed."

Beli raised his club overhead. Freyr leapt from his saddle and dodged low so the blow missed him. As he bent over he noticed the horn of a hart on the ground before him. Beli had his club raised up over his head preparing for his second blow. But, he was oafish and slow. His chest was unprotected. Freyr picked up the hart's horn and stabbed Beli through the heart before the jotun had a chance to bring down his club again. Beli toppled over, killed with one blow.

Freyr continued on his way to Barri Grove where he met Gerdr. He saw she was even more beautiful in person. Upon meeting him, she too fell in love, and they were a very happy couple. Gathered around them were the Æsir, Vanir and alfs. Even though there was some reluctance on their part to admit a jotun to their lands, the Æsir, Vanir and alfs blessed the union out of their love for Freyr.

The only thing for Gerdr that marred the wedding was the disappearance of her brother Beli. He had told her he was leaving for the wedding, but had never shown up. His whereabouts remained a mystery. Freyr remained silent on the matter.

Afterwards the couple went to Freyr's hall in Alfheimr to live. Their love deepened as time passed and they remained happy until the end of the world, when Freyr would have cause to regret the price he had paid for Gerdr – the sword Gambanteinn and the horse Blodughofi.

But that was far in the future. Their union flourished and soon they were blessed with a son whom they named Fiolnir.

Chapter 19

The Deception of Gylfi

Gylfi was a fair and just king who ruled over the land in Midgardr called Svithiod, now known as Sweden. He was so powerful enemies had long since given up trying to invade his kingdom. Without battles to fight he had many idle hours which he spent in the pursuit of knowledge. He had often visited the dvergar and alfs and had learned their secrets. He was accomplished at metal work and knew the fine things that could be wrought from gold. But he also had the knowledge of how to make weapons and useful household implements. He was well-versed in the knowledge of runes and often conjured up the dead and questioned them. He often ate with his warriors and learned from them. While at dinner he'd listen to stirring songs of valor. Of all his pleasures, music was the greatest. He would rather have starved than have done without it.

His skalds were absent from one dinner, which made Gylfi angry. But off in the distance he could hear sweet singing and harp playing. All there who heard it were moved to think of their greatest adventures or loves. The doors to the hall opened and a beautiful tall woman stood, noble in bearing, singing the praises of the Æsir. She went up to Gylfi and sung him a brooding song that sounded as if it came from the grave. She sung stories of great warriors, battles, and new beginnings. She told Gylfi secret knowledge. Long after her song had ceased the assembled sat thinking of the words she had sung.

Finally the spell was broken as Gylfi arose and spoke to her, "Tell me your name fair woman? What payment can I give you for the songs you have just sung? Truly it was the most magnificent I've ever heard. I will give you up to half my kingdom."

She answered, "I was called Gefjun by the Æsir and jotuns when I was young. The price I ask is meagre. I have four oxen, Hœfir, Hyrr, Raudr and Rikinni. I ask that I be allowed to own all the land I can plough during one day and night."

Gylfi readily agreed to her terms. Certainly it would cost him less than half his kingdom.

The next morning Gylfi went out with Gefjun to see her oxen. He was surprised at the sight. They were huge and powerful. The four were jet black with white foreheads. They had been harnessed to a plough which cut a deep trough, deeper than Gylfi had ever seen. Gylfi watched as the ploughing began. It seemed almost as if both Gefjun and her team increased in size before his very eyes. The plough cut deep down through the foundations of the land. They ploughed throughout the day and night. At the end of that time she drove the oxen out into the sea and waded in after them. The sea reached up to her waist. The oxen strained and the land which had been ploughed was pulled away from Gylfi's kingdom. She pulled it to a shallow section of the sea and anchored it there and named it Zealand. And that is why when you look at a map of the two areas you can see they can be fitted together as if they were parts of a puzzle. The gaping hole left in Gylfi's kingdom rapidly filled with water and formed a lake which is now known as Logrinn, and sometimes as Lake Malar.

Gylfi watched from a distance as Gefjun secured her land and guided the four oxen onto the land. She stepped upon the shore behind them and chanted spells and carved runes on the oxen. They were immediately transformed into four strong youths. Gylfi could hear her laughing and praising them. "I am proud of you my sons, as your jotun father would also be if he were able to be here."

In time Zealand flourished under their touch. Cattle grazed in vast fields and pastures. Crops of corn sprang up, tempting others to move there and be ruled over by Gefjun's kind justice. Eventually she married a man named Skjold and from them descended a long line of noble kings and valiant warriors. They lived in the city of Hleidra on the island.

Meanwhile Gefjun's songs had filled Gylfi's head with such stories that he hungered after even more. He wanted to know about the other Worlds of the Tree, and decided the best way to find out was to go directly to Asgardr. And naively he began his journey unaware that one can only journey to Asgardr with the Æsir's permission. Unknown to Gylfi, while he traveled on his way, many obstacles were cleared from his path so his journey was safe. Hints and signs were planted along the road so he could find his way when he was lost. But many deceptions had also been prepared for him once he reached Asgardr.

Gylfi took on the guise of an old man and began his journey. He walked for days and days which then stretched into weeks and eventually into months. But the time came when he reached Asgardr and stood before Heimdallr, who opened Asgardr's gates to him. To his left and right were monumental halls and palaces. He walked on until he came to what he thought was the most wonderful hall there.

Gylfi leaned back so he could see over the top of the hall. But he was blinded by the gold shields which formed its roof. Standing just outside the doors was Hermodr who was juggling seven swords and daggers at once with great skill. He kept them moving in a circle in front of him. Without stopping or losing his concentration he spoke to Gylfi, "Who has come to see us in Asgardr?"

Gylfi answered, making his voice shake with age, "My name is Gangleri. I've been walking for many weeks and am exceedingly tired. Can I stay here for the night? Who owns this great hall? Is it possible to speak to the owner of such a palace?"

Hermodr replied, "If you will follow me you can ask him those questions yourself." In a swift final motion Hermodr flung the swords and daggers he had been juggling so they landed in the ground standing up to form a circle.

As the two approached the hall the doors opened of their own accord, and once the two were through, the doors closed behind them. As he walked down the corridor to the main room Gylfi saw many different activities off in the side rooms – wrestling, music, all manners of games and sports, and feasts of every description. They came to the main hall which had three thrones set at the far end of it. Each throne was higher than the one before it. A man could be seen in each seat.

Gylfi asked, "Who are the three one-eyed men I see before me? They seem so alike, yet so different from each other."

Hermodr replied, "The one seated on the lowest level is Harr; Jafnhar is seated in the middle; while at the highest is Thridi. Yet all think alike and could be taken for one and the same."

Harr spoke first, "Why have you come to Asgardr? Who are you?" Harr signaled for food and drink to be brought.

A feast was set before Gylfi but he declined it saying, "The hunger I have can only be satisfied with knowledge. Answer my questions and I will be filled."

Harr answered, "A wise and foolish response to our hospitality. I must warn you, you can only leave Asgardr if you take with you more knowledge than you arrived with. So ask all your questions and we will answer them."

Gylfi asked his first question, "Tell me who is the oldest of the gods. Who do those in Asgardr worship?"

Harr answered, "We worship the Alfadir, who was before . . ."

Jafnhar continued, as if the thought were the same person speaking so flawless was the transition from one speaker to the other, ". . . the creation. The Alfadir made all things possible."

Thridi continued where Jafnhar had left off, "The most glorious of the Alfadir's creations was Midgardr and those who live there."

On and on Gylfi questioned the three, "What words of wisdom can you give me to take back to Midgardr to teach others. Tell me how to lead a just and true northern life."

The high one spoke, "Once in my youth I was lost. But then I met another and was no longer alone. I learned from him it costs nothing to say kind things and be friendly. Having but half a loaf and no drink I found I still had a friend. After awhile we parted. Later, my clothes I had hung on a stake. Naked I was common, yet my clothes were well made.

"Sometimes I arrived at homes too early before the mead was brewed, and at other times too late, after it was drunk. When invited for a meal I never went with my stomach growling. It is impolite to gaze on a meal with hunger when you are the invited guest. Never go to a friend hungry lest you stay that way afraid to ask for food. Remember, there is always the chance a meal may not be offered. Not everyone is invited to eat.

"Beware when visiting a house, and be on the lookout, for an enemy may be within. Look this way and that before entering. Be on your guard.

"'Hello,' I said, 'I am here. Where shall I sit?' In kindness I came, not with drawn swords, lest I be surprised with their number.

"And when one has traveled far across mountains and arrives cold and numb the fire will be welcome for its warmth. If possible clean and change from your travel clothes before joining the party.

"Before dinner you must needs wash and prepare. Only after friendly encouragement should you tell of your travels.

"It takes skill to live and travel by one's wits. If such are lacking it would be better if you stayed home, else you run the risk of being laughed at behind your back.

"But he who blows his own horn sounds a sour note, so do not boast. Rather tell of your deeds in a modest manner. If one is wiser than you your silence will bespeak wisdom. Open your mouth and they will learn you are a fool.

"Beware when first you sit at a strange table. Do not immediately join in. Wait and listen so you can learn the other's thoughts first. If you don't follow this advice you may find yourself unwittingly boasting of having killed your hosts' son, not knowing the slain warrior's true identity.

"Best it is in a lifetime to earn praise and favor from others. Think upon the advice given by those whose thoughts are evil. Very often their counsel is too.

"The best burden to bear on a journey far from home is wisdom. It is much better than wealth, and more useful too.

"The worst burden to bear on a journey is a fondness for drink. As one loses one's wits one becomes more the fool. As a fool you are slave to rather than a master of the situation. The best meals are when one can think about them and remember what happened the next day.

"In battle be silent, but brave. Live well till you die. Cowards, away from battle, and out of danger, think they will live forever. But they will have no rest in old age.

"The fool goes to dinner withdrawn at first. But drink loosens his or her tongue so everyone knows what a fool he or she really is.

"Be friendly and happy with your guests at dinner. Be modest in your speech, and speak fairly of others if you wish to gain their praise and knowledge. Fimbulfambi is the name given to the tongue-tied fool who sits silent while their guests eat.

"The one who has done many things and met many people can understand the minds and moods of those one meets.

"Drink mead, but not overly so. When you feel your senses leaving you no one will begrudge your retiring at an early hour. Drunkenness is best served in sleep.

"Those who gorge themselves at meals do harm only to their own bodies. Many will mock a fat stomach. Even cows and pigs know when they've eaten enough. The glutton does not know when he or she has eaten too much.

"A sour unhappy person makes fun of others ignoring him – or herself in the jests.

"But lie not awake at night with worry for then you will find yourself tired during the day with your problems still unsolved, and you will be ill-prepared to attend to them.

"A fool takes the laughter and company of other fools as coming from friends, not realizing the wise speak ill of the fool. If someday the fool finds himself or herself tried in council the fool will find the laughter will not stand at the fool's side. Be moderate with your advice at council. If you use loud and boorish behavior you will only find yourself set upon by those who are even more loud and boorish.

"One who is ignorant still thinks they are the wisest there when sitting alone by the fire. But with others the ignorant person finds out how little he or she knows.

"Ask questions and listen to the replies. Answer carefully and wisely when questioned. These are the traits of a wise person. Many a fool chatters away trying to answer questions that befuddle everyone. It's best to be silent if your knowledge is uncertain.

"If you are taunted at dinner, smile through it all with dignity. Ignore the rude remarks of others. Do not overstay your welcome or you might not be asked back. Remember the best loved guest becomes tiresome after awhile.

"Do not be so hungry and intent on eating that you do not talk to your host or choke on the meal while trying to make your statement.

"It is better to have your own small place than to be a beggar amongst the wealthy.

"Crooked and difficult is the road to an enemy, yet straight and true, no matter the distance, is the road to a friend.

"Never venture into an open strange land unarmed. You can't be certain what or who lurks there.

"If you have gained wealth do not lust for more. If you save something for a friend, often it will be taken by an enemy since things do not often work out as we would like. You should give presents to friends for the joy of giving. Such giving and receiving makes for friendship. Also seek out your friend and spend time with your friend talking and sharing your thoughts. Always be loyal to your friends, and to your friends' friends. But never be friends with your friends' enemies. That is disloyal. If you are involved with someone you don't trust, then be wary. Be as true as possible, but if necessary answer a person's lies with your own. But do this cheerfully. Often friendly smiles will win you what you want. The person who is without friends is like the fir that has died. It is without needles or bark. Barren there it stands. Its life will not be long.

"The grain of sand on the beach is small, the drop of water in the ocean disappears. Wisdom and abilities vary in people. All about are those who are half-wise. But best of all are those who are somewhat wise, having neither too much nor too little wisdom. They lead the best lives who are good at what they do. The one who is overly wise is seldom happy.

"One cannot conquer from the bed, but must rise early. The wolf starves that lies idle. You must hunt in order to find meat. If you lack helpers, then you must do things for yourself in order to win wealth. But never will this happen to the morning sleeper.

"Practically, one must know how many logs to put by for the winter, lest one freeze before spring comes. The wise person will see to this early in autumn.

"Remember, a secret can be told to one, and it is fairly safe. But telling it to two is risky, and sharing it with three is foolish, for then everyone will know it.

"The best things in life are fire for warmth, good health and the ability to keep it, and a life lived honestly without vice. But no one's life is entirely worthless. A person might be blessed with sons, daughters, friends or wealth. Some will derive pleasure form their good works.

"Life is better than death. Those who are lame can still ride a horse. The handless can still shepherd a flock. One who is deaf can still be a brave warrior. Blindness is better suffered than the flames of a funeral pyre. The dead perform no deeds. Remember, eventually all die. Mortals cannot be spared that fate. There is one thing that does not die. And that is a good name, which lives long after. A bad name also lives after, but not nearly so long.

"It is foolish to prize gold so highly. Wealth can be fleeting. Many lives will be spent sometimes wealthy, sometimes poor. But no matter your circumstances always live the same within yourself. The wisest will remain silent most of the time.

"It is best to praise these things at the end of the day: a weapon that has been used, the promise of a maid or lad, ice once it is crossed, and mead after you have drunk it.

"Cut down wood during the gale; sail when the day is clear; and woo your love at night away from curious eyes. Expect your ship to sail swiftly and your shield to give you protection. Want from your sword that it should be sharp, and from a maid or lad that she or he will give you kisses.

"Mead is for drinking by the fire, ice is for skiing on. Swords are best if they are tarnished. Judge a horse by whether it is sleek and sinewy, or not.

"Do not trust the field that has been sown too soon. Early praise for children can only lead to disaster. Never trust a bow that has been loosed, a flame that has been lit, a wolf that grins in the darkness, a boar grunting in the distance, a cawing crow, the tree that has no roots, the wave crashing on the shore, a kettle screaming with water, a loosed arrow, the receding tide, a snake coiled and ready to strike, the cold of the night, the words spoken by a bride at night, a wide sword, the playful games of a bear, the children of a king, the welcome of a volva, the slave's wit, an ill calf, the newly dead, your kin's slayer upon the highway, a half-burned, or a gimpy horse. Remember this advice, it is unwise to trust any of the above.

"Never trust the words spoken by a maiden or a young lad. And if a woman has been false, be wary of what she says. Following her advice is like riding an unshod horse over slippery ice, dealing with a badly trained two-year-old, sailing a rudderless ship on a violent sea, or catching a reindeer on a slippery mountain with a crippled hand. The wise man will not do these things.

"I speak of these things with wisdom. And well I know that men can be just as deceiving as women. Many a maid should beware a man's silky words. Often the most flattering comments are spoken from false thoughts. A man desirous of the favors of a woman will woo her with soft words and gifts. But if a love is true never find fault with it. Many times the wise become enthralled while the foolish escape. Do not find fault with the loves of another. Even the wise man can make a fool of himself in love. Only those in love can understand why, and sometimes even they are confused. The saddest thing is to love without return."

Gylfi noted what had been spoken, "I will carry your wisdom with me always. But I would learn more from you."

Harr, Jafnhar and Thridi continued, "Now we will tell you the story of Loddfafnir. He is also a man of Midgardr, like you Gylfi. He listened outside this hall and returned to Midgardr to follow the advice of what he had heard. You would do well to imitate him. This I told him, for I knew he was listening:

"Listen Loddfafnir and listen well. Learn the words I speak and follow the wisdom you gain. Sleep through the night and arise only if you need to spy upon others or to relieve yourself in the outhouse.

"Listen Loddfafnir and listen well. Learn the words I speak and follow the wisdom you gain. Avoid the woman who practices magic lest her chants and spells woo you away from

the company of others. Under her charms you will no longer desire food and joy will be a thing of the past. Sadly you'll retire to sleep.

"Listen Loddfafnir and listen well. Learn the words I speak and follow the wisdom you gain. Avoid another's spouse when your thoughts turn to love. It is unwise to make her your mistress.

"Listen Loddfafnir and listen well. Learn the words I speak and follow the wisdom you gain. If you travel over mountains and fjords be sure to take plenty of food with you.

"Listen Loddfafnir and listen well. Learn the words I speak and follow the wisdom you gain. Never trust an evil man for his trickery will bring you nothing but grief no matter how true your actions. Once I saw a man who was fatally wounded by the words of an evil woman. And though her words were untrue they still caused his death.

"Listen Loddfafnir and listen well. Learn the words I speak and follow the wisdom you gain. If you have a true friend whom you trust, then seek out that person's company and visit often. The untrod path is soon overgrown.

"Listen Loddfafnir and listen well. Learn the words I speak and follow the wisdom you gain. If you find a good and wise man or woman, keep that person as a friend and listen to their counsel. If you find a person who is a fool then avoid their senseless ramblings.

"Listen Loddfafnir and listen well. Learn the words I speak and follow the wisdom you gain. Treasure your friends and never be the first to dissolve a friendship. Troubles kept to yourself will eat you up, but those shared can be solved.

"Listen Loddfafnir and listen well. Learn the words I speak and follow the wisdom you gain. Avoid the fool and cherish your friends. The veiled enemy will speak untruthfully of you to others, but the friend will sing your praises. Don't waste your time arguing with someone who is evil. Often that person will win with tricky words.

"Listen Loddfafnir and listen well. Learn the words I speak and follow the wisdom you gain. Make shoes and arrows for no one but yourself. If the shoe should hurt or the arrow prove untrue, then the blame will be yours.

"Listen Loddfafnir and listen well. Learn the words I speak and follow the wisdom you gain. If you know a person is evil, then say so. Do not bargain with your enemies.

"Listen Loddfafnir and listen well. Learn the words I speak and follow the wisdom you gain. The evil you do will haunt you all your days. The good you do will be a pleasure all your days.

"Listen Loddfafnir and listen well. Learn the words I speak and follow the wisdom you gain. Avoid the gaze of warriors fighting against you in battle for their frenzy may enthrall you. Though a bird may be able to fly, a snake on the ground can easily catch it once their eyes meet.

"Listen Loddfafnir and listen well. Learn the words I speak and follow the wisdom you gain. If you desire to win the love of a good woman, then be just and true to her. Be thankful for the good she does you.

"Listen Loddfafnir and listen well. Learn the words I speak and follow the wisdom you gain. In all your actions be cautious but not afraid. Beware first of strong brew, second of a woman married to another, and third the smooth words of a thief.

"Listen Loddfafnir and listen well. Learn the words I speak and follow the wisdom you gain. Never make fun of the stranger met on the road. Never laugh at your guests. Very

often strangers at your table may surprise you with his or her knowledge or identity. There is no one so perfect they are blameless in life; there is no one so evil they are worthless.

"Listen Loddfafnir and listen well. Learn the words I speak and follow the wisdom you gain. Do not laugh at the counsel of the old. They speak with the wisdom of age.

"Listen Loddfafnir and listen well. Learn the words I speak and follow the wisdom you gain. Be kind to your guests and generous to the needy, but not overly so. The door that is opened often becomes weak. Attach a latch and use it lest your generosity ruin you.

"Listen Loddfafnir and listen well. Learn the words I speak and follow the wisdom you gain. Finally, there are medicines to cure many ills. Earth will cure the ravages of drink. Fire will help the sick, and the oak will cure constipation. Seek the aid of an ear of corn when magic and trickery are worked against you. Rye will cure rupture, while the moon will soften anger. Place grass and its roots against the sore and the wounds of the sword. The dirt of the field can be used to lessen the flood.

"Now have I finished with the words that you would do well to follow. Hail to the speaker and listener. Let those who can gain a profit from what they hear."

Gylfi stepped forward and spoke, "And now answer me this . . ."

But before he could ask the question Jafnhar spoke, "We have already given you the knowledge you will need to live an enjoyable life. There are no other questions you need to have answered. Return to Midgardr and live a life that others may learn from your example."

Gylfi showed that he appreciated their generosity, "Truly you have given me the gift I prize above all others – knowledge. I will do as you say and return to Midgardr and try to live a life worthy of the present you have given me. I will teach others so that they may know the wisdom of the Northern ways."

Before Gylfi could blink there was a flash and he found himself back on Midgardr near his kingdom. He returned home and passed on the wisdom he had received from the Æsir so that all who wanted to avail themselves of it could live honorable lives. And though the knowledge was available to all, many on Midgardr paid no attention to Gylfi's message and, instead, bemoaned their fate, cursing the gods that they had no way to better themselves.

Chapter 20

The Stealing of Thor's Hammer

Thor was the member of the Æsir most feared by the jotuns. What they feared most about him was his most prized possession, the hammer Mjolnir, forged by the dvergues Sindri and Brokkr. Though flawed by the evil machinations of the cunning Loki, even with its shortened handle it struck fear in the hearts of the jotuns. The threat of its use by Thor kept the jotuns within the bounds of Jotunheimr and out of the sacred land of Asgardr. But what if somehow it were stolen? Who would protect those in Asgardr and Midgardr then?

One day the worst fears of those in Asgardr happened, and the prayers of those in Jotunheimr were answered. Thor had been dozing beneath a tree in Thrudheimr, his estate. The regular rolling thunder echoed overhead with each of his snores. Gradually he awoke, and as he did so he automatically reached out for Mjolnir. But what he gripped was air, not the familiar thong of leather looped through the end of the short handle. His hand felt about. But his grasping yielded nothing. As his sense gradually returned from sleep and he raised up and looked all about, it sunk in on him his hammer was missing.

"Where could it be?" he thundered as he rushed through his hall overturning tables and looking under beds for Mjolnir. He called for Sif, Thrudr, Hlora, Modi, and Magni to help him search.

Sif looked at her husband patiently, "Maybe you dropped it? Or, perhaps while you were asleep and dreaming of killing jotuns you accidentally threw it? You know how you can toss and turn in your sleep?"

"No, then it would have returned to me. What am I going to do, Sif?" Thor continued looking up and down, hoping to find Mjolnir.

Sif tried to help, "Just calm down and think. Raging and storming about won't help. It's just making it wet in here. Can you remember where you last had it?"

Irritated, Thor shook his head no. "If I knew that, then I'd know where to find it, wouldn't I?"

The six continued looking, but without success. Thor called for the warriors in his hall to stop fighting and help him look for Mjolnir. Every portion of his estate was searched, all without success. Thor became more and more agitated as the unfruitful search wore on. His red hair tossed about wildly, and his red beard seemed to burn with anger. Then a thought occurred to him, and he spoke of it to Sif, "There is but one in all of Asgardr whom I consider my enemy. There is only one in this sacred land who could profit from our loss of Mjolnir – Loki!" The name boomed out from him.

Thor went to the center of Asgardr and yelled out for Loki to show his miserable, twisted face. Loki was easily found, since this time, oddly enough, he was in no way guilty of the mischief. It took him awhile to convince Thor and the other Æsir of his innocence in the matter. But he finally did. He even offered to help look for Mjolnir. Thor was suspicious, but so far his own efforts had failed.

Loki suggested they go see Freyja, "She has just returned from a journey to Midgardr searching for Odr. We shall borrow her falcon-guise, valsharmr, to aid in our search for Mjolnir. Hopefully we'll have more luck than she has had looking for Odr." Fortunately Loki had returned valsharmr just that morning, before Freyja's return.

They found Freyja in Sessrumnir, walking around crying tears of gold. Thor spoke first, "We've come to borrow valsharmr to use to help us find Mjolnir. Will you let us use it?"

Freyja signaled for her servant Fulla to fetch it. When it was brought into the room she took it from her and without even noticing its disheveled condition, handed it to Thor and motioned for the two to leave her alone with her sadness, "Here, I'd give it to you even though it was pure gold or silver. Just leave me alone."

Outside the hall Thor handed valsharmr to Loki who put it on and flew off heading towards Jotunheimr. As he flew through Midgardr he could see violent storms below him. There was flashing lightning. Thunder rolled over the land followed by downpours that swelled rivers beyond their banks. Then came blinding snowstorms with hail, all blown about by a fierce wind that bit through even the thickest fur coats. One look at all this told Loki who had stolen Mjolnir and was now playing with the hammer. The hrymthursar Thrym could of course cause snowstorms, but he didn't have the power of thunder and lightning. Loki flew towards Thrymheimr in Jotunheimr.

For all the trouble which was being caused on Midgardr, he found Thrym sitting on a grave mound leisurely braiding leashes out of fine spun gold for his greyhound dogs, and plaiting the manes of his horses, weaving adornments amongst the hairs in intricate patterns. When he tired of these pursuits he stopped long enough to feather his arrows with eagle's quills. Despite the fact Loki walked up on him from behind, he spoke to him without turning around, "How are things going in Asgardr? How are the Æsir and their friends the alfs? Things must be boring there if you're seeking out the company of those in Jotunheimr."

Loki replied, "You know very well how things are in Asgardr since you stole Mjolnir. I'm here to claim it and take it back to Thor, its rightful owner. Stop sitting there dishonoring the dead and fetch the hammer."

Thrym turned and spoke, "What concern is it of yours who has Mjolnir? You're as much an enemy of the Æsir as you are of anyone. You shame yourself helping them. How can I be sure your search for Mjolnir is in the Æsir's behalf? Why would Thor send you to fetch it? I hardly think you are one of his most trusted friends. If I were to fetch the

hammer, assuming I had it, and give it to you, how do I know it would find its way back to Thor?"

Loki became more angry, "Don't joke with me. Even if you do have Mjolnir, I'm more powerful than you. The longer I stay in Jotunheimr the more powerful I become. Don't seek to test that power."

The warning made Thrym back down a little, "It's true, I do have Mjolnir. But it's hidden eight rosts beneath the mountains of Jotunheimr. I'm the only one who knows how to retrieve it. So if you harm me you will lose the hammer forever. However, if you treat me in a fitting manner, perhaps we could talk about what I would bargain for to return Mjolnir."

The conversation was becoming interesting for Loki. There was nothing he liked better than to bargain for something, especially if the price to him was nothing. He was very good at dealing in the worst interests of all concerned. "What is it you desire?"

Thrym thought a little and then spoke, "I desire what just about everyone in Asgardr and Midgardr desire. It's very lonely and cold in Thrymheimr. The climate is harsh and unwelcoming. What chance do I have of finding a wife who would like it here. I've tried and tried and I have yet to be able to lure a wife here. So I would like you to arrange a marriage for me. That is the price for Mjolnir."

Loki thought it a simple enough request, "It should be easy to find someone in Thrymheimr for you. I'll leave now and be back by nightfall. While I'm gone you can fetch the hammer and have it ready by the time I return."

Thrym shouted out after the quickly departing Loki, "Hold on a moment. Don't leave in such haste. I have not agreed to your deal. Nor will I. I don't want just anyone to be my wife. I've thought about this a long time. And as I said, I desire what just about everyone in Asgardr and Midgardr desire."

Loki had returned and didn't like the sound of what he was hearing. It would be easy enough to find some ugly jotun with no prospects of marriage who would welcome a future of hearth and home, even with Thrym. But, it seemed Thrym had his eyes and heart set on something higher.

Thrym continued, "Many years ago I once saw Freyja. Since then I've been smitten by her and on long winter evenings have often thought how nice it would be if she were next to me sitting by the fire. So she is my price for Mjolnir. Bring her here and after the wedding ceremony has been successfully completed, and the marriage consummated, then will I gladly return Mjolnir. I'll also become a friend to the Æsir, wedded to them as well as Freyja, since I'll be so grateful for the happiness they will have brought me. Here is a ring set with a red ruby to represent my love. Give it to Freyja as the first of many gifts from me."

Loki agreed to the deal having no idea how he was going to fulfill it. "As is the custom, I'll bring your wife to you within nine nights." He donned valsharmr and flew back to Asgardr where he found Thor in the courtyard near the main gates pacing back and forth waiting for him. He yelled out to Loki before Loki had landed or changed from valsharmr.

"I don't see the hammer on you. Have you failed? Do you know where Mjolnir is? Quick, tell me what our fate will be."

Loki tried to calm Thor's anxieties, "Don't worry, all has been taken care of. The hrymthursar Thrym has the hammer buried eight rosts deep in Jotunheimr under a tall mountain. But he's willing to dig it up and return it and be a friend to the Æsir if we'll do a very simple thing."

Loki drew out the telling of the story as long as he could. Thor became more and more excited with the anticipation. "Well, what is it? Speak faster."

Loki continued more slowly than ever, "Thrym is a very lonely person. This has lead him to gain our attention by stealing Mjolnir. He'll give us his friendship if we'll give him Freyja as a wife."

Thor thought a moment, "That seems reasonable enough. She'll certainly make the sacrifice if she realizes it will get Mjolnir back for me. Perhaps this will take her mind off Odr, too. We'll be doing her a favor. Everyone wins."

Thus rationalized the two hurried off to Folkvangar to return valsharmr and give Freyja the good news of her upcoming marriage. Thor was so excited that he made his way unannounced through Sessrumnir to her private chamber. "Find the bridal dress you so recently wore. Put it on for I have good news for you. Loki and I are going to take you to Thrymheimr so you can become the blushing bride of Thrym. This will help you forget the sadness brought about by Odr's disappearance. And in exchange for the favor Thrym is giving us by making you so happy, he'll return Mjolnir to me."

Freyja had only recently managed to stop crying. But the news she heard from Thor, along with the mention of Odr's name set her off again. Soon they had to leave the room for another since it had rapidly filled with red gold from her tears.

Thor continued completely misinterpreting the situation, "Stop the tears of joy you have and begin your preparations. I will take you to Thrym today."

Freyja slowly recovered her composure and became quite angry at the very suggestion she go live with a jotun just because Thor wanted his hammer back, "I had nothing to do with the carelessness which allowed your hammer to be stolen. Since it was due to your carelessness, you go live with Thrym, for I will not. Get out." As she spoke her final words to Loki and Thor her chest heaved with anger breaking the Brisingamen Necklace.

Loki and Thor realized she was not to be reasoned with and left. They sent messengers to all of the other Æsir and Vanir telling them to meet at Urdarbrunnr Well for a Thing to discuss how Thor's hammer might be retrieved.

That evening at the Thing many suggestions were made, none of which seemed workable. One of the Æsir even suggested Freyja be forced to wed Thrym. But this was not a very popular idea. Freyja was much loved in Asgardr, particularly by the male Æsir, and her presence would have been sorely missed.

Njordr, Freyja's father spoke up, "I will not permit my only daughter to leave the protection of Asgardr. Anyone who tries to force her to wed the ugly Thrym will have to battle my son, me and all of the Vanir. I'm certain a few of the Æsir would also join us." Freyr walked over to his father's side, emphasizing the point.

So, that was settled. Freyja would stay in Asgardr. But what was to be done about the hammer? Heimdallr had stood silently gazing off before him during all of the arguments. Finally he spoke, "I've been looking into the future and there are sad times ahead for us as well as those in Midgardr if we don't retrieve Mjolnir. We have no obligation to give Freyja to Thrym or even to bargain with him since Mjolnir was stolen from us. But part of

the blame lies with Thor who was careless enough to leave such a precious object laying about. Therefore, it should fall to him to retrieve Mjolnir. He should not be hiding behind Freyja's skirts. Rather he should be wearing them. I suggest he dress as Freyja and go to Thrymheimr in that guise and retrieve the hammer himself."

There was a great deal of laughter at this solution to their problem. But soon there was silence, since no one had offered a better idea.

Heimdallr continued, "Thor's red hair could be braided. Brisingamen could be repaired and lent to Thor to wear, as well as Freyja's household keys which he could wear hanging from his side. With a virginal red dress on and a hood over his head to protect his maidenly modesty, as well as long petticoats to hide his hairy legs, he could easily pass for Freyja."

Everyone yelled their approval of the idea. Everyone, that is, except Thor. He roared out over all the others, "I'll not do it. There is no way to force me to go. You wouldn't let Freyja leave Asgardr to marry Thrym. Would you force Thor, who is much more powerful and useful to you, to do so instead? My answer is no, absolutely not. Even the mere thought of this charade has brought guffaws of laughter to some of you. What then would be your reaction if I were actually to wear such a costume? Some of our fiercest warriors would laugh themselves to death, which certainly wouldn't help us at the last great battle. No!" Thor stomped off causing the whole land to shake.

Forseti yelled out to the others, "We must restrain ourselves in this matter. It's for our own good that we keep our laughter in, for if we don't we'll have nothing to laugh about. Someone fetch Thor back here."

Thor was brought back and one by one everyone there pledged not to laugh if Thor would dress up as Freyja. Loki even went one better than everyone else, "And to show you it can be fun, I'll dress up as your handmaiden and accompany you to see Thrym." However, this was no great sacrifice on Loki's part since he often changed into a woman and was in fact quite fond of dressing up as one whether he was physically transformed or not.

Reluctantly Thor accepted their assurances they would not laugh at him, and agreed to the ruse.

Heimdallr supervised the outfitting. Odin gave Freyja permission to remove Brisingamen, which had since been repaired, and lend it to Thor. Then he went off to make a magic salve from the blood of a bear and wild boar's suet. When rubbed on Thor, this salve caused all of his battle scars to disappear as well as his chest hair and beard. He refused to have his leg hair removed. "I'll not do that. Imagine Thor with smooth legs? It would be unseemly." He didn't even consider the impression a hairy-legged Freya would make.

Two of Freyja's red dresses were sewn together to make one for Thor. Fortunately, Thor's favorite color was red which made wearing the dress a little easier. But he insisted on wearing his hauberk under the dress and no amount of persuasion could get him to remove it. A leather bodice was laced around his chest in such a way as to give him the appropriate bulges. Hoping to take Thrym's gaze from his intended's face, Hermodr fashioned two round shields out of copper which were attached to the front of the bodice to accentuate Thor's front. Brisingamen was hung around his neck, and a set of household keys were hung about his waist. Thor insisted on also wearing his boots, belt and gloves, as well as his battle helmet. Fortunately the dress hung long enough to cover his hairy legs and boots. Some of the Asynjur wrapped material around his helmet to try and disguise its true purpose. Hnoss bound together a bunch of peonies, sunflowers and hollyhocks into a corsage which she attached to the front of Thor's dress, telling him all the while that it would make him even more beautiful than he already looked.

Still something was missing, which Odin provided. He took a scarlet rope and wrapped it across his son's shoulders and attached a veil to the helmet so it hung down over Thor's face. "Now you're ready, my son, to go and get your hammer back. Maybe next time you won't be so careless with it. As a father I can only look at my son in wonder at his wedding preparations."

While Thor was being attired Loki had gone to dress himself. His problem was not one of having dresses sewn for him, but rather of choosing which one to wear from his wardrobe. He tried on outfit after outfit, flouncing around in front of his mirror, this way and that, to see how the dresses fell on him. Back and forth he went until finally he settled on the perfect little number. But, he took an assortment of others with him. He certainly didn't intend to be seen in the same gown twice.

Thjalfi had seen to the readying of Thor's chariot. It was bedecked with flowers and misted over with various fragrances. He had also shod the goats with golden shoes and sprayed them lest their smell offend anyone in Thrymheimr. Now all was in readiness.

Thor and Loki boarded the chariot. With reins tightly wrapped around his wrist, Thor yelled for the goats to proceed. As they flew off Loki could be heard instructing Thor in the ways of women, "You're going to have to talk in a higher voice, Thor, if we are to convince Thrym of your femininity." Thunderbolts shot forth from the chariot.

The chariot flew swiftly over Midgardr towards Thrymheimr. Loki's taunting all throughout the journey made Thor angrier and angrier. By the time they neared Thrym's castle, storms, thunder and lightning bolts had set the sky ablaze. Hardly the genteel arrival Thrym expected.

Everything had been in readiness for Freyja's arrival for several days. But when Thrym saw the chariot approaching in the distance he jumped up and started yelling out last minute orders, "See that the benches are covered with fresh straw so my bride will sit comfortably during dinner. Make certain all of the food is set on the table. She'll be hungry after such a long journey. Soon I'll have all I want in life. I own precious golden-horned cattle. My jet-black oxen are the envy of all in Jotunheimr. I have treasures of gold and jewels stolen from the Svartalfheimr. She is all I lack in life." He was practically jumping up and down as the chariot landed. He sent forth six of his servants to greet Freyja while he went to his throne to await her arrival.

One servant was dressed in cloth woven of gold. Another wore shining silver. A third was dressed in black mail forged from lead. A fourth wore a similar outfit made of iron which shone blue in the sun. The fifth emissary wore reddish copper. And finally, walking behind the others was a servant who wore mail made of tin. Although it shone almost as brightly as the silver, if one looked at it closely it could be seen to be a lot cheaper.

The six were surprised at the two images alighting from the chariot. Loki held out his hand to be helped down. When the tin servant tried to help Thor/Freyja he was unceremoniously shoved to the ground. The six quickly organized themselves as an honor guard around Thor/Freyja and Loki and with great majesty escorted the two to the throneroom where Loki and Thor/Freyja were presented to Thrym, whom they found seated on his golden throne and dressed in purple and gold awaiting his bride.

Thrym spoke to Thor/Freyja, "Freyja, my love. I have waited with great longing for you. And as anticipation in my thoughts has enlarged you in my mind, so do you seem enlarged in person. I've seen you from afar, but I must have misjudged the distance. Because you seem so much larger than I imagined your height. And you seem so much more powerful and muscular than I recall you being when I've seen you. But, you look wonderful so let us be married right away and retire for the night to our wedding bed, so we might get to know each other better, much better."

Thor/Freyja answered, "I'm hungry. What have you got to eat?"

Thrym was slightly taken aback at this reply to his suggestion, but quickly answered her, "Anything you wish, my love. But first wouldn't you rather get acquainted with your groom? My what a deep voice you have?"

Loki answered in a high falsetto voice, "She is suffering from a slight cold and her voice is hoarse. However, she wouldn't be dissuaded from this visit with you."

Thrym's eyes shone with love.

Thor/Freyja turned from the throne and followed a servant through room after room in the castle until they reached the banquet hall. He sat at the head of the table and began eating, not even waiting for the others to seat themselves. Loki whispered into Thor/Freyja's ear, "Try to be a little more genteel and ladylike in your eating. The grease is dripping off your veil down the front of your dress." Then Loki sat down to the right of Thor/Freyja and asked for a servant to cut his meat for him.

Thrym arrived in the hall and headed straight for his intended. He reached for the veil, "Let me lift this door that hides my treasure. I want to give you a little kiss."

Thor/Freyja pulled his head back sharply which surprised Thrym. Loki spoke up with an explanation, "Freyja is virtuous and shy. She has only just met you. Let her become more comfortable here before you make any further advances."

Thrym was impressed, for he had heard awful stories about Freyja's easy virtue. Her behavior convinced him she was pure and innocent, despite being married to Odr. "Such modesty in women is almost unknown here in Thrymheimr. What a refreshing change." He sat down to the left of his bride and took her hand in his. Thor/Freyja squirmed in his seat which only endeared him all the more to Thrym, "My what a strong grip you have?" Thor/Freyja bent back Thrym's hand.

Loki intervened before Thor/Freyja broke Thrym's hand, taking Thor/Freyja's hand and holding it upturned for Thrym to inspect while explaining the strength of her grip to Thrym, "Her grip has been made strong from sewing all day long."

Loki noticed just as Thrym noticed that Thor/Freyja's hand was covered with battle scars. "And look at the scars she has suffered from needle and thread. Earlier she could not find a thimble but still insisted she sew her own wedding dress." Loki pulled Thor/Freyja's hand away and instead thrust the sleeve of the wedding dress towards Thrym. "Just look at the fine stitches."

Thrym smiled at the domesticity of his future wife. He didn't even notice how large and hairy the hand was and how ludicrous a needle would have looked in it.

Loki, not to be outdone reached to his side and took the hand of the jotun next to him and began to enjoy the dinner. What there was of it, considering how much Thor/Freyja was wolfing down.

Thor/Freyja was quite hungry. By the time Thrym had seated himself Thor/Freyja had already eaten an ox. Then he ate eight large salmon in one gulp, without even taking a breath. Having finished with the main course he started on desert. Sweetcakes and fruit had been prepared in a beautiful design on a tray which Thor/Freyja hoisted to his mouth and tilted so all the delicacies slid down his throat. He washed it all down with three tuns of mead.

Thrym turned to the others and proudly said, "Has there ever been a bride with a greater appetite than that? Just think what her other appetites will be like?"

Loki thought an explanation for Thor/Freyja's gluttony was in order. "Dear Thrym, Freyja was so excited at the prospect of becoming your bride she forgot to eat and has tasted neither food nor drink in eight days."

Thrym was truly touched. He quickly bent over and raised the veil again, hoping to have better luck stealing a kiss. But what he saw startled him so much he sat back and fell off his chair. "Her eyes are so burning and piercing. They burned through me like fire. It's almost frightening."

Again Loki came to the rescue with an explanation, "She has slept for the last week so she would be well-rested when she arrived here. What you've seen is the burning look of love and the expectation of what is to come later."

Thrym picked himself up and sat down in his seat, "Was there ever a happier bridegroom than I?" He turned to all those assembled.

Everyone looked at him and he took the pity in their eyes for envy. He snuggled up close to his beloved.

Thrym's ugly gaunt and drawn sister entered the banquet hall and walked directly to the head of the table and demanded Freyja give her her bridal gifts, as was the custom, "If you want my love and friendship then honor our customs and give me my presents."

A great quiet filled the room. Thor/Freyja just stared at her. Loki spoke up, "We haven't brought any gifts with us. I fear love has made Freyja absentminded about the bridal gifts. Perhaps we can bring something at a later date?"

Thrym's sister was clearly angry as she spoke to Thor/Freyja, "If you have brought nothing, then give me the gold rings on your fingers and the beautiful necklace you wear about your neck."

Thor/Freyja started for the sister, but was pulled back into his seat by Loki who spoke to Thrym, changing the subject. "Thrym, I see everyone has finished eating. Isn't it about time the wedding ceremony was begun? Why not have Mjolnir sent for so the nuptials can be hallowed and consecrated in the name of the Asynjes Var and Frigg, as well as Odin and Thor as is the usual custom?"

Seeing that what he had waited for was now so close at hand Thrym seized upon the suggestion, pushed his sister out of the way and signaled for several dvergar to go and fetch the hammer. Soon they returned weighted down by the treasure they carried hoisted on their shoulders. It was brought to the head of the table and placed in front of Thor/Freyja. The dvergar swore holy vows to the Asynjur Var which were repeated by Thrym who was now standing behind his bride. They called for blessings of a good home from Frigg, and success in the marriage from Odin and Thor. Then all eyes turned to Thor/Freyja whose turn it was to repeat the vows. Thor/Freyja was reluctant to speak, but did so at Loki's urgings, promising to be faithful and loving to his/her husband. After he finished the hammer was placed in his/her lap. Thor/Freyja reached for it, closed his hand around the

handle and stood up. He ripped the veil from his face and all in front of him immediately recognized Thor the thundergod. Thrym still didn't know what the commotion was about until Thor turned around to face him. Never was there a more surprised bridegroom.

Everyone began shrinking back from the table. Some turned and ran for the exits as fast as they could. But it was too late. Thor swung Mjolnir overhead and let loose lightning and thunderbolts. The first to die was Thrym, followed by his greedy sister. Soon the roof was ablaze and the walls were crumbling as Thor set about slaying all of the wedding party. Loki had hurried out to Thor's chariot and hid under it until Thor was finished. When Thor's rage finally subsided all that was left was smoking rubble.

Thor calmly, stepping over fallen walls, walked over to his chariot and spoke to Loki, "You can come out now, Loki. All has been taken care of. Be certain when we are back in Asgardr and you tell your story of how bravely you fought in the regaining of Mjolnir, that you don't leave out the part about hiding under my chariot in the filth where my goats had relieved themselves."

They started on their trip back to Asgardr.

Alviss the Dvergar

Meanwhile in Asgardr a cunning dvergar named Alviss had come walking boldly up Bifrost the day before Thor's return. He had heard of Mjolnir's theft and the terms Thrym wanted for its return. He decided he might be able to gain a little something for himself using this knowledge.

He was stopped on the bridge by Heimdallr, "Why do you tread on Bifrost and act as if you have some business in Asgardr?"

Alviss replied, "I don't deal with underlings. Take me to Odin for I have a message meant only for his ears. There's not a moment to be wasted. I have important news about the jotuns and their plans to attack Asgardr."

Heimdallr was not impressed, "There are many who use that story to try and see Odin, pale nose. You'll have to do better than that."

Alviss changed his strategy, "I'm the dvergar Alviss, which means all wise. I have come to take Freyja away."

Heimdallr laughed and replied, "I hardly think you are the god of her dreams. She is in love with Odr who is considerably larger in all ways than you. What makes you think you can fill his shoes? However, I'll take you to Odin so that he may share in your humor."

Odin sat on his throne looking down on the dvergar, "So you want to take Freyja. Why is that?"

What the dvergar said next startled Heimdallr and Odin, "Thor and Loki have been found out in Thrymheimr and both are now bound and trapped in the cellars of Thrym's hall. The real Freyja must come with me in order to save not only Mjolnir, but now Thor and Loki as well. Other jotun's have heard Thor and Mjolnir have both been captured and are now preparing to invade Asgardr. Only Freyja can stop them."

His story had the ring of truth to it, and Thor and Loki had been away a lot longer than had been expected. However, Odin was still a little skeptical, "Why has such an important mission been entrusted to you? Why hasn't Thrym sent one of his jotun servants to impress us with his size?"

Alviss thought for a moment. He hadn't anticipated his story being doubted. But he quickly thought of a reply, "Because I'm the wisest of my kind, and it was thought intelligence was needed to persuade Freyja to come with me rather than using brute force."

Odin thought for a moment and then answered, still suspicious, "In that case you must prove your intelligence to me before we can believe your story and give Freyja up to you."

Alviss was puffed up with how he had so far fooled them and readily agreed to the quiz.

Odin began, "How are the heavens named in all the worlds?"

Alviss smiled, "That's an easy one. Those in Midgardr talk of the heavens. The Æsir refer to sky or height, while the Vanir think of it as the wind roof or windweaver. In Jotunheimr it is called Upheimr which means high home, and the alfs call it fair-roof. The dvergar, like myself, call it drip-hall, since we suffer more from its effects than others do without benefiting from its beauty."

Odin nodded that that had been the correct answer and continued with another question, "And what of fire?"

Alviss answered, "Fire for men, eild or flame by the Æsir, the flickering one or wild-fire by the Vanir, and the consuming or hungry wolfish biter by the jotuns. It is all-burner by the alfs, furnace to the dvergar, and corpse-slayer or destroyer to those in Niflheimr."

"And what of the earth?"

Alviss replied, "Earth by men, Midgardr or fields amongst the Æsir, ways by the Vanir and all-green by the jotuns, burgeoning or growing by the alfs."

Odin asked yet another question, "So far you're doing quite well. The names of the moon, if you know them?"

Alviss grew more and more confident with each question, "Moon amongst those on Midgardr. The Æsir and Vanir know it as mild light, whirling wheel by those in Niflheimr, speeding or rapid traveler by the jotuns, and gleamer or splendor by the dvergar, and teller-of-time by the alfs."

Odin nodded that the dvergar was correct, "What of the clouds?"

Alviss answered, "They are clouds in Midgardr, rain-carriers in Asgardr, windblown or wind-ships in Vanaheimr, rain-hope in Jotunheimr, weather-might in Alfheimr, and hiding or helmets of darkness in Niflheimr."

Odin looked at Heimdallr. Could what this dvergar had said about Thor and Loki be true? He continued the questioning, "The wind?"

Alviss was getting tired of such simple questions, but gave the correct answer, "Men and women of Midgardr call it wind, the Æsir call it wafter, whiner by the Vanir, roarer amongst the jotuns, traveling noise by the alfs, and whistler by the doomed in Nilfheimr."

"And the calm that follows the wind?"

"Calm by men, sea quiet or stillness by the Æsir, wind-lull by the Vanir, sultry or humid by the jotuns, day rest by the alfs, day's refuge by the dvergues. There is no calm in Niflheimr, so they have no name for it."

Odin thought he had tricked him with that one. But the dvergar had answered correctly. He continued, "The sea?"

Alviss smiled, realizing he was winning, "Sea by men, smooth gleaming by the Æsir, wave by the Vanir, eel home by the jotuns, drink stuff by the alfs, the deep by the dvergar."

"Wood?"

"Alright, I'll answer that one, but can you come up with some harder questions? Wood by those in Midgardr, mane of the fields or Midgardr's mane by the Æsir, wand of charms by the Vanir, seaweed that grows on the mountains by those in Niflheimr, fuel or firewood by the jotuns and fair bough by the alfs."

Odin asked another, "Night?"

Alviss quickly replied, "Night by those in Midgardr, murk by the Æsir, mask or covering of darkness by the Vanir, lightless by the jotuns, sleep's joyful rest by the alfs, and weaver-of-dreams by the dvergar."

"The seed sown on Midgardr?" was the next question asked by Odin.

"Men who sew it call it barley, you call it corn or breadstuff, the Vanir call it growth, the jotuns call it edible, the alfs grain or drinking stuff, and those in Niflheimr curse it as the hanging since all they are tempted by are its roots."

"And what of beer?" continued Odin.

"Surely that's not an important question?" queried Alviss.

Odin answered, "If you don't know the answer, just say so."

Alviss responded, "I will answer it. Ale by men, beer by the Æsir, foaming strength or wassail brew by the Vanir, clear mist by the jotuns, mead by those in Niflheimr for they have none and treasure it greatly, and feast draught by the jotuns. Have you any better questions for me?"

Odin smiled and replied, "I think the best ones are these last two. First tell me the name Nott the daughter of Narfi is known by in each of the worlds?"

Alviss replied, "Night by those in Midgardr, Nott or the dark amongst the Æsir, and the hood by the Vanir, unlight by the jotuns, sleep-joy by the alfs, and bringer of dreams by the dvergar."

Odin asked the final question, "I'm surprised at your wisdom. So here is the last question whereby you can gain the hand of Freyja. After Nott comes her son Dagr and the start of the day. And with him comes the sun. How is the sun known in all the worlds?"

"That's certainly easy," replied Alviss, confident that he was assured of Freyja's hand with his answer, "Sun by men, circle of the sun by the Æsir, all-bright by the Vanir, everglow by the jotuns, fair wheel by the alfs, and finally Dvalin's Doom by such as myself. Now send for Freyja, that I might take her as my bride."

Odin stood up and pointed to the east as he spoke, "We have instead sent for Dvalin's Doom. I've quizzed you all this night and now the sun has come. You may be smart but you're not smart enough to hide from the day or your fate of uppr dagr. You've forgotten to wear your red tarnkappe that would have protected you from the sun's stiffening rays."

There was a surprised look upon Alviss's face as he began to speak. But his head had already turned to stone and the rest of him was quickly stiffening. His knowledge and ambitions had been too much for him. He was carried out to the courtyard and set up as a statue for birds to rest upon.

Later that day Thor and Loki returned from their journey having successfully retrieved Mjolnir and killed a lot of jotuns in the process. Altogether a successful trip.

There was peace once more in Asgardr, but only for a short while.

Part Three

The Ending of
All Things

Chapter 21

Odin Seeks After Knowledge

There was an uneasiness in the air. Odin felt its intenseness and knew the time of Ragnarokr was fast approaching. "I must go in a quest for more knowledge," Odin said to himself as he sat in his hall, Valaskjalf, in his watchtower on his throne Hlidskjalf, surveying the restlessness in all the Worlds of the Tree. "The more I know the more I will be able to stave off the terror that awaits us all."

Odin set off from Asgardr. As he passed Heimdallr on Bifrost he gave his son a look which told his son more than speech could ever convey. Heimdallr watched his father make his way to Yggdrasyll. What he saw next shocked him and he thought of leaving his post on Bifrost to go to his father's aid. But, instead, he continued his duty and stayed, and watched.

Odin tethered Sleipnir to Yggdrasyll and then sacrificed himself on that windswept Tree, a sacrifice to himself. He hung himself and for nine days and nights he swung back and forth from its mighty branches. The spear Gungnir pierced his side and Odin was given neither food nor drink. As he fasted and thirsted for those nine days he penetrated the depths of unknown worlds and learned nine mighty runes from the son of Bolthorn, the father of Bestla. Odin called out as he learned the runes:

"Knowledge began, and from one word I gained others and my knowledge increased. The knowledge of one deed taught me more deeds. I read the runes written by Odin for the Æsir, Dain for the elves, Dvalin for the dvergues, and Alsvidr for the jotuns and those on Midgardr. New ones I wrote. Wise is the one who can cut them and read them. Wise is the one who can stain them and use them. Wise is the one who can call them and offer them. So learn them and use them.

"The mighty charms I learned are unknown to rulers and kings of Midgardr. The charms I learned were eighteen in number. They are:

"Help is the first. Use it to bring comfort and for the release of agony and the defeat of illness.

"The second is known by those who work with helping the sick.

189

"The third is to be used in battle to keep my enemies at length, to dull their swords and turn away their spears.

"The fourth is useful in releasing the bonds and locks that might chain me.

"Useful is the fifth for catching arrows hurled at me. My vision is swift enough so I can see them coming and catch them in hand without injury.

"The sixth one will prevent the charms and runes others might carve on a green tree's roots to be used against me. Instead the magic will be turned back against them.

"If flames consume my friends's house I can use the seventh to put it out.

"The eighth can cause hatred to leave the minds of my enemies.

"The ninth will cause the raging sea to calm around the ship I am aboard.

"Useful is the tenth in disrupting the activities of troll-wives and making it so they fly about in their true shapes rather than in disguise to fool the unsuspecting.

"Those I lead in battle can hear the eleventh charm and gain in strength by it and be protected and return home from the battle unharmed.

"With the twelfth I can carve runes and learn the knowledge of hanged men. I can call them forth and quiz them at my will.

"If I chant the thirteenth over a child and sprinkle it at its naming day it will forever be protected in battle and not fall in combat.

"The fourteenth charm taught me the names of the Æsir and Alfs. This knowledge is granted to only a few.

"The fifteenth was that self-same charm sung by Thjodreyrir at Dellingr's gate. It increases the strength of the Æsir, the prosperity of the alfs, and increases Hroptatyr's knowledge.

The sixteenth may be the most powerful of all. With it I can woo and win the heart of the woman I desire.

And those whom I woo and win will be true and loyal to me ever after, once the seventeenth charm is chanted.

"Finally, the last rune. The eighteenth is a secret charm which will only be heard if I am sleeping in the arms of my own sister. As such it will remain secret, which makes it more powerful. Knowledge known by all is deluded and worthless. Knowledge known in secret and away from others is all powerful."

After learning these runes Odin lowered himself from the Tree and returned to Asgardr. He passed his son on Bifrost without speaking. Although Heimdallr had witnessed all this, his keen vision had been unable to penetrate the depths Odin had. He could only guess at the grimness of the wisdom which had put such a gloomy countenance on his father's face.

Back in Asgardr Odin drank a sip of the Precious Mead from Odrœrir and sat on his throne thinking. He was never known to smile again.

His first command after his sacrifice was that the runes he learned be carved on Svalin, the shield set in front of the sun. Next they were risted on Arvakr's ear, Alsvin's hoof, the wheels of Rogner's chariot, the reins guiding Sleipnir, the paws reaching out from the bear, Bragi's tongue, the claws of the wolf, the beak of the eagle, on wings dripping with blood, at the end of Bifrost, and then on glass, gold that shining metal, in wine, on herb's, Vili's heart, Gungnir's tip, Notung's edge, Grani's breast, the nails of a Norn, and the beak of an owl. All this was done so that that knowledge and protection would help the Æsir.

Ever after Odin became known as the god of the gallows. Whenever he came upon anyone who had been hung he would carve runes and raise the dead person back to life so they could talk and Odin could learn the secrets the dead might know. But even with all this he was not satisfied. For the more he learned the more he realized he was in darkness. Then his raven Huginn whispered in his ear about a jotun named Vafthrudnir who possessed great wisdom. Odin was determined to seek him out and gain what knowledge he could. He informed Frigg of his plan to visit Jotunheimr.

"If I learn but one thing which can be helpful to the Æsir in staving off Ragnarokr, then the journey will have been worth it, no matter what the risk."

Frigg expressed her concern, "I hope I can persuade you not to go. Vafthrudnir is known to exact a high price from those who seek to match wits with him. He is just as evil as his children, the skeleton maiden Modgudr and Imr. If you should lose, then all of Asgardr and Midgardr would lose; and if you should win it would probably be for only the slightest bit of knowledge. The cost is too great for the risk involved. I advise you not to go."

But Odin was not to be dissuaded, "I shall go in disguise. Then he'll have no cause to think I'm such a special prize. Perhaps if he doesn't realize who I am then he will accidentally give up more knowledge than he would in the normal course of events if he knew he was matching wits with Odin."

Vafthrudnir

Odin left Asgardr once again and soon found his way through Jotunheimr to Vafthrudnir's high-timbered hall. He introduced himself to the gatekeeper, "I'm called Gangraaf and wish to match wits with Vafthrudnir, the father of Imr and the skeleton maiden Modgudr. I hear he treats those who best him to his generous hospitality and great wealth. I hope to gain much in our encounter."

The gatekeeper replied, "You're not the first to try your wits against Vafthrudnir. Nor will you be the last. But as yet no one entering here has ever left. Which means my master has bested them all, and has lost no wealth by the contests. Why do you think you are any different?"

Odin/Gangraaf replied, "I think all who enter think they are different, and in that respect I am no different. But they have all lost. I will be the exception and win. I have little time to waste. Show me to your master. Maybe his mind has tired from the difficulty and strain put upon him by the previous contests? Or, perhaps, he is frightened of more competition?"

The gatekeeper opened the gate to admit the stranger. "That he is not. Give me your name again and I'll have you announced."

Odin/Gangraaf was shown to the great hall where Vafthrudnir and a host of his friends were assembled enjoying a feast. The gatekeeper bowed before them and announced, "This is Gangraaf who boasts he can beat you in a battle of wits."

Odin/Gangraaf stepped forward. Vafthrudnir turned to him, seemingly bored by the challenge, "As with everyone who seeks this contest, I will make you the same offer. If you fail in our contest then you will lose your head."

Odin/Gangraaf replied, "I accept that punishment. But what if I win?"

Vafthrudnir laughed as did those around him, "So far we haven't had to contend with that possibility. I suppose you would win my head and kingdom." Odin/Gangraaf gave a very knowing smile which seemed to take Vafthrudnir back a bit. Why was this stranger so confident? He continued immediately with some questions for the stranger, "But here are some questions for you to guess at. Then perhaps we will change your name to Sanngetall." Vafthrudnir motioned for Odin/Gangraaf to come and sit beside him.

Odin/Gangraaf declined. He was a bit angered from the insult of being called Sanngetall, which meant one who guesses, "I'll stand until I've won the right to sit next to you. Ask me your first question."

Vafthrudnir thought for a moment, then asked, "What is the name of the river protecting Midgardr from Jotunheimr?"

Odin/Gangraaf answered, "That's easy since I've just crossed the mighty river which has never been known to freeze over to get here. It is the river Ifing. Have you nothing harder with which to test me?"

Vafthrudnir was surprised the stranger had known the answer. There were many who had lost their head with that first question. "Very well. Name the horses who belong to Nott and her son Dagr and pull their chariots on their journeys around Midgardr."

This proved easy for Odin/Gangraaf to answer, "Nott's horse is called Hrimfaxi. Her son has two noble stallions named Skinfaxi and Gladr."

This, too, surprised Vafthrudnir. For many could name Nott's horse, and some could name at last one of Dagr's. But no one had ever named all three. "I will quiz you about other horses. Name the riders of Stufr, Kertr, Vakr, Fakr, Holvir, Mor and Fokvir?"

Odin/Gangraaf did not pause, but immediately answered, "Those noble steeds are ridden by Vifill, Bjarr, Morginn, Haki, Hogni, Meinthjofr and Haraldr."

"Very well, then," continued Vafthrudnir, "can you answer this riddle? Who are the two who to the Thing go? Three eyes have they, ten feet and one tail?"

Odin/Gangraaf laughed, "Such a simple question. It could only be Odin riding Sleipnir."

Vafthrudnir was impressed, "Clearly you are a worthy opponent Gangraaf. Tell me where the last great battle will be fought?"

This was no ordinary question since the last battle was in the future and only someone with unnatural knowledge would be able to answer it correctly. But Odin/Gangraaf easily answered, "It will be fought on Vigridr Plain which is one hundred rosts on either side."

"Give me an ekename for Vidarr, and as many as you can for Thor?" asked Vafthrudnir. He thought he had the stranger with this question.

Odin/Gangraaf smiled and easily answered, "Vidarr is also known as the hinn thogli ass, which means the silent god. Thor is known as the herthrumu gautr, the otti jotna, Oki-Thor, the hinn almattki ass, the hafra drattin, the hafra njotr, and the Midgardsveor, ekenames which mean the thundergod, the jotun terror, charioteer-Thor, the all-powerful god, the lord of goats, the goat user, and the protector of Midgardr."

"You're right. Now tell me ekenames for the Precious Mead, those who live in Midgardr, and Maane?" He leaned back in his chair satisfied these questions were unanswerable by the visitor.

Odin/Gangraaf did not hesitate as he answered, "That wondrous drink is also known as odhrœris dreckr and the hinn dyri mjodr. Two names for those who live in Midgardr are Fitjung's Sons and the Mogthrasir. Finally, Maane will also answer to the name Fengari."

Vafthrudnir motioned for the stranger to sit next to him, "You are a worthy adversary and I think not an ordinary man of Midgardr. Come sit next to me so I can quiz you further. Perhaps I can also learn your secrets?"

Vafthrudnir asked him questions far into the night. His questions concerned jotuns who had been as well as those who were yet to exist. He asked questions about other worlds and worlds which did not yet exist. He quizzed Odin/Gangraaf until finally he could think of no more questions. Every question he had asked had been answered correctly. Finally, he threw up his hands in despair saying, "You know all that I know. You have won the battle, what is it you want?"

Odin smiled and said, "The contest is not yet finished. I want your head and what is in it. Therefore, I'll quiz you. If you can answer all of my questions then we will both be even. If you miss just one question then you will lose."

Vafthrudnir had no choice but to agree to the terms Odin/Gangraaf set before him. Odin/Gangraaf asked his first question, "How was the creation of the heavens and Midgardr brought about?"

Vafthrudnir easily answered, "They came from the jotun Ymir, also known as Aurgelmir. His body became Midgardr, his bones became the hills, the sky was formed from his skull held aloft at four corners by dvergues, and his blood became the oceans, lakes and seas."

Odin/Gangraaf nodded that that was the correct answer and gave his next question, "Where did we get the shadows on the face of the moon?"

Again Vafthrudnir answered with ease, "Vidfinnr was an evil jotun who forced his unfortunate children to perform arduous labor for him. They are now those shadows, having been rescued from their slavery by Maane."

Odin/Gangraaf continued, "And what of Nott? Who is she?"

So far Vafthrudnir was having no trouble answering the questions and began to feel at ease. "Nott is the daughter of Narfi. She married Dellingr and had her son Dagr by him."

"Here is the hardest question yet. Before the Æsir there were the old gods. Where did Winter and Summer come from?"

This was truly a difficult question. Vafthrudnir thought for a moment until he vaguely remembered the answer, "Vasuth had a son named Vindsval who had a son named Summer."

Odin/Gangraaf asked him another question, "Name Ymir's first sons?"

Vafthrudnir replied, "Thrudgelmir was the first, a noisy six-headed son. Another son was Bergelmir. But the oldest born in that time was Aurgelmir himself?"

"And where did he come from?"

Vafthrudnir continued, "From the heat of Muspelheimr and the cold of Niflheimr."

"How were the sons of Ymir born?"

"They came about from under the arms of Ymir and from one foot begatting unnaturally upon the other."

Seeing that he easily answered these questions Odin/Gangraaf switched to another topic, "What causes the wind?"

Vafthrudnir seemed pleased, "That's easy since I've been to the far ends of the north and have seen the jotun named Hræsvelg who sits in the form of an eagle flapping his wings and sending forth the wind."

"Where is Njordr's first home?"

Vafthrudnir answered, "He is one of the Vanir and originally lived in Vanaheimr."

"What's the fate of those killed in battle?"

"They are accepted as brave warriors and known as the Einherjar and dwell and die over and over again in Valhalla."

Odin/Gangraaf paused for a moment to drink some mead and complimented Vafthrudnir on his wisdom, "You have great knowledge. Where did you gain it?"

Vafthrudnir was pleased he was holding his own, for the questions had been a lot more difficult than he had expected. "I've traveled and asked questions all my life. I've been to all the Worlds of the Tree. So far these questions have been quite easy. Have you any harder ones?"

"Very well," said Odin/Gangraaf, "let me question you about the ending of all things. Who will live after the last great battle?"

This was a much more difficult question. It frightened Vafthrudnir that Gangraaf would know it. What frightened him even more was that Gangraaf also seemed to know the answer. "Lif and Lifthrasir will eat the dew of the morning and hide in Hoddmimir's Holt. When it's safe they will come out again."

Odin/Gangraaf pursued this topic. "Will there be a sun after the old one is eaten by Fenriswulf?"

Vafthrudnir knew the answer. But he could see his knowledge was being sorely tested. "Alfrothul is the sun who has a daughter before she is swallowed by that evil son of Loki's. Her sunlight will shine ever after."

"Who are the Norns?"

"They are three jotun sisters from the east who have crossed over Mogthrasir's Hill. They weave their cloth which tells the future. When their tapestry is done the worlds will tremble and crumble."

From Vafthrudnir's hesitancy before answering each of the last few questions Odin/Gangraaf could sense the jotun's knowledge was less precise on these matters, so he continued along the same line, "Name others who will live on after the great battle that is called Ragnarokr?"

Vafthrudnir had begun shaking. These questions were ones no ordinary person could ask. For the first time he sensed he was going to lose this contest. "That's a difficult question that only a few can answer. And none of Midgardr know the reply. I believe some who live will be Vidarr the Silent, Vali the Avenger, Modi and Magni who shall become owners of Mjolnir after Vingnir falls in battle. If you give me more time I can think of others."

But Odin/Gangraaf was satisfied with the answer, "How will Odin die?"

"He'll be swallowed by Fenriswulf. His avenger shall be his son, Vidarr the Silent."

Odin/Gangraaf stood up, "Now for my last question. But think carefully before you answer, for your head depends on it. What does Odin whisper in Baldr's ear before his son begins his journey to Niflheimr?"

Vafthrudnir's trembling hands knocked over his goblet. "I don't know. I believe I've been tricked. You aren't Gangraaf. You couldn't know that answer unless you were…the only person who would know that answer is…I can't believe it, but you must be…"

Before Vafthrudnir could finish Odin quickly picked up a sword, "That's right. I am Odin and you have lost our contest." With that he cut off Vafthrudnir's head.

Odin made his way back to Asgardr. He wasn't happy at having won the contest, since he hadn't won using knowledge of the past, but rather using what he knew of the future. He had learned nothing and there were undoubtedly many more questions to which Vafthrudnir had knowledge that Odin did not know the answers. What had he gained after all, but more killing? Odin now knew the jotuns had great knowledge of the ends of things and they wouldn't fear to fight the last battle.

Odin sat on Hlidskjalf brooding, waiting for things to happen. And the events started occurring one by one and he felt so powerless to stop them, although he continued to try.

Chapter 22

Idunn Leaves Asgardr

Now things were inevitable. The predestined events of Ragnarokr were beginning to occur. There was a sense of helplessness and despair permeating Asgardr. The first to suffer from these feelings was Idunn. Her black mood became greater and greater until it engulfed her entirely. When this happened she picked the last of the golden apples from the only tree in Brunnakr Grove still putting forth fruit. Without telling anyone where she was going, she departed Asgardr.

That evening Bragi returned from one of his journeys and noticed Idunn was gone. He searched amongst the dead trees of the orchard, but couldn't find her. He went to Odin's hall, Valaskjalf. Odin had been sitting in the watchtower on his throne Hlidskjalf, brooding and had seen Bragi coming. He sent word his son was to be allowed to enter.

Bragi was so excited he didn't even ask leave to speak, "Idunn has left and I don't know where she's gone. I'm so very worried. I returned this evening to find all of the trees in Brunnakr Grove dead. She's taken the remaining apples with her. Where can she be?"

Odin answered, "I know all of this, for I have watched her departure. She has gone to seek protection and make her home in the branches of Yggdrasyll. If you would see her, you must go there to do so."

Bragi thanked his father and hurried to Yggdrasyll.

He stopped to asked directions of the Norns, "Have you seen my wife, Idunn? I'm told she's around here."

They ignored him. He entreated them again. Finally, moreso to get him to leave rather than help by answering his questions, Verdandi raised her hand, unraveling a thread about Baldr living a long and happy life, and pointed her bony finger towards Yggdrasyll.

Seeing what she had done, Verdandi tried to repair the damage, but only made it worse. Her two sisters, Skuldr and Urdr, scowled at her ineptitude and began furiously weaving as if they were trying to get things done, resolve unresolved conflicts, or provoke new ones. Didn't matter how or what was done, only that it was done. Whatever, they concentrated on their tasks, ignoring Bragi. They knew they were running out of time. Urdr took the mistaken section about Baldr they had just worked on and quickly rolled it up with the rest of the fateful fabric. Maybe it would be alright rolled up with the rest of the future? Out of sight they soon forgot what had happened and started on the section concerning the last great battle, Ragnarokr. They had to get that done quickly because it was coming on fast.

Bragi walked under the sheltering branches of Yggdrasyll and called up to Idunn but she didn't seem to hear. He sang out beautiful songs to her. The birds in Yggdrasyll stopped their singing to listen. Even the Norns were moved and frequently stopped their weaving of the fates of all things, to listen. And when they did, the inevitable stopped in its tracks. But, eventually, they returned to their task and the future began again.

Sometimes Idunn turned her head towards Bragi, but she wouldn't speak, nor would she come down. Bragi was over come with grief, yet every evening he would go to the tree, stand beneath its branches and sing to her.

One morning Idunn awoke feeling very faint. Eventually she was overcome by this feeling and lost her balance. She fell from Yggdrasyll, floating down from the tree even as the dead leaves of summer lose their hold on the branches and drop to the cold ground below. She fell to the depths of Niflheimr, on and on, ever downward, reaching Helheimr, where she lay paralyzed in terror at the awful visions in Hela's domain. She lay there trembling with fright and from the cold, unable to do anything and too terrified to turn her gaze from the sights she beheld.

That evening Bragi came to Brunnakr Grove to sing to her. Looking up he saw her place deserted. He gazed at other branches but she was nowhere to be found. He walked around the tree and finally over to the Norns where he questioned them, "Have you seen Idunn? I've come to sing to her and try and persuade her to come back to Asgardr with me. But it appears she has already left. Can you tell me if I will find great happiness when I return to Asgardr? Will she be there waiting in Brunnakr Grove?"

The Norns didn't reply. However, Skadi pointed to a section of their tapestry that had been woven that morning. Terrified Bragi saw the weaving and read the story the threads told. The section he saw showed Idunn falling from Yggdrasyll. As Bragi sought to catch a further glance which he hoped would tell him where she was, the tapestry was rolled up from his sight, and torn slightly in the process.

Then Skadi spoke, "Things aren't right. We have troubles of our own to worry about, for you can see the water from Urdarbrunnr Well is no longer helping Yggdrasyll. For many lifetimes we have spread its goodness on the tree and helped it to be nourished and grow. Now the water has no effect. The tree is wilting even as we speak. Tell Odin something must be done about this." She turned back to her sisters.

Bragi hurried back to Asgardr and the hall, Vingolf, that had been built for the Asynjes, and called for a Thing to be held there.

At the start of the meeting Odin sent off his raven Huginn to search for Idunn. The raven quickly made his way to the many Worlds of the Tree seeking information about Idunn.

Finally he arrived in Svartalfheimr where he came upon Dain and Thrain. Instead of finding them hard at work casting precious objects in gold and silver and working with precious jewels, he found them slumped in a deep sleep. The black raven pecked at them.

But this didn't rouse them fully. Dain was heard to mumble about the severe cold and about the flames that would come after. Thrain, however, chanted over and over that Idunn was in Helheimr, the darkest reaches of Niflheimr, and all was lost. Having gained the information he sought Huginn returned to Asgardr and whispered the knowledge in Odin's ear.

Odin commanded Heimdallr, Loki, and Bragi to go to the depths of Niflheimr, to Helheimr to seek Idunn out and persuade her to return to her home in Asgardr. "Take this white wolf skin with you as my present to her, so that she might be comforted by it and be reminded of those in Asgardr who love her and hope for her safe return. But she must agree to return with you willingly. That is the only way to break the bonds which hold her in Niflheimr. She is held there by her own fears, and only she can conquer them and free herself."

Odin watched from Hlidskjalf as the three made their way to Idunn's side. They rode three monsters on their journey into the depths of Niflheimr, downward and downward, as they chanted magic songs, and carved magic runes to protect them in the evil land. Eyes seemed to watch them from dark corners. Bony hands beckoned them on, encouraging them to enter the evil realm – and stay.

The three came upon Idunn still transfixed by the horrible sights in her field of view. Bragi stood in front of her to block out the visions. Heimdallr gently wrapped her in the white wolf's skin hoping its warmth would help break the spell. All three talked to her trying to persuade her to come back with them. She neither looked nor spoke to them. But she did hear them, for at the mention of those who loved her and her home in Asgardr, her eyes filled with tears which rolled down her cheeks.

The three talked to her for many hours, but her sadness was too great to be broken through. Finally Heimdallr suggested they return to Asgardr with a report of their journey. Loki agreed. Bragi did not.

"I can't leave her here alone. You two can go back if you like, but my place is at her side to protect her from the monsters who are lurking about everywhere I look. I'll stay here and sing songs to her and hope we will leave this horrid place some day. Songs of hope and love. Songs of valor and kindness and goodness." Bragi spoke words of hope, but they seemed unconvincing. There were tears running down his cheeks. He spoke of hope, but knew it was hopeless.

Heimdallr and Loki started to make their way from that wretched land. Heimdallr turned back for one last look. He saw Bragi place his harp at his side and embrace Idunn in his arms. The song he sang was sad; so sad the walls of the cave wept. And from out of the darkness, slipping from around a rock, a skeletal hand reached out and stole the harp Bragi used to accompany himself while singing stirring songs that had brought such happiness to everyone. Its soaring melody was never to be heard again in that existence.

Heimdallr and Loki arrived back at Asgardr late that night. They went to Vingolf and gave a report of their journey, for the Thing had not yet broken up, so intent was the discussion on what to do to make things better in Asgardr.

There was silence all around as the two entered the hall. Everyone hoped Heimdallr and Loki brought good news with them. But then they saw Bragi was missing from their ranks, and everyone was afraid.

Finally Odin spoke, "There is little more to say. Now we have lost Bragi, too. But perhaps this evening we can each reflect by ourselves and think how the upcoming battles may yet be won. We still have the hope Bragi may persuade Idunn to return to us. With tomorrow's dawn perhaps our problems will seem less grim, for there is always hope." Those listening remained unconvinced.

Those assembled were feeling a bit fatigued and all agreed to try and have a pleasant night's rest. But there were some who whispered the tiredness was unnatural, that Loki had been seen mixing something in the drinks. Suspicion was growing amongst some of the Æsir he was not to be trusted and something had to be done about him, and soon.

But for whatever reasons, sleep came easily to the Æsir that night. Even Heimdallr, who for the first time ever nodded off while standing watch on Bifrost.

As Odin bade Frigg good night, he told her of a journey he was going to make, "I think I'll have to seek more knowledge. But the knowledge I seek can only come from those who cannot speak." Frigg went to her bed to rest while Odin went once again to Hlidskjalf and sat watching and worrying.

Chapter 23

Baldr's Draumr

Balder was Odin and Frigg's son. He was beautiful to behold. He had long blond hair and was tall and physically the most perfect of the Æsir. He had never been known to treat anyone unfairly, or refuse anyone if their request was something he could fulfill. He and his wife, Nanna, brought happiness with them wherever they went. Baldr often visited Midgardr and taught those he met the art of healing and using herbs. He brought with him happiness and goodness wherever he went. Arguments stopped when he approached and goodwill would abound between longtime enemies. No one had ever heard anything bad said about him. Nor was there any slander attached to his name. There were no stories of him cheating anyone, or causing ill luck to another. Perhaps that's why Loki disliked him so much.

Breidablik was Baldr's estate. Usually it could be seen from afar glistening in the sunlight. But for some strange reason a mist had settled over it and his silver and gold hall, Feikstaf, could barely be discerned.

Baldr's two closest friends in Asgardr had been Bragi and Idunn. He had frequently been seen in Brunnakr Grove talking to Idunn, or taking long walks with Bragi, both singing songs as they went on their way. So he was more affected than anyone else when Idunn and Bragi left Asgardr. For the first time in his life he was sad, and not even Nanna could lift his spirits. He was inconsolable. At night he began having nightmares from which he awakened screaming. At first he couldn't remember what they were about. But as they became more dreadful they stayed with him in his waking hours. One dream showed all of the Æsir in mourning at his funeral. In another he saw Breidablik deserted and overgrown with weeds. Baldr knew his death would bring the last great battle even closer. He felt things were changing much too rapidly and it made him uncomfortable.

After awhile he started keeping to himself in Feikstaf, allowing no one but Nanna to visit him. He confided his most recent dream to her, "I have had unsettling dreas and feel my death coming, and it will be at the hands of another. My slayer looks familiar but his countenance is shadowed from me. My eyes glaze over in blindness when I try to make out who he is."

Frigg was worried about his behavior. He had been the happiest and most outgoing of the Æsir. Rarely would a day pass without him visiting someone else in Asgardr or dropping by to see Frigg. When Nanna told Frigg about the dreams and Baldr's change in mood she called a Thing at Urdarbrunnr Well. She was well aware how serious the matter was.

Baldr rode his horse to the Thing. Everyone else was already gathered there. As he approached, his horse tripped and fell, throwing Baldr to the ground. Although both horse and rider were uninjured everyone felt the fall was an omen of ill luck and bad things to come. But no one spoke these thoughts out loud.

The Thing continued. Odin cut runes to foretell the future. But these were not sufficient to tell the assemblage what they wanted to know. The dvergars Thrain and Dain were sent for. They cut more runes. Thrain stared transfixed at what he was watching. His eyes darting back and forth. "I see the end of all things. But first will come Baldr's death."

Frigg was very upset at this confirmation of what she felt. "We must do something to save Baldr's life. Tomorrow the Æsir must journey throughout all the Worlds of the Tree and get everyone and everything to pledge not to harm my son."

All agreed. Some of the Æsir were so anxious they didn't wait for the morning, but started out that evening. By the next day most animate and inanimate objects had pledged their loyalty to Baldr, vowing not to bring harm to him. Baldr needed no longer fear water, fire, metals, stones or animals either tame or wild. Such vile creatures as serpents, snakes, and spiders had pledged not to harm him. Even sickness and old age had pledged to hold him safe from their weakening grasps.

Frigg had spent the day gathering pledges. She was just to the west of Valhalla returning to her hall when she stopped to rest beneath an oak tree. To the east of the tree she saw a sprig of mistletoe, called mistilteiin. It was quite a distance away and she was very tired. Anyway, how could a small thing like that hurt her beloved Baldr? So, she neglected to get its pledge before returning to Fensalir.

By evening almost everyone was feeling a lot better than they had the day before. Now Baldr was safe and the last battle had been postponed, some thought, forever. Perhaps things would turn out all right after all?

Odin Journeys to meet the Prophetess Volva

But there were two who were not cheered by the promises made that day, for different reasons. Loki was disappointed Baldr seemed to be protected from harm. Odin still felt things weren't right and set about to gain more knowledge from the dead. He saddled Sleipnir and rode down the winding roads which lead to Niflheimr.

As horse and rider neared Gnipahellir Cave, Garmr came out to greet them. His chest was covered with the blood of others who had not made it past him. He licked his lips at the large meal he saw approaching. It had been quite awhile since someone had dared come near him.

Three times Odin tried to get past the baleful hound. Three times the wolf lurched forward snapping at the air. His chain was not long enough to reach the two strangers, but was long enough to allow him to harass them. Finally Odin geed Sleipnir who in one mighty leap cleared the obstacle barring their way. The wolf strained at its chain, but the links held fast and all who followed after Odin into the cave was the wolf's howls at being cheated out of a meal.

Modgudr heard the commotion at the entrance and allowed the stranger who had gained entry without the payment of a hel-cake to pass by, thinking he might prove too powerful if she challenged him.

Odin rode eastward until he came to the grave of the prophetess called Volva. She was a sibyl from a long ago time who had had many lives. Once she had been the same Angroboda whose heart Loki had eaten and then subsequently born three children: Fenriswulf, Midgardrsormr (Jormungandr), But now she rested beneath the musty dirt waiting to be called forth.

As Odin knelt next to the grave he noticed a light to the north and walked a short distance over to it. There he saw a banquet hall which had been set out for a great feast. The walls were covered with tapestries depicting events from the past as well as those which had not yet come about.

He could see Sleipnir leaping over Garmr; there was one of strange sporting events taking place in Asgardr. He couldn't quite make out the one which bent around the corner of the wall. It seemed to be a funeral procession. As he turned his attention back to the hall he saw goblets overflowing with mead, plates filled with meat. Couches were covered with rings of gold as gifts for the special guest. Flowers were strewn along the floor and everything seemed to be in readiness awaiting the arrival of whomever was to be honored. Yet the room was empty. Odin called out but there was no answer. Maybe the party had gone off to greet the warrior?

Odin returned to the Volva's grave, stepping over some others who lay in his way. He turned back to the hall before kneeling at the grave. A strange mist seemed to rise up and engulf the vision which had attracted his attention. He turned his thoughts to other matters. First he carved runes on the stones marking the burial cairn and chanted magical charms three times. He sang mystical corpse-songs called kvad gladra, which were designed to awaken the dead. He sang them three times also, so their magic would work. Slowly the dirt moved. Particles tricked down the side of the mound as a bony hand broke through the soil. Then a ghastly skeletonlike form sat up and spoke in a scratchy voice.

"Who dares disturb my hellish sleep? I have rested here for long ages, so long the worms have already eaten me through and crawled in and out of where my eyes used to be. Now the sights I see I perceive without ordinary vision."

Odin spoke with the voice of an old man, to match the form he had taken, "I'll learn of orlog's decrees from you, and the nature of what is to come."

Volva slowly responded, "Why do you want to know that which cannot be changed?"

Odin responded, "But perhaps things can be changed."

The spectre stood up, grave wrappings hanging around her bony skeleton. Some green flesh hung from her cheekbones, slowly sliding down her cheeks onto her shoulders. Her jaw ground back and forth as she spoke, but her lips didn't part from their perpetual grin.

Odin faced her without shrinking back in fright which is what most would have done. "I am called Vegtamr Valtamssonr and have come on a long journey to seek out your knowledge of things. Why does that hall seem prepared for a feast, yet no one is there? Why are the seats stacked high with byrnies and battle armor, yet no warriors prance about? Who is to be welcomed at this feast?"

Volva wearily replied, "Why do you waste my time with these silly questions?"

Odin/Vegtamr Valtamssonr interrupted. "I should think you have plenty of time to waste. You don't look like one who has pressing engagements waiting."

Volva continued grinning as much as she was able, "You will not insult me when you hear for whom the table is laid. It is for one of the Æsir. Baldr will soon come here to live. The shield which protects the cauldron from spells will soon be removed and the beer ladled out to those attending his welcoming. But ask me no more of these events. I'm tired and wish to sink back into the rest from which you have disturbed me."

Vegtamr Valtamssonr wouldn't let her depart. "Stay, I have more questions. Who will be the instrument of Baldr's wyrd?"

She replied, "Ah, you ask me a riddle. Do you wish to know who the instrument is, or whom it is who plays the instrument which will be Baldr's downfall? I will whisper it to you."

Her cold clammy hand clutched at Vegtamr's shoulder and drew him near to her. Her icy breath whispered a name in his ear that sent shivers through him. "Don't forget the name I have just told you." But how could he? It was his own son and Baldr's twin brother, Hodr.

"All murders must be avenged. Who will avenge his death?"

She answered, "That is also easy. The one whose name you would know has not yet been born. His mother is a woman of Midgardr living in Vestraslir. She is Rindr. Her husband will be Odin, and her son will be but one day old when he has performed his noble deed. He will neither wash nor comb his hair before his destiny is met and the vengeance performed."

The questions went back and forth. The subjects were of the future and of the far past, times which mortals would know little of. Finally, in despair Odin yelled out, "If only everything would weep at Baldr's death. Then there might be some hope."

Volva shuddered and realized she had been called forth by Odin himself. "You've lied to me about your identity. Your name is not Vegtamr Valtamssonr. Indeed, I believe you to be Odin. You may think you have fooled me, but our conversation has kept you away from Asgardr a long time. Perhaps too long. I'll tell you now that strange things are taking place there. Maybe Loki has taken over by now? If he has not, it will only be awhile. In the meantime I will return to my sleep and await the breaking of the bonds which keep us all in check. Then our time will come and we shall walk in Asgardr, and blood will finally be shed there. Until that time, chants and runes will not disturb me. I will next be awakened by the quaking of rocks and the splitting apart of worlds."

She disappeared back into the mound. The dirt followed in the opening after her, sealing her resting place once more.

Odin cursed at her. "You may call yourself Volva now, but I recognize you as the evil Angroboda. You have deceived the Æsir in the past and we burned you for it. Your children are imprisoned by us. We shall fight you and defeat you. Never more will you rise up to taunt the living."

Odin mounted Sleipnir and hurried back to Asgardr, not knowing what he would find there. One thing he knew, though. Baldr's time was short unless he was able to do something. But what? Suddenly things seemed hopeless. He had already seen the hall laid out for Baldr's entry into Niflhel. Could it be prevented?

Back in Asgardr Odin came upon Baldr and many of the Æsir assembled around him. Everyone was laughing and having fun. No one seemed to have a care in the world, for all thought Baldr was now safe since everything had sworn to never harm him. They took advantage of this to develop their latest entertainment.

The sport was held in a sacred field where no harm could be caused to anyone. Angry words and oaths were not permitted. Because of the vows everything had given they had no fear of desecrating the land with the shedding of blood.

Finally there seemed to be laughter in Asgardr. They had fun with Baldr's protection. At first they timidly threw light objects at him. One-by-one whatever was tossed either fell short or swerved to miss Baldr no matter how true the aim. As they became more confident they hurled greater and more dangerous objects until finally they were throwing battleaxes, spears, swords, shooting arrows, dropping boulders and doing anything else they could think of to test the truth of each vow. Some even charged up to him with swords drawn and hacked and hewed away at him with no harm done. Even Thor joined in and threw Mjolnir at the motionless target. Mjolnir, never known to miss, missed. Even Odin's spear Gungnir missed. Surely the worlds were safe now, since harm had to come to Baldr before events could proceed to Ragnarokr? No one thought the Worlds of the Tree were all out of kilter if enchanted weapons defied their enchantment. Gungnir was never meant to miss. Nor was Mjolnir. Now they missed. This wasn't right. These things alone should have worried the Æsir more than anything. Enchanted weapons enchanted never to miss, were missing. What were the Æsir missing in this fact? Why did they not see they were in worse trouble than ever? Yet they went on playing their dangerous games, becoming more confident with each deflected blow at Baldr. Arrogance is never a good thing. Arrogance and defiance is always a deadly combination.

Loki strolled up to the gathering. He had been keeping to himself on the sidelines watching. He had always been jealous of Baldr. Indeed he was probably jealous of everyone, but now Baldr was getting more attention than he had ever gotten, no matter how much attention an evil deed he had done should have warranted. And the worst thing was that Baldr was unharmed and didn't even seem to be enjoying himself. He just stood and let things be thrown at him. Loki would have tried dodging back and forth, making a game of it for entertainment's sake. But Baldr seemed totally unconcerned with whether or not he was hit. Loki thought, "He probably still misses Bragi and Idunn. I don't see why? They were such a boring couple, never getting into mischief. He was always singing and she was always gardening." Loki left, determined to find a way to make things right and get the attention he deserved.

It didn't take him long to plot his revenge. For soon he found out about the carelessness which could have prevented the events now fated to occur.

Frigg sat spinning in Fensalir as usual, content her beloved son would not be taken away from her. She turned as she heard footsteps approaching and saw an old crone hobbling across the marble floor leaning on a bent staff for support. The old lady came closer and in a slow weak voice spoke, "My name is Thokk, and I've just come from the sacred field where everyone is having fun with Baldr, using him as a target. This caused me great concern since we have all recently been worried about Baldr. Surely you should not permit him to be used like this?"

Frigg smiled at the stranger. "It's all right. He's safe now since everything has vowed to protect him. I no longer fear for his life. He is protected by sacred vows and we can rest easier now." She resumed her spinning.

The old lady continued her questioning. "Are you certain nothing thrown at him will harm him? I wouldn't want Baldr to be injured by accident."

Frigg replied, "Nothing thrown at him will harm him. Nor will illness or accidents plague him. He is safe. Everything has sworn to protect him, except…"

The old lady started at the 'except' and seized on it. "Except! Except, what? Surely you're just joking?"

Frigg felt safe with the old lady now and didn't mind telling about how tired she had been that day. "I had been gathering pledges all night and by late that afternoon was quite weary. So I stopped to rest and noticed a sprig of mistletoe in the distance. But it was so small and insignificant I didn't bother to walk over to it. Besides, it was a plant Baldr was raising and I knew it wouldn't harm him anyway."

Frigg was continuing with how long her walk had been back to her hall that day when she noticed she no longer held the old lady's attention. In fact the old lady seemed anxious to leave. "Would you care to join me for something to drink?"

The old lady turned and answered as she left, "No, I have urgent business in the east to attend to. Perhaps some other time you will invite me again, although I rather doubt it."

Frigg watched as she left. Her steps seemed considerably lighter and she no longer seemed to be leaning on her staff as she walked. Something certainly revived her youth.

Frigg would have been terrified if she had seen what happened just outside the hall. The old woman tore off her garments and there standing in the entryway was Loki. He lost no time making his way to the field where the mistletoe was.

He had no trouble finding the mistletoe and knelt down before it and drew circles and cut evil runes and chanted spells before the tiny twig. He struck at it with his staff. Immediately it grew to the height of his staff. Loki got up and pulled the plant from the ground, roots and all, and cut away the branches and sharpened the end to a point. But it was still only wood and not very strong. Clearly more skill was needed for making the spear. He hurried over to Svartalfheimr to have it worked on by some wretched dokkalfar.

The little dvergues took the mistletoe and plunged it into some boiling water to wash away any impurities. They sent Loki out to find a child of Midgardr who was pure of heart. He soon returned carrying a frightened boy with him, and held the child while the dvergar stabbed the spear into the child's heart, killing him. The blood covered the spear whereupon it immediately became iron-hard. The tip was flattened and filed to a fine point, though it still had a greenish hue and resembled a leaf of mistletoe. Loki took the spear and breathed on the tip. As his breath disappeared he could almost see the events which were to take place reflected in the flattened end. He muttered to himself, pleased with what he had in his hand. "Frigg thought you too weak to have you utter a protective oath to Baldr. But now think of the oaths you'll soon inspire."

Loki hurried pack to the sacred field. He was now ready to join in the fun his way, but first he had to impatiently wait his turn. Of course, Loki being Loki, he wasn't going to wait like everyone else.

Impatiently he waited behind a group of dirty, ugly trolls who had been allowed in Asgardr to try their hand at throwing objects at Baldr. They delighted in this. After all, their goal was to destroy those in Asgardr and all their friends, and here they were being cheered on in their quest by those whom they sought to destroy. One-by-one they hurled their stone hammers at Baldr, and one-by-one the hammers careened out of the way to miss their mark, smashed to the ground and exploded into gravel. The trolls had never seen anything like this and tumbled in somersaults of laughter as they retrieved the pepples of their weapons and stumbled all over each other racing to get back in line to have another chance at Baldr. While in line they pressed the pepples back into hammer shapes, chanted magic incantations, and their weapons were restored, though weakened. Why they thought weapons which weren't as strong as before would do the deed they'd already failed at, was odd. Bascially, they just liked throwing things at anything. And throwing at Baldr was almost the best thing of all. Throwing at Thor would have been better, but there would have been deadly consequences if they'd done that. The best they could hope for was that bits of their shattered hammers might hit the flint in Thor's head and cause him more pain, maybe enough to distract him at the last great battle. They were always trying to do their part for those who fought against the Æsir.

Finally, it was Loki's turn. As he took his place, ready to throw the spear he realized if he killed Baldr, Thor would probably seek vengeance against him immediately. With all the Æsir around it would have been impossible for him to escape. So, at the last minute he called out to Hodr, Baldr's blind twin brother. Hodr was the Æsir of darkness and was as quiet and reserved as Baldr was shining and outgoing. His hair was as dark as Baldr's was light. Even though the brothers were a study in contrasts, there was a mysterious bond of love between them. They had often taken long walks with Baldr describing the things he saw in such great detail that Hodr knew what shapes looked like and all about colors. His life had been lived in darkness, but his brother had brought him light.

Hodr had been standing apart from the others, sad at not being included in things. He raised his head at the sound of his name being called. Loki walked over and touched his shoulder. "Don't you want to join in the fun? Everyone has had their turn except you." Loki's voice had an unusual tone of concern in it. Of course, the "everyone" was everyone except Loki, too.

Hodr was glad to have been noticed. "I would like to join in but I can't see where Baldr is standing and wouldn't want to risk accidentally throwing something at someone who hadn't Baldr's protection. I have no skill in sport. Also, I have nothing to throw."

Loki patted him on the shoulder in commiseration, "I'll let you have my turn. Here you can use my spear. I'll position you and guide your aim. There's nothing to it."

Before he knew it Hodr was standing in Loki's place with a raised spear in his hand preparing to toss it at his brother. Loki turned him slightly, moved him over a bit and whispered in Hodr's ear, "Now you're ready. I'll stand back. Throw as hard as you can."

With that the spear was loosed. Everyone was yelling with laughter as the spear flew straight and true towards Baldr. Mere moments of innocence left. Could no one see Loki was doing this? And, everything Loki touched turned bad. If only someone would reach over and flick at the spearpoint and deflect it.

But, your wyrd is your wyrd. No matter how you or others try to avoid it, it is unavoidable. The norns looked at what was appearing on the loom, a series of images showing a spear hurtling towards Baldr. Skuldr covered her eyes and turned her back to the fabric. She knew the tragedy that was about to happen, and she was thinking of more than just Baldr. For the first time a tear fell down her cheek. Forever she had been helping weave this tapestry. She'd seen injustice, but had not sought to right it. Threads of murders and murderers had woven their plots throughout the warp of the fabric. All that she'd seen unmoved. But, Baldr's death was different. It changed everything.

But, moments passed and no one stepped in to deflect the fateful spear. It was held true on its course cheered on my laughter and encouragement. It took just a moment to penetrate through to Baldr's heart. He went down on his knees, slumped over the spear which momentarily propped him up, dying amongst the axes, swords, rocks and other weapons that had glanced away. Everyone was overcome with shock and at first couldn't believe what had happened. But the scene was so macabre they couldn't take their eyes off of Baldr on his knees in front of them, blood streaming down the front of his white tunic onto sacred soil which had never had to absorb blood which began puddling around him.

Hodr felt something was wrong. Instead of cheering and laughter there was dead silence. "Loki, tell me what's happened? Is everything all right? Why has the laughing stopped?" But Loki was gone from Hodr's side. He had slipped away to stand with a group of Æsir just as the spear had been thrown.

No one answered him directly. They were all too shocked. Hodr heard a murmuring that Baldr had fallen. Blood was seeping into the sacred ground for the first time. The sky darkened and no one noticed Hodr quietly slipping away into the nearby forest.

Gradually, what had happened sunk in and some of the Æsir rushed to Baldr's side. Others started yelling, "Hodr threw the spear." "Catch him." "He ran into the forest." Loki was now yelling louder than the others and led some of the Æsir into the forest to hunt for Hodr. Hodr was unused to hearing his name being called. And now it was being yelled in hatred. Still confused about everything, he moved even deeper into the forest to elude his pursuers. He was frightened. He loved his brother more than anyone. Had he harmed his brother somehow?

Frigg heard the yelling and came out of her hall to see what all the excitement was about. She saw her son's bloody body being carried to Feikstaf and was overcome with grief. She hurried to Baldr's side and never left it for the three days he lingered between life and death. Then the moment all had dreaded came. The deed was done. Baldr was dead.

Grief descended on Asgardr. Frigg was inconsolable. Odin brooded more than any for he knew the end was nearing and there seemed to be nothing he could do to halt fate's inexorable movement. All the Æsir kept their thoughts to themselves, still finding it hard to believe Baldr was dead. Only a few days before Baldr had been the focus of all the joy and fun in Asgardr. Now he lay in his hall while the burial preparations were being made.

Finally, Frigg could contain her grief no longer. She pleaded to all in Asgardr for one to come forward and make the treacherous journey to Helheimr, Hela's Hall in Niflhel in the furthest reaches of Niflheimr, to see if there were some way to persuade Hela to permit Baldr to return to Asgardr. A messenger brought a rod to her and said his master would be willing to undertake the journey. Frigg sent for him.

The rod belonged to Hermodr, one of the most valiant of the Æsir. He was Baldr's brother, Odin and Frigg's son. He was known as the messenger of the Æsir and had often undertaken journeys for many of the blessed in Asgardr. In gratitude for the missions he had performed, the Æsir had once presented him with a wonderful corselet and protective helmet. He had also once owned the sword Gambanteiin, which had become the property of Freyr who had given it to Skirnir in gratitude for helping him win Gerdr's hand. Hermodr loved battles and when he wasn't attending to errands he frequently rode with the Valkyries. On such occasions Odin lent him his spear Gungnir to cast over the battlefield. He helped escort the chosen slain part of their way to Valhalla, often rushing ahead so he could wait at the gate with Bragi to welcome them to Valhalla.

Odin was proud his son had stepped forward. He offered him the use of Sleipnir for the journey to Helheimr. "He's swift and knows the way there as well as the way back, so there will be no fear of losing you, too. Your journey will take you down helveg, the road to Hela's domain, through the Myrkvyrdr Forest where you will see horrible sights. Eyes will watch you and disappear when you return their gaze. It is good Sleipnir will be your steed. Only an extraordinary horse would enter that frightening place. But even worse sights await you when you arrive in Niflheimr and travel ever deeper through Niflhel into Helheimr. It is a dangerous journey and we are all grateful you love your brother enough to make it."

Hermodr replied, "I'm not afraid, father."

Odin continued, "We are all depending on you to try and win Baldr's release. The Worlds of the Tree are depending on you. For its branches shake. Even now leaves and twigs fall from it."

Sleipnir was saddled and brought from the stables. He reared and backed away as Hermodr, clad in shining armor, approached. No one but Odin had ever ridden him. Hermodr grabbed the reins and patted Sleipnir's neck. The touch was unfamiliar but seemed friendly and sure. Sleipnir nervously shifted about, snorting and whinnying, shying away as Hermodr tried to mount him. But Hermodr was patient and Sleipnir finally calmed down enough to allowed Hermodr to mount. Gifts for those in Helheimr were loaded onto the saddle. Then, they were off.

After Hermodr left preparations were made for Baldr's funeral. His ship, Hringhornr, was hung with tapestries telling the story of his life. Weapons, gold, silver, and other precious objects were used to decorate the ship. Garlands of flowers were looped from mast to mast. They placed everything they thought Baldr would need on his journey on the ship including tools and supplies of food. They built a pyre at one end and twined thorns around it and carved it with runes which would help him sleep peacefully. His favorite horse, fully saddled and ready to ride, as well as his hunting hounds, were slain and placed onboard.

While the ship was being prepared Nanna supervised the laying out of Baldr's body. He was dressed in his best armor. A pair of helskor, or deathshoes made of lead, were placed on his feet so should he have to wade through the raging river Slidr he would be protected from its poisonous waters and be assured of steady footing. Next his nails were trimmed so they couldn't be used to build the ship Naglfar, madeof dead men's nails.

Odin went to Feikstaf and asked to be left alone with his son for a few moments. After everyone had left he walked over to Baldr, opened his mouth and carved magic runes of protection on Baldr's tongue and blessed his journey hoping this would help keep him safe from the evil that was in all the reaches of Niflheimr. Once this was done Odin called everyone back in. Baldr was wrapped in a shroud and carried on the shoulders of the best warriors from Valhalla to Hringhornr.

Nanna stood next to the pyre, overcome with grief. She bent over to kiss Baldr one last time when her heart filled with such sadness that it broke and she died. Another pyre was quickly built. She too was prepared in a similar manner to Baldr. Her nails were cut, deathshoes were placed on her feet, and finally she was wrapped in a shroud and placed on the pyre next to Baldr.

The ship was drawn to the shore and set on rollers in preparation for its launching. Wood was piled high around the pyres. After saying their last goodbyes, everyone left the ship except Odin. He walked to where his son lay, removed his arm ring Draupnir from his arm and laid it on Baldr's chest. Bending over he whispered a single word into his son's ear, "REBIRTH!" and left the ship.

Odin's ravens, Huginn and Munnin circled overhead. Everyone stood on the shore watching the ceremony. Odin stood at the water's edge, unsmiling. His two ravens returned to his shoulders. His two wolves, Geri and Freki, stood beside him. Frigg stood nearby disbelieving it was really happening. The Valkyries, Æsir, Vanir, Einherjar, Ljosalfar, and other friends of the Æsir – all were there. Even Loki was there, although he didn't seem to be upset by what was happening. At times it even looked as if his gnarled mouth was smiling.

Freyr stood on the shore in his chariot pulled by Gullinbursti and Slidrugtanni. Freyja stood nearby weeping in her cat-drawn chariot. Heimdallr had left Bifrost and sat watching astride Gulltoppr. Even some hrymthursars and rock jotuns had come to pay their respects. Although they generally didn't like the Æsir they had been fond of Baldr. He had never done any harm to them and had even been known to give them help if they were in need. They moved back a little when Thor appeared, hoping he wouldn't see them, not wanting to arouse his anger.

Finally the moment to launch the ship came. Several of the strongest of the Æsir went up to the ship and pushed at its stern. But because of the wood and all the gifts piled aboard it didn't budge an inch. Again they tried, with the same result. Some hill jotuns walked over to help. But their added strength was of little use. Suddenly grief was forgotten while they pondered how to launch the ship. One of the hill jotuns had an answer, "I know a storm jotun living in Jotunheimr who would be strong enough to move this ship. She has been known to move mountains with but a flick of her fingers. This ship would be no problem for her. Her name is Hyrrokkin. It would take little time for one of us to go and fetch her."

A messenger was dispatched. Soon he could be seen returning accompanied by Hyrrokkin. She rode astride a giant wolf using two writhing vipers for a bridle. It took them but a few steps to travel from the horizon to the gathering anxiously waiting at the shore. Everyone stepped back a pace when they saw how monstrous the wolf was. There were whispers Fenriswulf had returned, and was on the loose again. But luckily fearsome as it was, it was not Fenriswulf.

Hyrrokkin dismounted and yelled for help in holding the wolf. "Have four of your strongest berserkers brought to hold him. He has little use for the Æsir and since I come today as a friend I wouldn't want him tearing through those standing nearby."

The four berserkers grappled with him without gaining much control. Finally Hyrrokkin grabbed at the reins again pulling the head of the wolf to the ground, twisting him onto his back, and binding his feet. She handed the ends of the rope to the berserkers to hold. Then she tied a restraint around the wolf's gaping jaws. Though he continued to struggle against the ropes he was sufficiently bound to offer no further threat.

Hyrrokkin now turned to the ship and shoved. Her action was so swift it startled many who had already tried to move the vessel. Hringhornr moved forward on the rollers so fast they burst into flames. The land shook so much from the force of her shove many of the Æsir lost their balance and fell to the ground. One who did not was Thor. He saw the rollers burst into flame and felt Hyrrokkin had caused it to happen on purpose in order to insult the dead. He ran forward holding Mjolnir aloft ready to strike her down. As she turned around she saw Thor's upraised hammer and prepared to defend herself. But before either could strike a blow Odin interceded, "Remember, Thor, she has come here under my protection and has done us a great service. Now is not the time for vengeance, especially in this land. Have you forgotten the shedding of blood is forbidden in Asgardr? Already that sacred law has been violated. Let's not further compound the tragedy of all this."

Some of the Æsir pulled Thor back. He lowered Mjolnir but his face still burned red with anger. Odin continued, "Put your hammer to better use. Although it fights many battles for us, it also hallows our sacred meetings. Bring honor to Baldr by blessing his ship. He has a long journey ahead of him and will need all the help we can give him."

The ship settled into the water and was rolling lazily from side to side. The rollers were still burning causing the water in the front of Hringhorni to boil and sizzle. Thor strode to the edge of the shore and swung Mjolnir overhead. Lightning broke through the sky and struck one of the masts of the ship, traveled downward and ignited the wood which had been piled high on deck. A dvergar named Litr had been standing near Thor. He was so frightened by the thunder and lightning that he started to run past Thor hoping to seek safety behind a rock. Thor was in an angry mood anyway, and when he saw a dvergar turning his back and running away from the ceremony he felt Baldr had been insulted once again. As Litr ran towards him he booted the dvergar with his foot. The dvergar sailed out over the water and landed on the ship and immediately burst into flames as he bounced back and forth careening all over the deck like a ball.

The flames roared higher and higher as more of the ship caught fire. Finally the flames touched the sky and were so brilliant many in other worlds could see them and wondered what was happening in Asgardr.

The ship gradually floated away from the shore towards the western horizon. Soon it looked as if the entire sky were ablaze. Then suddenly it plunged into the sea and was gone. The red sky calmed down into darkness. Everyone stood on the shore waiting, it seemed, for the ship to return. But it didn't and eventually they went one-by-one to their homes to await the outcome of Hermodr's quest.

Hermodr's Journey to Helheimr

Hermodr and Sleipner were nine days and nights on their journey before they reached the Gjoll river leading to the entrance of the cave Gnipahellir. Garmr came out and barked at them, but Sleipnir easily leapt over the hound. Next they came to Gjallarbru, the echoing bridge roofed with gold and held up with a single strand of hair. There they met the skeleton maiden Modgudr, guardian of the bridge.

She spoke to the stranger, "I see eight legs but they are not the mourners bearing the dead holding up each corner of the pallet? You haven't the light tread of the departed. It was only five days ago that nine bands of warriors came this way. Yet their footsteps combined didn't make the bridge bend as you do. You have an unusually healthy pallor for one crossing into the land of the dead. Who are you? Why do you calmly seek to enter a land others run from in fear, only to be caught and brought back trembling and quaking in their shoes? You can only bring envy to the staring unblinking eyes of those in Niflheimr."

Hermodr approached her without fear. "I'm Odin's son, Hermodr. I have come to ask Hela to return Baldr to the living. Has my brother come this way yet?"

Modgudr nodded she had. "Yes, he was accompanied by Nanna and a funny little dvergar. I'll let you pass on your journey. Continue downward and northward and you'll find the place you seek. But I warn you, the gates will be closed and you will not be allowed to enter. First, though, you must pay your toll of blood before crossing the bridge."

Hermodr responded, "That I refuse to do since I am not yet amongst the dead. My blood will never flow into Gjoll to make its level rise so that that awful ship Naglfar can be launched."

Modgudr stepped in front of him blocking the bridge, "Then you can't cross this bridge. Your body, filled with blood, would be too heavy."

Hermodr tried to assure her his horse's feet would not even touch the bridge, "I will fly swiftly across so that Sleipnir's feet do not touch it at all. If you refuse me we will walk slowly and see if that strand of hair will hold our weight."

Modgudr stepped aside and Hermodr flew across the bridge on Sleipnir. It waved side to side a little, and the hair stretched. But it held and the bridge remained there for more dead to cross over.

Hermodr and Sleipner galloped on into the darkness until finally they reached the barred Nagrindr Gate. The river Slidr, which passed in front of Nagrindr Gate, was frozen over. Cautiously Sleipnir walked on the ice until they reached the gate. Hermodr tried it but found it tightly shut and secured from the other side. He dismounted and tightened the girth around Sleipnir, remounted and pulled on the reins to back Sleipnir up a bit. Then he dug his spurs into the horse's side. Sleipnir in a mighty leap cleared the gate. They rode on to Helheimr up to the Hela's hall Elidnir where Hermodr dismounted and entered.

He could see Hela seated at the head of the table wearing diamonds, silver, and gold. But even their brilliance couldn't hide her deathly countenance. Baldr sat to her right and Nanna to her left. Baldr looking pale and tired, wore a crown of withered flowers. The feast was spread out before Baldr and Nanna, along with many precious gifts. Yet the two Æsir had not touched any of the offerings. Hela reached over and picked up another crown of flowers to set on Nanna's head. The flowers shriveled up and died at her touch. She handed them to Litr who scurried around behind Nanna, climbed upon a table and placed the wreath on Nanna's head.

Hela looked over and noticed Hermodr. "Who are you to enter here while still having the hue of one who lives?"

Hermodr shuddered at her half-living and half-dead face. "I have come to ask that you allow Baldr and Nanna to return to Asgardr and the living. They've been done a great wrong. Their time to visit you has not yet come so I am here to ask for their release."

Hela dismissed his arguments. "What argument can you present to convince me their time has not yet come? They are here, aren't they? Only those who belong are here."

Hermodr simply replied, "But then I am here and I don't belong. So, it's not always true that only those who belong are here."

Hela thought for a moment.

Hermodr remained silent.

Hela signaled for Litr to fetch a drink for Nanna and continued, "These two are honored guests here and I'm treating them quite well. Spread about are the gifts I've given them. I'll see to their needs from now on. Tell the Æsir Baldr and Nanna will be taken care of. I'll treat them as if they were my own beloved brother and sister."

The words she spoke reminded Hermodr of how the Æsir had dealt with Fenriswulf and Midgardrsormr, Hela's siblings. The thought of harm coming to Baldr and Nanna was almost too much for him. But before he could speak Hela left the hall.

Hermodr went up to Baldr and Nanna to embrace them. The three spent the night talking. Try as he might, he couldn't cheer them up. He tried to offer them hope. But, that's difficult when it's all hopeless. Baldr and Nanna seemed resigned to their fate and to the inevitability of the events which had begun with Baldr's death.

Hermodr persisted, "I'll try to talk to Hela again tomorrow. Perhaps there's still some way I can convince her to let you both go. Maybe there's some offer I can make her which she'll accept."

Baldr spoke, "She'll never let me go. I'm the prize. But she really has no interest in Nanna, and I think would prefer she wasn't here. So, perhaps, you can at least persuade her to let Nanna leave this awful place."

Before Hermodr could answer, Nanna broke in, "I'll never leave your side Baldr. If you are doomed here, then so am I. I'll leave only if you are at my side when I do."

Hermodr and Baldr both tried to convince her to return to Asgardr. But she was adamant about staying wherever Baldr was and the subject was dropped.

The next morning Hermodr went to another hall where Hela was holding forth, passing judgment on the new arrivals into her domain. Her voice was clear and strong as she damned those who passed in front of her to eternal torment. Even the raging waters in the great cauldron Hvergelmir and the swords and axes which clanged against each other in the river Slidr could not drown out her sentences.

He could see off in the distance those who were walking to Nastrond, the strand of corpses. They waded through streams of poison, back and forth with no conceivable purpose. But even that was preferrable to what awaited them after they were finished with that punishment. For then they were cast into Hvergelmir and served up as food for the serpent Nidhoggr.

Hermodr approached the throne. "I would have a further word with you."

She looked down on him, "You again? If you don't leave soon I'll cast you into Hvergelmir. I have no further use for conversation with you."

Hermodr clenched his fists as he spoke, "Your threats don't scare me. You have power only over the dead. Everyone here looks on me with jealousy and envy, for I'm still alive and breathing, with blood coursing through my veins. My heart yet beats. So let's stop the threats and get on with what my purpose is. As I look around here I see you have many fine warriors to fight your battles. Many who are willing to do your evil deeds. How could Baldr, who is so unwilling to be here, be missed? All of Asgardr weeps for his return."

Hela sat up abruptly, "What is that you say?"

Hermodr had to think for a moment. His speech was unplanned and he had just been saying whatever came into his mind. "All of Asgardr weeps for his return."

She seemed surprised. Perhaps because no one wept for her return. "All cry for the loss of Baldr? That I can't believe, for no one is loved that much. But you have given me an idea for a wager. If what you say is true, and all do weep for Baldr's return, I'll allow it. It's as simple as that. But if only one person or thing resists mourning his passing, then he'll stay with me and you'll make no further efforts to get him back. Do you agree? Or, were your words only that, words?"

All at once Hermodr had some hope, "What I say is true. I'll return to Asgardr at once and gather the proof you need."

He left the hall and rushed back to Baldr and Nanna with the news, "Soon I'll return for you and then all will be right again."

Baldr and Nanna seemed doubtful. "I'm not certain all will weep for me. So, in case this is the last time we meet, Nanna and I would like to send some gifts back with you."

Baldr handed Hermodr the arm ring Draupnir to be given back to Odin. They both sent a small golden ring to Fulla. But they sent the most gifts to Baldr's mother, Frigg. She was given an embroidered tapestry, some linen, a carpet of green, a mourning veil, and a handkerchief with which to wipe her eyes.

Before Hermodr left, Baldr once again tried to get Nanna to return with him. But she again refused. So Hermodr bid them a sad farewell, leapt on Sleipnir, and hurried back to Asgardr.

He was spotted by Heimdallr on guard on Bifrost. As soon as he saw Hermodr, Heimdallr mounted Gulltoppr and rode to Odin's hall and burst in with the news, "Father, Hermodr approaches. He cannot be more than half a day away."

Odin just stared out the window."

Heimdallr was confused why Odin wasn't as excited as he was, "He's returned with news of Baldr and Nanna. Why aren't you excited."

Odin answered, "I have also seen Hermodr in the distance. And that's what's troubling."

Heimdallr still didn't get it, "But he has returned. He's journeyed to the darkest reaches of Helheimr and has returned."

Odin responded, "Yes, he has returned. But did you see Baldr or Nanna with him? If Hela had granted our request for Baldr's and Nanna's safe return they would be riding with him."

Heimdallr's spirits sank. His father was right. Hermodr had failed.

Odin looked kindly on his son, "Go back to Bifrost so you might welcome Hermodr home to Asgardr. And, as soon as he returns bring him to the courtyard for a Thing, so he can report any news."

The Æsir gathered in the courtyard waiting for Hermodr's return. But there was no joy as they waited. Everyone knew Heimdallr's message had said only Hermodr could be seen riding back. There was no sign of Baldr or Nanna.

Heimdallr on Gultoppr, and Hermodr on Slipnir, rode into the courtyard. The Æsir quickly gathered round and began pummoling him with questions even before he dismounted. He waved them aside, dismounted and turned to Odin, "Hela would not let Baldr leave."

There were many sighs as Hermodr spoke those words. But he continued, "She has made us an offer, though. If everything will weep for Baldr, then Baldr and Nanna will be allowed to leave Niflhel. But if only one thing refuses, no matter how trivial, then she'll keep Baldr and Nanna with her."

Word spread quickly through the crowd. There was some hope. Baldr and Nanna might yet return. And if they did, then Ragnarokr would be pushed further into the future. The Norns would be wrong.

Odin signaled for the Valkyries, "I command you to go to all the Worlds of the Tree and spread word that everything and everyone is to weep for Baldr. And those tears will cry Baldr out of Niflhel. He's sadly missed by all, and I'm sure many already weep for him. Baldr will soon be back with us."

The Valkyries rode off spreading the word. And everything complied. Throughout Midgardr, Asgardr, Jotunheimr, Svartalfheimr, Alfheimr; to the north, south, east and west; all things wept.

Soon the Valkyries were on their way back to Asgardr, their mission accomplished. Everything had wept. As they rode through the Jarnvidr Forest they came to a cave. Crouching in its entranceway was a gnarled old crone.

The Valkyries stopped and discussed the old crone. None could remember having seen her before, which meant, she had not been asked if she had wept for Baldr.

Most of the Valkyries stayed where they were so as not to frighten her. Only a few quietly approached so as not to frighten her, "Have you wept for Baldr so he might be returned to the living?"

Another of the Valkyries continued, "He is beloved by all and I'm sure your tears have flowed as greatly as the others we've met."

But, instead of acknowledging what they had hoped to hear, she laughed, "Me? Cry for Baldr? Why should I cry for him? His goodness disturbs me. No one should be that good. It's unnatural."

She retreated into the cave. Some of the Valkyries followed, "Who are you that you would wish someone so pure and good as Baldr to be kept in Helheimr with Hela?"

The hag answered through her twisted mouth, "I'm Thokk and I'll never weep for Baldr. He has never given me joy. If it falls to me to save Baldr then I refuse. Let Hela keep what she has."

The Valkyries begged the old hag to reconsider. She answered with derisive laughter. The more they begged, the harder she laughed, until all, even those in Niflhel heard. One of the Valkyries recognized the laugh. "That malicious laugh can belong to only one. And I can only think of one who would be evil enough to deny Baldr a chance to return to us. It's Loki."

The Valkyries rushed forward to grab the hag. But she disappeared, and where she had been standing there flowed a poisonous stream. As they left the cave the entrance closed behind them and merged into solid rock.

They sadly took the news back to Asgardr that there was one who had not wept. So Baldr and Nanna had to remain in Helheimr with Hela until the ending of all things and the last great battle. Only then would they be freed.

Chapter 24

Vali the Avenger

Now that it was certain Baldr and Nanna were to remain in Helheimr, his death had to be avenged. It mattered little the murder had been unintentional. The fact remained that blood had been spilled on the sacred ground of Asgardr and some sort of atonement had to be made. Hodr would have to be killed.

Hodr sought refuge in Breidablik, Baldr's estate. Since the land was a gridastadr, sacred place, none of the Æsir could enter and slay him. If they did, their crime would be judged just as great as the one they sought to avenge.

During the day Hodr stayed in Feikstaf. At night he roamed through the dark forests on the property. In the darkness no one could see to find him. And if someone did hunt him he'd meet them where he had the advantage. In the dark a blind man is king.

By tradition the avenging of a death fell to the closest kin. Hodr being Baldr's immediate older brother, by a few minutes, should have been the avenger. But he could hardly have been expected to slay himself. If Odin fathered another son, that child would become Baldr's closest kin and thus the avenger. Odin remembered the prophecy from Volva that he would have a son named Vali by Rindr of Vestraslir. But he didn't know who Rindr was.

Odin remembered once Mimir had spoken of Vestraslir. So, he paid his uncle a visit at Mimirsbrunnr Well, "What can you tell me of Vestraslir, its customs, the people there, who rules it?"

Mimir's knowledge was sparse. "I know very little about Vestraslir or it's people. But, I'll gladly tell you all I know. Baldr was my kin, and I'll do what I can to help avenge his death."

Odin had learned some new information from Mimir, but he needed more. He sent for Hermodr. "I have another task for you. Take Sleipnir and ride to the northernmost region of Midgardr, to the land of the Finns, and seek out the green ice castle of a wizard named Hrossthjof, whose name means appropriately enough, horse thief. His name should tell you a little about his character, so be careful he doesn't trick you. And always keep

one eye on Sleipnir. Though, I think Sleipnir can take care of himself he would be a fine specimen for Hrossthjof to steal.

Hrossthjof's sister is Heidr. His brother is the hrymthursar Hrimnir. He alone of the men in Midgardr can see into the future. Learn what you can about the woman who will bear my son. Learn of the one who will be known as Vali the Avenger.'

The Valkyries brought Hermodr's armor to him. As he turned to leave, Odin gave him a final admonition. "Remember the warnings I have given you about Hrossthjof. He has been known to transfix those who visit him and then rob and slay them. Be not a bird to his snake. In order to help you I want you to take my runic staff Gambanteinn instead of your spear. It will give you more protection. You will not fool Hrossthjof about who you are. He will know. Be prepared and be on your guard. A story of your death would make a fine addition to the evening tales he tells. There is great danger where you are going."

Hermodr was off immediately. Sleipnir rode swiftly northward through Midgardr. The closer they came to Hrossthjof's land the more the storms raged around them; driving rain, then sleet and snow. Finally, a raging blizzard marked their entry into Hrossthjof's land. High mountains whose distances were distorted by the perpetual twilight loomed before Hermodr. But Sleipnir was able to fly over them. And once past these obstacles things became suspiciously easier. It was almost as if Sleipnir were drawn to Hrossthjof's ice castle. But this didn't last long. As they neared the castle they were plagued by demonlike monsters and ghostly apparitions which nipped at Sleipnir's feet and lunged at Hermodr seeking to pull him from his mount. But Hermodr fended them off with Odin's magic runic staff.

Hrossthjof had laid various traps for them in the snow. Sometimes what looked like sure footing was just a thin covering of ice over a bottomless crevasse. But somehow Sleipnir was able to sense where the true path lay and avoid the false way set before them. Infuriated Hrossthjof sent avalanches of snow cascading down on them, but these Sleipnir was able to outrun until finally they reached the castle's front gate.

Here they met Hrossthjof who had taken on the form of a jotun. He came at them with a magical lariat and tried to loop it around the two. Instead Hermodr used Odin's magic staff to cause the rope to wind back around Hrossthjof until he was securely fettered. Hrossthjof realized he was not dealing with an ordinary mortal of Midgardr, but a messenger sent from the Æsir. "I didn't realize with whom I battled. Often I have to contend with visitors who are not very nice, so I'm always prepared. Now that I know you carry the magic of the Æsir with you I will no longer attempt to harm you. I swear this by the river Leiptr, upon whom vows are sacred and I cannot break lest I risk eternal damnation in Niflhel."

Hermodr was satisfied with the oath and released Hrossthjof. "I've been sent by Odin to quiz you about the avenger who will be born to slay Hodr. Tell me what you know of a woman named Rindr and how Odin might woo and win her love and gain a son by her.'

Hrossthjof went into a trancelike state. He carved runes into the frozen snow and began chanting spells in a language which Hermodr did not understand. The sky darkened and the earth shook. In the distance he heard the sounds of tortured souls reluctantly giving up the knowledge which dead men have.

Still in a trance Hrossthjof lifted up his arm and pointed off in the distance. "Look to the mountain. It will tell you the future."

Hermodr looked in the direction Hrossthjof indicated. The clouds darkened and the sky parted. He could see a mountain white with snow. But suddenly blood flowed from the peak until the side of the mountain ran red. Then rising up out of the snow was a beautiful woman carrying a baby cradled in her arms. She set the child on the ground whereupon he immediately grew into a youth. He carried a long bow in his hand and a full set of arrows hung quivered on his back. He moved apart from his mother, drew a sharp-pointed arrow, fitted it to his bow and fired. The loosed arrow arched into the sky in a flame of light that disappeared into the night as darkness closed around the vision.

Hrossthjof interpreted the vision for Hermodr. "The blood of Baldr has stained Asgardr and must be avenged. The woman is Princess Rindr, the daughter of King Billingr of the Ruthenes. Her son will be Vali who will slay one brother to avenge the death of another. He will be the last born of the Æsir. But for this to come about Odin must cast off the mantle of one of the Æsir and win Rindr as a mortal of Midgardr."

Hermodr sat astride Sleipnir pondering the knowledge which had been revealed to him. Hrossthjof walked away until he seemed to merge with the snow, then disappeared from sight. Hermodr made no attempt to stop him since he had the knowledge he wanted. He hurried back to Asgardr.

Odin listened to Hermodr and knew what he had to do. He quickly outfitted himself as a mortal of Midgardr. Wearing a blue cloak, a broad-brimmed hat pulled low to hide his missing eye, and carrying his spear Gungnir and his sword Notung, he immediately set off for King Billingr's realm.

Once he arrived in Ruthenia he sought an audience with King Billingr. "I've come a long distance to offer you my services. I know you're beset by those who are preparing to invade your kingdom. It might be of interest to you that I'm skilled in all the warrior arts and have commanded many armies. If there is anything I can do to help you, you have but to order me."

King Billingr was too happy at this serendipitous occurrence to be suspicious. "As you can see I'm too old to command my army, yet you don't look that much younger?"

Odin responded, "Appearances can be deceiving. Although I'm older than many realize, my body remains firm and able."

Billingr nodded in agreement, "My generals are young and lack experience. Many years ago I defeated the last of my enemies so my generals have not had to fight. They are at a loss to know what to do. Would that I had a son to take over for me. But I have only been blessed with Rindr, my daughter."

Odin replied, "Surely she has given you a grandson who can be taught all the skills necessary to lead?"

Billingr answered, "Alas, no. She has ambitions in life. She wants to be a Valkyrie and ride to the battle with Odin's messengers. Although she has many wooers, none have succeeded in winning her hand. She insults them and turns them away, knowing that only those maidens untouched by a man can be chosen as a messenger for Odin and ride the Wild Hunt with him. I doubt I ever will have a grandson. You seem to have the wisdom of your age so I accept your offer to lead my army against my enemies. Teach my generals all you can about the maneuvers of war."

Although Billingr thought the meeting had concluded Odin added one last thought, "I will easily defeat your enemy. And perhaps, after my victories have once again restored calm to Ruthenia, I can try my hand at winning Rindr and bring a grandson into your life. Rindr's suitors have been young warriors. Perhaps their inexperience was all too obvious. Maybe my age and what I can teach her will win her hand."

Billingr replied, "After you've commanded my army and defeated my enemies, you have my permission to see what you can do with Rindr. I think of all the tasks before you, Rindr will be the hardest. But, I haven't anything to lose for your trying, and perhaps an heir to gain."

Odin took command of the army and inspired such confidence in the troops that it took very few battles to rout the enemy and win the war. The men were amazed at the courage of their leader. Many in Ruthenia thought the soldiers were exaggerating the abilities of the stranger. There were some who said during the last battle the general rode off against the enemy alone. He waved his spear and caused such fear in the enemy they discarded their weapons and ran.

No matter how much his legend grew, or was exaggerated, there was no doubt but that it was because of him the land was no longer under attack. King Billingr offered him great rewards and a permanent role in the ruling of the kingdom. "Take what you want from me. It's because of you I still have a kingdom left to govern. I offer you whatever you desire as your reward."

Odin knew what he wanted, "I remind you of our first conversation. I would like Rindr's hand in marriage."

Billingr answered, "I would be proud to have you as my son-in-law. But that is something I can't command from her. She is free to choose her own husband. If she willingly chooses you, then I will gladly perform the ceremony."

King Billingr motioned for a servant to leave and ask Rindr to the meeting. Moments later, when she arrived her father introduced her to the stranger. "This is the general I have talked of during our dinners together. He has saved our country from the barbarians who sought to overrun us and enslave you and me. He has brought freedom to our country. I've offered him riches and power, but all this he has refused and seeks only your hand in marriage. I have judged him a worthy son-in-law and have agreed if you also agree. If it weren't for him then you might now be forced into a marriage with one of our enemies and someone of considerably less stature than this noble warrior. What say you?"

Rindr was angry she was being bartered about, "You may give away your kingdom, and your power to strangers, but I am not to be given away. If he wants my hand I will gladly give it to him." She stepped up to Odin and slapped him, then continued looking at her father, "You know I'm promised to Odin. In order to ride as a Valkyrie I must maintain my purity of mind, heart, and spirit. No husband."

Her father answered as all fathers answer their daughters, "Rindr, be practical. Being a Valkyrie and riding the Wild Hunt is a dream. No one from this Land of the Tree has ever become a Valkyrie. Just look at him. He is the finest warrior I've ever seen, a great general, and I might add not half bad to look at even though he's a little old for you. He'll make a fine husband."

Rindr spoke her final say before turning to leave, "If you like him so much then you marry him, for I will not." She went back to her chamber and gave orders to the servant in the outer chamber, "No one is to enter my room." With that she went in to her room, slammed and locked the door behind her.

King Billingr apologized for his daughter. Odin cast off the insult. "I'm no longer needed here. I'm going to leave immediately to set off on other journeys. Maybe I'll have better luck with them."

King Billingr tried to persuade him otherwise. But it was no use and Odin departed. But he was not gone long.

Outside he cast off the guise of the general and took on the form of a middle-aged, one-eyed man. He called himself Rosterus and set up shop as a goldsmith in Ruthenia. Soon his fame spread throughout the land. The necklaces, bracelets, and rings he made from bronze, silver, and most of all gold, were highly prized in the realm. His designs were intricate. The links almost a puzzle as to how he got them to twine about, in and out, over and under each other. His clasps were ingenious and magical in the way they held the jewelry to the wearer. And no amount of tugging could cause his jewelry to break. The pieces were so highly polished they could reflect even the smallest amount of light at the darkest hour. And the appearance of the wearer seemed to be favorably enhanced by the jewelry.

Many of the ladies-in-waiting who attended Rindr wore his jewelry. Yet she seemed unimpressed by his handiwork as she commanded her ladies-in-waiting, "Keep your baubles away from me. My wrists must be unencumbered if I am to wield a sword properly. And a clanging necklace bouncing up and down on my chest as I rode to the Wild Hunt would only be a distraction."

Still Rosterus had hopes. He journeyed to the castle and sought a meeting with her, bringing a necklace, bracelet, and ring to present as gifts for her. They were the best pieces he had ever made. "I give you these as tokens of my love."

She threw the gifts to the floor, "That's what I think of your love. I'm not to be bought with trinkets, baubles, or gew gaws. I don't seek the company of men. It's at cross purposes with my desires. Leave at once and never return."

Rosterus left Ruthenia never to be heard from again. Soon his jewelry became the most valuable in the land because there was never anyone else who could match the skill of his artisanship.

Odin returned to Ruthenia for a third time. He took the form of a young warrior, handsome beyond belief. His only fault was a missing eye whom many thought he must have lost in some great battle.

It became known throughout the kingdom that his sole purpose was to win the hand of Rindr. King Billingr approved and gave him permission to woo his daughter. He brought her presents and talked to her of love. He sang songs in praise of her beauty and spoke of the rich full life they would have together. He was most persuasive and at last it seemed his efforts were to be rewarded. At the conclusion of one of their meetings Rindr whispered in his ear, "Come to my chamber tonight. But let no one know of your visit. Then I'll properly reward your efforts, which I have so far disdained."

That night after everyone in the castle had retired, Odin quietly went to her room. The servant in the outer chamber had been dismissed and found the door unlatched and slightly opened. He took this as an invitation and went in and made his way to her bed. She seemed to be asleep. Odin bent forward to kiss her. As he did so she let out a

scream and struck him on the chin with her staff. He fell backwards, startled. She yelled a robber was in her room. Two guards appeared with an attack dog and surrounded Odin.

Odin surprised his captors by running between them. They released the dog, but before it could catch him Odin pulled a piece of bark covered with runic inscriptions from beneath his cloak. He touched Rindr lightly on the breast and brow with it, chanted the sixteenth charm he had learned while hanging on Yggdrasyll, and then leaped out the window never to be seen again.

Rindr was immediately affected by the magic. She fell into the arms of her guards and was carried to her bed. She seemed dead, and lay in this state for many days. When she finally awakened she was morose and despondent. Nothing could bring her out of her black mood. She rarely spoke and eventually kept to her chamber. Meals were brought to her room where she played at her food and ate very little. She grew weaker, thinner, and more depressed. King Billingr sent messengers throughout the kingdom in search of someone to cure his daughter.

A wise woman named Vecka arrived at the castle and sought an audience with King Billingr. "I have heard from your messengers you seek someone to cure your daughter. I am skilled in medicine and am blessed with the skills of Menglod. I think her madness will be an easy illness to remedy."

King Billingr was elated someone had come forth to help his daughter. "You shall have all you desire. Tell me what medicines you need and how many helpers you require. Here at the castle we have the best leeches in the land for bleeding. Just say the word and I will have them brought to you."

A servant had already started to leave the hall when Vecka held up her hand to stop him. "I won't need them, nor will I need any assistants. I work alone. But I will guarantee my results."

She was shown to Rindr's chamber and began her ministrations at once. She attended Rindr by first giving her foot baths and warm massages. She mixed strange elixirs which had a calming effect on Rindr. But Vecka didn't seem satisfied. She went back to King Billingr. "I'll need to use some drastic measures."

King Billingr was surprised. "But she seems better now. Her color has returned and she is no longer as nervous nor as jumpy as she had been. She no longer shrinks from me when I approach."

Vecka continued, "But she'll get no better than this unless I can give her the final treatment. I would like her bound to the bed hand and foot so she'll be unable to resist. I'll spend the night with her. There are likely to be many screams from her room, but don't enter. It's for the best. I must have your word on this if she is ever to get better."

King Billingr gave his word all conditions would be met. "Is it necessary she suffer so much her screams will be as frightening as you say? Will the resistance be such that she has to be bound?"

Vecka answered, "I assure you there is no other way. But after it's over she'll be happier than you have ever seen her before."

Everything was prepared according to Vecka's instructions and she was left alone with her patient. King Billingr ordered the guards to leave the outer chamber and allow no one to enter until Vecka gave orders that it was all right. King Billingr waited in the hallway outside his daughter's chamber, staying awake all night. But, he heard no screams.

Vecka approached Rindr and touched her on the brow and breast. The madness departed. Rindr looked up at the wise woman who leaned over and whispered in her ear, "You'll have my child who will be the last born of the Æsir. He'll be Vali who will avenge the death of Baldr. It isn't fated that you remain a virgin and ride with the Valkyries. Your wyrd follows another course."

Rindr nodded in agreement and the bonds fell away and she was free. She held out her arms awaiting the embrace of her lover.

The wise woman lay down on the bed beside Rindr. And as they kissed and made love throughout the night the disguise Vecka wore was momentarily discarded and Vali was conceived. They slept locked in each others' arms until late the next morning. Vecka left never to return.

King Billingr never left his vigil outside the door to Rindr's chamber. The next day he was surprised when Rindr left her room and invited him to join her for an afternoon meal. He had never seen her so radiant.

He went into his daughter's chamber and yelled for Vecka to give her his thanks but she was nowhere to be found. Where had she gone? He knew she hadn't gone out the door because he had kept guard all night. Nor had any of his soldiers seen her leave the room, hallway, or castle. The only other way out of Rindr's room was through the window. But they were high off the ground. A fall would kill anyone from that height.

Rindr didn't explain anything, just took her father's hand, "Please, let's go eat. I'm famished."

They went to the banquet hall where King Billingr ordered a magnificent meal and invited others to a celebration in honor of his daughter's recovery.

Soon it became obvious Rindr was with child. King Billingr was happy but extremely puzzled. He thought perhaps the young warrior had managed to make love with her after all one of those nights he had stayed at the castle. No matter, what was important was that he was going to be a grandfather. Rindr would not be the last of his kin to rule his land. His would have a grandson to carry on after Rindr had ruled.

Odin made his way back to Asgardr to await the arrival and coming of age of his son. He found things had not changed. Hodr still stayed within the safety of Breidablik's boundaries, his loneliness haunting him. He followed the same routine. During the day he stayed in Feikstaf, at night he wandered in the forest waiting for the warning from the birds telling him when morning was approaching so he could return to the hall's safety and hide away from others.

He now had several aids the troll Mimring had made for him. These included a shield of darkness, a magic shirt which made him invisible, and a magic sword. But none of this really mattered. He cursed the Norns for weaving the fate that had made him the slayer of the only friend he had ever had, his brother Baldr.

Although not meaning him harm, the other Æsir had always shunned him because of his blindness. They were always testing their warrior skills and battling with each other in fun. He had been unable to join in. The only ones who had understood his need for companionship had been Baldr and Nanna. Now they were gone. He had decided that, although, now he carried powerful weapons he would try not to use them. He had already caused enough trouble and seemed to want someone to avenge Baldr's death and put him out of his misery.

Then one mid-winter day the moment came which had long been hope for. Heimdallr saw a young child approaching in the distance on Bifrost, no more than a baby really, carrying a bow and quiver of arrows. When the child finally reached him Heimdallr barred his way. "No child whose hair is messy and uncombed, and whose hands have never been washed, may pass into Asgardr. No child who still has that pungent odor of a baby about him may enter Asgardr. Depart and return when you have grown up and bathed."

The child looked up to Heimdallr and spoke in a commanding voice, "Take me to Valhalla so that I might meet with my father."

Heimdallr was impressed with the courage the child showed and escorted him to the entrance of Valhalla where they were stopped by Hermodr. "No visitor may enter here who has not met with a valiant death in battle. I see no wounds on you. Although I see dirt, try as I might there is no blood encrusted on your skin. Depart and come again when you are older and have proven yourself."

The child spoke. His voice had already deepened since the last time he had spoken, "I wish to see Odin, my father. Delay me no longer for I have important work ahead of me."

Hermodr followed the command and stood to one side and motioned for him to enter. The Æsir, Einherjar and Valkyries stopped eating and stared as Vali approached the head of the table where Odin was seated.

Odin stood up to welcome his son, "I acknowledge to all assembled this child is my son Vali by the Princess Rindr, daughter of King Billingr of Ruthenia. He is the one for whom we have waited so long. He shall avenge the Baldr's death and make things right once again in Asgardr. He will bring us all honor. I hereby give him permission to use my hall, Valaskjalf as his own." He motioned his son over beside him. "Speak to the brave warriors gathered here." He picked Vali up and stood him on his throne, since no one could see him because his head barely reached above the table.

Vali cleared his throat, his voice continuing to grow deeper. "I vow before all of you that I shall neither comb my hair nor wash until my deed is done and I have restored honor to this land."

There were many doubters and one yelled out, "How can a mere child, a baby, slay Hodr? He now has powerful weapons to protect himself. Even the birds have become his friends and warn him when anyone approaches. Many of the Æsir are afraid to face him. Are we to expect you to slay him?"

Vali drew himself to his full height, which wasn't much, barely past the knees of most of the warriors, and spoke, "Though I am but one night old I am gaining strength from Asgardr. By tomorrow I'll be fully grown and strong enough to best Hodr."

He seemed to grow even as he spoke.

And true enough by the next morning he was fully grown and had donned a magnificent warrior garb he found in Valaskjalf. Stopping to neither eat nor drink he went to Breidablik to find Hodr and avenge Baldr's death. He tried to enter the hall, but there were charms protecting it. He would have to wait until evening and go into the forest to find Hodr.

Hodr had returned to the darkness of the forest While roaming about he noticed the birds were quiet. He yelled out to them, "Why aren't you talking with me? Is something wrong? I am lonely for your songs. My life is nothing but darkness. Your chirping eases my thoughts and guides my way."

Still there was no response. The darkness engulfed him. He was so alone.

The silence lasted but a few moment more, then he heard a small peep, "All of the other birds have flown away. I'm still in my nest and too young to fly or I would leave also. I must warn you, there's a stranger in the forest who will do you great harm. Vali the Avenger has come."

"Vali the Avenger has come...Vali the Avenger has come...Vali the Avenger has come..." The little bird's song echoed in the trees.

Hodr was truly frightened and turned around in circles not knowing where to hide. He was alone in the dark and could sense the danger all round him.

Then he heard a voice call out to him. "Hodr, I'm your brother Vali. Protect yourself for the hour appointed by the Norns has come. The moment of your wyrd has come."

Hodr was frightened. He had never engaged in battle and wasn't quite certain what to do. No one had taught him warrior skills. He raised his shield of darkness before him and ran towards the sound of Vali's voice, waving his sword of terror every which way. Vali stood his ground and loosed one arrow after another toward the area of the waving sword. Because, though Hodr was hidden by the shield, he held the sword in front of the shield, making it visible and giving Hodr a place to aim.

Suddenly, the shield of darkness dropped to the ground, balanced briefly and then fell to one side revealing Hodr to Vali. One arrow had pierced clean through his heart and he was dead. He was finally at peace.

Vali's shouts of triumph were heard throughout Asgardr and the Æsir ran to the forest to see what had happened. They saw a tall physically beautiful young warrior standing over Hodr's lifeless body. He had brought honor to himself and the Æsir.

Hodr was carried to a funeral pyre and sent on his journey to Niflhel. No one knew if his journey would take him deep enough to see his brother, but many hoped it would. Some of those gathered were sad at the events which had occurred. Many thought in the backs of their minds the wrong person had been slain. After all, Loki still walked amongst them, and hadn't he been the one to give Hodr the spear and direct his aim towards Baldr?

Soon Hodr arrived in Niflheimr and continued ever downward to Niflhel, Helheimr, and to Hela's hall, Elidner. He stood apart from everyone else in the hall wondering what was to happen to him. He looked about and for the first time realized the infirmities of life had been cured and he could see. A man approached him with a compassionate look on his face. Hodr was calmed just looking at him. He seemed different from the others in the hall. He was tall and well-formed, whereas the others were thin and downcast. The stranger spoke to him and Hodr recognized Baldr's voice. "Welcome my brother. I'm glad you're here. We can be a great comfort to each other."

Hodr realized he had been forgiven for his crime. "But how can you say that? I was responsible for your death."

Baldr replied, "Don't be deceived. It was Loki who caused my death, and Loki who prevented Nanna and me from leaving here. There is no fault on your part. I'm sorry you

have had to suffer so much. Let's go to Nanna and talk. She'll be so happy to see you. For the first time since we arrived here I feel our sadness is gone and we can be happy."

Baldr put his arm around his brother's shoulder and led him off. There were tears in Hodr's eyes.

Back in Asgardr Odin sat silently in his hall. Were things really set right by Baldr's death being avenged? At least Asgardr had an additional warrior for the final battle.

Odin continued brooding. He knew things still weren't right.

Chapter 25

Odin is Banished

The story of Odin's unnatural wooing of Rindr and Vali's subsequent conception gradually became known, with a little help from Loki. A Thing was called to discuss the matter. The assembled generally agreed Odin had performed a disgraceful act when he turned himself into a woman in order to gain entry into Rindr's chamber. They all agreed the only adequate punishment was banishment. Odin accepted it.

Odin reluctantly bid farewell to Frigg, who remained behind weeping bitter tears for him. He then said his farewells to the few in Asgardr who had defended him, and went to Midgardr where he wandered throughout the land hoping to gain additional knowledge which might help him at the last great battle. He waited patiently for his eventual return to Asgardr.

While he was suffering his banishment, Ullr, Sif and Aurvandil's son, Thor's stepson, assumed the role of leader of the Æsir. He was chosen for this position because of his noble bearing and courage as a warrior. He was an expert archer and known throughout Midgardr as the god of the skis. He was married to the ambitious Skadi who delighted in his promotion to the highest throne because her status was increased, too.

To minimize the impact of his reign he assumed Odin's name and tried to rule as wisely as Odin had. He managed to do so for ten years, but without achieving a great deal of success in turning back the ongoing events of Ragnarokr. Everything was progressively getting worse. Soon there were plots against him and eventually an evil sorcerer named Mithotyn deposed him and reigned in his stead. But Mithotyn's reign was short-lived and remembered as one of great evil and filled with tragedy. Times became so bad and his rule in Asgardr so dictatorial, that he too was overthrown.

The next to assume the rule of Asgardr were Odin's two brothers, Vili and Ve. They immediately tried to restore calm and called a Thing to discuss the unsettled rule of Asgardr since Odin had been banished. They presented their ideas on how the situation might be improved.

Vili spoke, "We have been badly ruled under Ullr and Mithotyn. Ve and I don't wish to rule in place of our brother who is the rightful ruler here. So, we have decided to use

our present authority and send messengers to Midgardr to find Odin and bring him back so he can once again assume his rightful position as leader of the Æsir. We decree his banishment is over."

Cheers went up amongst some of the Æsir. Ve continued, "It was a mistake to send Odin away, a mistake we've paid for ever since. I only hope Odin's banishment all these years has not hastened the last great battle." But, in his heart, he knew it had.

It took the messengers many months to find Odin. But when they did and told him the news that he was once again welcome in Asgardr, he quickly returned and claimed his throne.

Seven months had passed from when Mithotyn had been deposed until Odin's return in the month of May. Those in Midgardr sensed things were once again right in Asgardr and put on merriments to celebrate. The May Festivals continued ever after at that time of the year to celebrate Odin's return to Asgardr.

Frigg greeted her husband warmly as he entered the courtyard to attend the Thing. Odin paused only briefly to speak to the assemblage. "I've tried to use my time in banishment wisely and to learn. I only hope I've learned enough to be of some help in bringing peace once again to our land. I hold no bitterness towards those who caused my banishment. Time is too short to waste on useless revenge. My first act will be to banish the use of all forms of galdr and seidr. We shouldn't have to use mystic arts to bring about events which are good and just. They should come of their own accord."

Unfortunately, Odin's first command brought some dissension from the Vanir. Galdr and seidr were their major forms of power and protection. They just did not have the brute strength the Æsir did and had had to rely more on other arts to achieve their victories in battle. But there was nothing they could do about the command from Odin. They accepted his leadership and, therefore, followed his orders, even though those orders served to actually weaken the defense of Asgardr, rather than to strengthen it.

After the Thing Odin went to his hall, Valaskjalf, to the watchtower and once again sat on his throne Hlidskjalf and began his surveillance of all the Worlds of the Tree, to familiarize himself with what had been going on while he was gone, to see how the balance of powers had shifted, and hopefully to see something which might help the Æsir. Frigg joined him on her throne and looked over at him. She smiled and was glad for his return. He didn't return her smile. Matters weighed heavily on his mind. But he was glad to be with her again.

Chapter 26

Loki is Banished

Asgardr settled into a calm, even hopeful state. True, Idunn, Bragi, Baldr, Nanna, and Hodr were gone, but the other signs of Ragnarokr had not yet come about. Many hoped the prophecies had been wrong and things would go on as they were for many generations to come.

One thing irritating many in Asgardr was Loki. He seemed to flaunt his presence more and more. Many felt he should be gotten rid of. But he had been clever, and as yet there was no cause. So, generally, he was ignored. And the more he was ignored the more outrageous his behavior became trying to be noticed. Many felt it wouldn't be long before the patience of even the most moderate and forgiving of the Æsir would reach its limit. Clearly something had to be done.

At the moment Loki was away and Heimdallr had vowed not to let him cross Bifrost when he returned. Just because Loki wasn't banished didn't mean things should be easy for him to come and go as he pleased. He'd have to try a longer route for his journey back to Asgardr. For now, everyone was grateful Loki was away and the problem of what to do about him didn't have to be dealt with, yet.

The troubles with Loki were soon forgotten when invitations from Ægir arrived. Everyone remembered the fun at Ægir and Ran's last feast. The mead had been strong and plentifully brewed in the giant cauldron acquired so long ago by Thor and Tyr. The fall had been beautiful, and having a feast in honor of the harvest would be the perfect way to celebrate. Many of the Æsir sent their messengers to Ægir assuring him they would be there. Even Bragi had decided to attend, after receiving permission from Hela to temporarily leave Niflhel. He tried to persuade Idunn, but she would not leave. She was too sad to attend any celebrations.

The Feast at Ægir's Hall

The places were all set out in Ægir's great hall. Bragi was given a seat of honor to Ægir's left. Odin sat on Ægir's right. Frigg sat to Odin's left wearing a deep azure robe and a helmet made of heron feathers. Just about everyone was in attendance. Thor had arrived a few days before and set up the brewing kettle since he was the only one strong enough to lift it. Then he had departed to Jotunheimr to settle some feuds with a few jotuns, promising to return for the feast if he could.

Loki was unaware of the feast since he hadn't been sent an invitation and no one had bothered to tell him about it. He found out quite by chance when he overheard some gossiping dvergues. A lack of an invitation was a small matter. He hurried to Ægir's hall. Everyone was disappointed to see him and no one made an effort to welcome him. He tried to sit at the table but no one moved over so he could take a seat at one of the benches.

They found it suspicious when he walked to the kitchen and didn't fully shut the kitchen door behind him. They could see him talking to Eldir, Ægir's cook. What was he plotting? He had to be plotting something. It would be unusual if such were not the case. He did not return to the main hall, but stayed in the kitchen. Actually, this was because it was the only way he could have some food and mead. He knew no one in the dining hall would let him eat or drink.

Many of the Æsir had arrived at the feast very sad because Baldr, Nanna, Hodr, and Idunn were not there. Then the feasting started and the mead was served up in plentiful quantities. Gradually everyone's spirits rose and they temporarily forgot all about the evil which seemed set upon destroying them.

Ægir sent for Eldir. He raised his cup to toast his servants and the cook, "My warmest thanks for the bountiful and delicious meal my cook and his aides have prepared for us today."

All assembled raised their cups to join in the toast. Eldir humbly bowed and returned to the kitchen. Just inside the door Loki stopped him, "What's all the shouting and clapping about?"

Eldir proudly told him about the toast, "They feel this is the best meal they've ever had. And even if I do say so myself, I quite agree."

Loki quizzed him, "Enough of that. What else do they talk of?"

Eldir replied, "I've heard them talk of the great battles won by the Æsir, and the great acts of kindness performed by the Vanir. Then, again, they are all boasting of each other's adventures. I've not heard an unkind word spoken amongst themselves."

Loki seemed displeased, "And what do they say of the noble Loki?"

Eldir answered, "Well, I have been listening as I've carried in trays of food, and as yet I haven't heard a word of praise for you, though there have been many against you."

Loki was angry because everyone except him was receiving praise. Even the servants had been praised. "Perhaps I should take a seat now, no matter whose it is. I feel inclined to talk amongst them. I'll mix my insults with their mead." The mischief could be seen in his eyes as he started for the hall.

Eldir put up his hand to stop him, "Be warned of what you do Loki. They don't have a great deal of patience with you. If you treat them badly they'll give you the same in return, and more."

Loki shoved him aside, "Tend to your pots and pans. I'll not have a cook tell me what to do."

Everyone ceased talking when Loki entered. He alone spoke, "Well, I see everyone is interested in my arrival. I'm sorry I haven't brought my invitation with me. It was misplaced and never reached me."

Some of the Æsir mumbled that perhaps he hadn't been sent one.

Loki continued, "Speak up, I can't hear what compliments you have for me. If some of you will move over I'll sit amongst you. That is, I'll sit next to anyone but the craven Bragi. Whom amongst you will share a place and a cup of mead with me?"

No one moved or spoke so Loki continued, "Why do you shun me so? I've as much right as anyone to be here, and more so than most." He looked directly at Bragi.

Bragi replied, "Please leave us so we can enjoy our feast."

Loki became angry, "Why should I leave when the fun is only beginning?"

Bragi made an offer to Loki, "If you'll leave us I'll give you my hall, since I no longer need it, and my horse, since I no longer ride him. In addition, you may have my sword and this precious arm ring. Only leave us in peace."

Loki spurned the offer, "It's true you are no longer worthy of a hall in Asgardr. And why do you need a horse and a sword since you are too weak to fight in battle? Your arm ring probably belongs to Idunn since it's cut like a woman's. And what of Idunn? Where is she now? In whose arms is she resting now that you're away from her? After all, if she will sleep with you, her brother's killer, then she is likely to sleep with anyone. I see many of the Æsir turning their eyes away in guilt. Why even I…"

Bragi rose as if to attack Loki, "You're a liar. No wonder your reputation has brought you the ekename of arch deceiver. I would challenge you to combat if we were elsewhere. But Ægir's hall is hallowed and I'll not defile it out of respect for our host."

Gefjun, who had been sitting to Bragi's right pulled at Bragi's arm. "Sit down, Bragi. Don't waste your words with someone like Loki. Soon his punishment will come."

Loki turned to Gefjun, "Be silent, or I'll name the name of your secret lover, the white god who has to pay you with jewels for your favors – which is the only way he can get any favors." Loki then turned to Odin and continued, "You sit there unsmiling. And well you should. Often you have given victory to the wrong side for your own selfish purposes. You have unjustly caused the deaths of many warriors so the ranks of the Einherjar in Valhalla would swell. What say you to that?"

Odin answered, "How would you know? You haven't been in Asgardr that often, preferring to travel to other lands and father, excuse me, mother monsters. Of course, we shouldn't forget the eight winters you spent on Midgardr disguised as a peasant woman where you went about milking cows for your living and bearing children. You've always had odd ways about you."

Changing into a woman was not a crime Odin should have accused Loki of, for it left Loki with an immediate retort, "Have you forgotten the time you were on the Isle of Samsey? There you practiced all the black arts of seidr, including ergi, sleeping with your own sex. Changing into the form of a woman, since only women can conjure using that magic, you performed many wicked abnormal experiments. Let's also not forget the reason you were banished and also walked on Midgardr, from where you have only so recently returned. You lived there in banishment for ten years, I stayed there of my own free will for only eight years. Tell me, when you visited Midgardr during your banishment did you again become Vecka and visit Rindr? Perhaps you took her away for another unnatural reunion?"

Frigg tried to calm the two, "It seems you both have brought up acts which would be better forgotten."

Loki broke in, "And, of course you have many deeds which would better be forgotten, also. Why didn't you accompany Odin to Midgardr during his exile? Could it be you enjoy being the consort of whomever is leader in Asgardr? After all, Ullr did change his name to Odin. Perhaps he also took what went with that name?"

Odin jumped up to speak, but Loki would not be interrupted, "Now Odin, remember how ages ago we were friends and we mixed our blood together and swore oaths of foster-brotherhood together. You loved me then, did you not? And in that love you vowed never to see me in want. You pledged you would always share with me. If you were drinking I would also be drinking. If there was food on your plate, there would also be food on my plate. Yet how do you treat me now? There you sit drinking and eating and I am not served. I am not even seated."

Odin nodded agreeing what Loki had spoken was true. He motioned to his son, Vidarr, "Give the vile mother of Fenriswulf your seat. It's true that in my youth I did swear such a foolish oath, as we are all wont to do when we are foolishly young."

Vidarr followed his father's wishes and offered his seat to Loki. But as Loki climbed over the bench to sit down a strange thing occurred. The rest of those seated at the table got up to leave. Loki moved away from the table angered by the insult. Everyone, including Vidarr, sat back down.

Loki walked around the banquet hall and began hurling insults at everyone again. He knew all of their faults and wasn't reluctant to shout them out.

Freyr answered back after Loki had paused from insulting the Æsir, "You're a coward and a braggart. Unfortunately you don't have much to brag about, which makes you the worst kind of boaster."

Loki walked over to him, "You don't have long now, Freyr. Soon your words will be silenced. At the last battle you won't be able to defend yourself since you had to give away your weapons in order to win your wife. How does it feel to know the only reason Gerdr lives with you is because she is blackmailed into doing so?"

Before Freyr could respond his sister, Freyja, spoke up, "You tread on thin ice Loki. Be sure of your footing before you slip, or the ice breaks." She had just recently returned to Asgardr from Midgardr with Odr after having found him meditating in a stand of myrtle. In honor of this many couples on Midgardr had begun wearing myrtle during their wedding ceremonies to bring them luck in their marriage.

Loki turned his insults to her, "What have we here, sister defending brother? Or is it mistress defending lover? Of course if you were to speak up and defend your lover you could be champion to all who are here, as well as countless multitudes who are not present including the alfs and dvergar, too. Especially the dvergar. Your necklace Brisingamen speaks for you in that matter. It's no wonder your chariot is pulled by cats." He lifted the necklace, inspecting it, and then let it fall back gently to her breasts as he passed his hand down to her waist.

She pulled his hand away before it could grope any further and spoke in icy tones to him, "You must surely have lost your wits to insult us all like this."

Heimdallr sought to restore some calm to the situation, "Loki, you are now drunk and saying things you don't mean. Why not go outside and sober up a bit. Then come back in and we'll try to start fresh and welcome you."

But Loki was not to be stopped now. He was just getting started. Before he could continue Skadi spoke up, "Loki you are nothing but a cur. Don't feel too smug, your punishment is coming. I see you bound with fetters made from your own sons. The time draws near for you."

Loki answered her remarks, "So you would attempt to insult me. But you have secrets too. Shall we speak of your son Sæming. Odd he doesn't look like Ullr. Could it be because he is your son, but Odin is the father? Have you forgotten I helped bring about your father Thjassi's death? Perhaps my talents as a lover have made you forget?"

Skadi mumbled to herself, "Would that I could forget our vile encounters. You were a hurtful lover."

Sif went over and poured a goblet of ale which she brought to Loki to try and calm him, "Here is some ale for you. We are here for a celebration, not to open old wounds amongst ourselves."

Njordr tried to help, "We are all friends here. You're welcome amongst us if you'll be pleasant and not hateful. My son, daughter, and I were not born in Asgardr, but we have lived here long enough so we are not strangers. You, too, could have many friends if you tried. Freyr, Freyja, and I are held in the highest esteem by the Æsir."

Before Njordr could continue, Loki broke in, "Held is the correct word, or do you forget that the three of you are hostages? I'm told the children of a brother and sister are monsters. I look at Freyr and Freyja and see this adage has been proven true."

Tyr sought to defend his friends, "Don't speak so to Freyr and Freyja. The one amongst us who has monsters for children stands insulting us."

Loki laughed at Tyr, "You wave and gesture at me with a stump. My son Fenriswulf was the cause of that. Never was a father more proud of the deeds of his son."

Tyr responded, "I lost only a hand while Fenriswulf lost his freedom. And you have lost your honor, on more than one occasion."

Loki shot back, "May I remind you that one of those occasions was with your wife. Perhaps it will surprise you to learn the son you raise as your own can claim a title as one of my monsters."

Freyr sought to threaten Loki, "You forget where your son Fenriswulf lies. He is fettered by the river Van, a place where you will be brought and shackled so that father and son can see each other and talk over old times together, forever."

Loki replied, "Not forever. Nothing is forever. And the bound lose their bonds and conquer their jailers."

Two of Freyr's servants, Beyggiver and Beyla, were helping with the serving. Beyggiver had just filled a tankard of ale from the large vat which was so designed that it filled itself automatically from the main cauldron, making the servant's task easier. He was walking past Loki and dared to speak to him, "If I were one of the Æsir I wouldn't hesitate to crush you and do away with your evil."

Loki had never been spoken to like that by a servant before, "Who's your master?"

Beyggiver answered, "I am servant to the noble Freyr."

Loki looked towards a serving woman who was standing near the kitchen doors, "Is that smiling hag over there your sister? Maybe she's your wife since she has a stupid look of love on her face as she looks at you. Or, perhaps since you work for Freyr, you follow his example and she is both."

Beyggiver answered, "My wonderful sister Beyla stands in the corner waiting to fill the tankards of those who run dry."

Loki gruffly shoved him away, "No doubt your mind has been addled from sleeping in the straw so much. Your sister Beyla looks as if she has been sleeping in straw which has been cleaned out of the stables. Keep her away from me for she smells."

Loki gestured for another servant to bring him some more ale, "What's your name and whose servant are you?"

The servant replied, "I am Fimafengr, Ægir's personal servant. My master has often told me that I am his favorite."

Loki took the ale, "Don't brag about yourself, it's bad form. Now I'll turn my attentions to Sif, who has often turned her attentions to me." He walked over to her and ran his fingers through her hair, "What lovely golden locks. Too lovely to be real. In fact I cut your real hair and now use it stuffed as a pillow on which to rest my head. Would you care to come to my bed and see?"

Sif drew away.

All of a sudden there was a great rumbling. Beyla, who had been standing in the corner near a window yelled out, "You had best hold your tongue Loki, Thor is coming and will take care of you."

Loki yelled back, "I thought I had made it clear I didn't wish to be addressed by servants. Perhaps I should teach one of you a lesson so the rest will remain quiet." Loki reached out and struck Fimafengr who fell to the floor dead.

Everyone was shocked at the sudden action. A few of the Æsir rose to rush Loki, but they stopped in their tracks as Thor entered the hall. Bolts of lightning bounced off the wall. Deafening thunder drowned out Loki's words, but Thor's carried over the thunder, "Loki, shut up, or I'll fling Mjolnir at you and silence you for good."

The thunder had quieted enough for Loki to answer, "And dishonor the Æsir by using your sacred hammer to defile Ægir's hall? I stand here trembling at the mighty Thor who stood quivering with fright in the thumb of Skrymir's glove, and who looked so beautiful as she was wooed by the hrymthursar Thrym."

Thor yelled with anger, "If I can't use Mjolnir, then I'll do the job with my fists." But Thor was held back by some of the Æsir as he tried to go for Loki with his clenched fists. Thor cursed at Loki. "May you go to Nastrond and suffer every torture imaginable."

Frigg spoke up, "I wish Baldr were here to help his mother, I'm sure his goodness would be able to calm everyone down."

Loki laughed at that, "You have me to blame for Baldr's death. And worse yet, you have me to blame for Baldr being kept in Helheimr."

Frigg looked at him disbelievingly, "What are you saying? Everyone knows it was an old hag named Thokk who refused to weep for Baldr. What did you have to do with that?"

Loki laughed, "Thokk is the same old woman you confided your secret laziness to. Too bad you didn't walk that extra little bit to get the mistletoe to pledge an oath of protection to Baldr. Too bad you confided in Thokk. Thokk with her gnarled lips which wouldn't tremble and bring forth tears for Baldr was none other than I, Loki, in disguise. So I have killed Baldr twice, and you have killed him once."

Frigg began to cry. Thor broke from the grips of those holding him and headed for Loki. But Loki was too swift and as he ran from the hall he tore torches from the walls and threw them on the path behind him yelling, "I've finished with the Æsir. I damn Ægir's hall to burn for the insults I've suffered here. Look for me as much as you want, but you'll never find me."

Outside Loki ran towards the nearby shore. Some of the Æsir yelled after him, "The water will stop him since there's no boat he can steal to ride away in."

But they were surprised. At the banks of the water he turned himself into an eel and slithered into the water and swam away.

Loki fled to Midgardr and began looking for a secure hiding place. Eventually he came to some high mountain ranges. Inbetween them lay a deep valley. He'd be safe there. He built a house next to a river called the Franangr Falls in a secluded part of the valley. This house was constructed with four doors, one in each wall, so Loki had an escape out of the house if anyone finding him tried to corner him.

He spent many weeks there, yet still felt unsafe and pursued. He decided to change himself into a salmon during the day and hide in the Franangr Falls. But after awhile he began to feel safer. No one had come near his house and he felt that perhaps the Æsir had given up the pursuit. So he began to think up mischievous things to do. He had often seen Ran weaving nets with which to catch sailors. He set about with some flax and yarn to weave a net so he could easily catch more fish. He continued thinking of new tricks to play on others.

Odin sat in his hall, Valaskjalf, in his watchtower on his throne Hlidskjalf surveying all the Worlds of the Tree looking for Loki. This was the only task occupying his waking moments since returning to Asgardr. Suddenly he caught sight of Loki sitting outside his cabin, weaving a net. Odin immediately sent for Thor and Hœnir, "I've found Loki. He's living in a valley and has built a cabin beside the Franangr Falls. Let's seek him out and use whatever force necessary to return him to Asgardr so we can exact a fit and proper punishment."

Loki was deeply involved in weaving the net, and was working so intently he failed to notice Odin, Thor, and Hœnir approaching until it was almost too late. When he glanced up he could hardly believe what he saw. He ran into his cabin and cast the net into the fireplace, then ran to the river, changed himself into a salmon and plunged in, quickly swimming to the deepest part to hide.

Odin, Thor, and Hœnir found the cabin deserted. Looking around inside Hœnir spotted the net and retrieved it from the fireplace, "Why don't you two repair it. It may be of use to us. I'll go outside and search for Loki."

Odin and Thor set about reweaving the net and tying new knots to replace the burnt out sections. But the damage was too extensive and by the time Hœnir returned Odin and Thor had given up trying to repair it.

Hœnir had an idea, "Odin, do you remember when we went with Loki on a journey throughout Midgardr and Loki caught the dvergar Andvari with Ran's net after he had tried to escape by turning himself into a fish and hiding behind a waterfall? I have a feeling Loki is trying to elude us by the same deceit, which is why he tried to burn the net. So,

I suggest one of us goes to Ran and borrows her net, which I'm sure she'll give us when she finds out we intend to capture Loki with it."

Thor quickly left. It didn't take him long to reach Ægir and Ran's hall. When she heard why the net was needed she sent a servant to fetch it and gladly lent it to Thor. On his way back Thor passed through Asgardr and summoned some of the other Æsir to come with him to Midgardr to help trap Loki.

Thor and Hœnir stood on opposite sides of the river, each holding an end of the net. They walked upstream dragging the net with them. Loki escaped being entangled in it by hiding between two large stones on the river bottom. The net passed over him barely grazing his back. They gathered up the net and searched through it releasing all of the real fish. Loki wasn't amongst them.

Thor spoke, "I know he's down there but somehow he has escaped the net. Let's weight it down with a rock so it'll drag along the bottom and pick up everything, including rocks."

This was done and again they dragged the net upstream. This time Loki saw there was no escape. He waited until the net was almost upon him and then jumped over it and swam towards a waterfall which was at the point where the river ran into the sea. Odin, Thor, and Hœnir quickly gathered up the net and headed for the waterfall. Thor waded out to the middle of the river and cast the net out again. As the net came towards him Loki again jumped over it heading back downstream. Each time the net was cast Loki had to make the decision of whether or not to leap over the net or jump over the waterfall and into the jaws of Ægir, as the sea was often called. It was a difficult choice. He didn't want to enter Ægir's realm. He had greatly insulted his host at the feast, including burning down his hall. Now he certainly regretted that deed. There was no good that could come of rushing into the sea. Ægir would have all the fish looking for him so he could be captured and suitably punished. So Loki continued leaping back and forth over the net, gradually tiring. He couldn't keep it up much longer.

Yet again Thor cast the net out before him. But this time he was going to try something different. When Loki made his attempt to leap back over the net Thor reached out and grabbed him. Loki's body slipped through Thor's hand, but Thor clenched his fist tighter and held onto the only part left, the tail. His grip crushed the tail to a tapered point, which is why salmon's to this day have a tail shaped in that manner.

Thor waded back to shore where Odin changed Loki back into his regular form. Loki remained silent during the return journey to Asgardr. Even when quizzed by Thor or Odin he refused to talk. What good would it have done anyway? To beg for mercy would have been out of the question. There was no chance the Æsir were going to be merciful with him. The insults he had hurled at Ægir's feast were bad enough, and, perhaps, could have been forgiven. But no one was going to forgive him for bringing about Baldr's death and then being responsible for keeping him in Helheimr. And bragging about it.

That evening as they passed through Midgardr the people jeered at Loki. The dvergar encouraged the Æsir to kill him then and there, "Why wait for later? Just turn him over to us, we'll take care of him." But the party continued on with the dvergar accompanying them part of the way, prodding Loki with their pick handles or throwing rocks at him. Nor did animals spare him. He was mercilessly stung by insects, birds attacked his eyes and snakes crawled under his feet trying to rear up and bite him.

Oddly enough the person offering Loki protection was Thor. He told all in Midgardr to spare Loki, "Don't harm him yet. We have plans for dealing with him. You have nothing to worry about. Rest assured he'll be justly rewarded for his heinous crimes."

They took Loki to Mt. Idavollr where they met up with the rest of the Æsir and Vanir. From there they proceeded to Hvergelmir. They entered a cave near Hveralund which was in the ninth and deepest region of Niflheimr and prepared the area for Loki's punishment in a bottomless pit whose entrance was next to where Garmr was bound.

Odin commanded some of the Æsir to bring in three of the largest boulders they could find. While this was being done Odin gave further instructions, "Loki has two sons, Vali and Narfi, by his wife Sigyn. Have them brought here."

While some of the Æsir went to fetch Loki's two sons, the others returned with the three boulders and stood them on edge inside the cave. Thor hammered them into the ground securely using the might of Mjolnir. They cut holes through the top of each boulder as well as a wedge.

Loki's two sons were brought into the cave, each struggling madly to get free. Sigyn followed behind begging for mercy for Loki and her two sons. Odin touched Vali and instantly he was changed into a wolf. His animal instincts took over and he leapt at the nearest object to him, which unfortunately happened to be his brother Narfi, whom he ate. Then some of the Æsir attacked Vali, killing him and eviscerated him pulling out his guts.

Loki was carried to the three boulders and heaved his body every which way, struggling to break free, but unable to do so. He was placed in the indentations left where the wedges had been cut from the boulders. He was held to the boulders with one rock under his shoulder, another under his loins, and a third under the backs of his knees. His sons' entrails were twined in and out of the holes which had been cut in the rocks and wrapped around Loki. As soon as the strands touched him they turned to iron until finally he was held fast and could not escape.

Skadi, Thjassi's daughter, bent over Loki, "It's nice to see you like this. I know things are a bit easy for you right now and you're having such a good rest. But I'm going to do my part to make things more difficult. While you lie here for the rest of eternity you can spend some of your time thinking of how you killed my father."

She took a snake and tied it in a knot around an overhead hanging stalactite. Its venom dropped down onto Loki's face. With every drop he writhed and twisted in agony. Sigyn couldn't stand seeing her husband tortured. She ran outside the cave and grabbed the first container she saw, which was a conch. Running back to Loki's side she held it over his head in order to catch the venom. Ever after that Loki was unable to sleep. He worried about the conch filling, at which time Sigyn had to turn to empty it. While she did this the venom once again fell on him causing him to twist and turn, writhing, trying to avoid it, which was impossible considering the way in which he was bound. Sometimes Sigyn fell asleep and the conch filled up and overflowed. Loki's screams woke her and again he suffered as she emptied the vessel.

Those in Midgardr suffered from his punishment also. The three rocks to which he was bound had been hammered through to the center of Midgardr. Every time he tossed and turned in agony Midgardr trembled and shook in response. But this was the price they had to pay to have Loki bound and punished.

Certain that Loki was finally taken care of the Æsir returned to Asgardr.

Thorkill

Legends of Loki's torment spread throughout Midgardr and grew larger with each retelling. After many generations there came an explorer who decided to find Loki. He was an adventurer named Thorkill who had often sought out the legends of Asgardr. He was the same adventurer who had once searched with King Gormr and found Geirrodr's Garth.

He raised a crew. This time, although he offered space to King Gormr, the king refused, having had enough adventuring to last him the rest of his life, which he thought would be considerably longer than Thorkill's.

Thorkill steered his vessel northward until they reached a land where darkness was eternal. Even at midday there was no light. Though his crew was frightened they followed Thorkill's orders and sailed on hoping they would soon be away from this frightening land.

The journey wore on. Their food supply was dwindling until at last they were forced to eat some meat which looked as if it should have been thrown overboard. Many of the crew died. And just when everything seemed hopeless the lookout spotted land.

But disappointment was theirs. As they neared they saw sitting on the shore were two jotuns who were roasting some fish. As hungry as they were, and as much as they wanted to stop and ask to share the jotun's food, Thorkill realized it would not be safe to do so. As they sailed passed, the jotuns yelled at them, offering them safety. But Thorkill didn't want to take the chance of trusting their word. Instead he yelled riddles back and forth with them until their ship was safely passed and out of their range.

They sailed on until they reached a region where men of Midgardr had never ventured. They landed the vessel and lit a fire on the beach. Bearing torches for light Thorkill and some of his men went off exploring. Soon they came to a cave, which they entered. Snakes slithered passed their feet trying to avoid the light, seeking cover in holes and beneath rocks.

The party came to a brackish shallow stream of black water which they easily waded across. The walls of the cave narrowed until they had to travel single file. This passageway suddenly opened into a vast cavern.

Bound on three rocks before them lay Loki. Sigyn must have been out emptying the conch since there was no sign of her. Loki's body was covered with mud and dirt. His hair was matted with poison and stood out stiffly from his head. One of the sailors reached out to pluck a lock to take back to Midgardr with him. At this action Loki strained at his bonds and the ground shook under them causing the sailor to fall forward into a stream of poison. He died instantly.

A snake turned its attention to the visitors near him and spat out a stream of poison at one of the sailors. The poison hit him across his neck severing his head as if it had been hewn off by a sword. Some of the poison splashed from the fallen sailor and hit another in his eyes which were immediately eaten away. Yet another sailor was so frightened he covered his face with his cloak so as to protect himself. He put out his hand to feel his way along the wall as he retreated and accidentally touched a stream of poison. His arm was eaten away.

Thorkill, and those who could, retreated. Only five made it out of the cave alive, and of those one had been blinded, another was minus an arm, and two had been driven mad. Only Thorkill escaped whole.

They rushed back to the beach, passed the sailors who were standing by the fire, and boarded the ship signaling for the others to board so they could depart at once.

Thorkill told of their adventures as they set sail. But more tragedy was to beset them. On their journey southward their ship ran aground and all aboard were killed except Thorkill. He made his way back to his homeland and told all who would listen of his adventures and assured everyone Loki was indeed securely bound.

Chapter 27

Ragnarokr

Now that Loki was securely bound many of the Æsir felt the events leading to Ragnarokr were again held in check; once more they had battled and won. A new sense of optimism swept through Asgardr and Midgardr. But Odin knew differently. He sat in his hall, Valaskjalf, in his watchtower on his throne Hlidskjalf looking into all the Worlds of the Tree. Here and there he'd see something out of place, something which wasn't quite right. It might be as insignificant as a plant dying and no new one springing up to take its place, leaving a bare spot where once some beauty had been. Or, it might be the troubling sight of seeing the witch Heidr living again and passing from house to house spreading evil throughout Midgardr.

After seeing her Odin put on his wide-brimmed hat, pulled low to conceal his missing eye, donned a blue cloak, and carried his spear Gungnir with him disguised as a staff. He set out for Midgardr to find Heidr and quiz her about the knowledge she had of Ragnarokr and the endings of all things.

She was easy to find. Odin just followed her trail of strife and pestilence until he caught up with her. She was sitting just inside a cave on an island near Denmark staring out over the sound as if in a trance. Odin approached, interrupting her divinations. He offered her gifts of rings and necklaces encrusted with precious jewels. These she disdained, "What use have I of mere baubles and gew gaws? I can get the same from my friends in Svartalfheimr any time I want. You can't fool me with your disguise, nor buy my knowledge with your bribes. I can see you're Odin and sorely troubled by events. I'll not give you the knowledge you seek."

Odin threw the treasures into the sea, "Perhaps I have other gifts which will interest you?" He reached inside his cloak and took sticks carved with runes, rocks carved with mystic treasure-spells, and other objects of divination, and handed them to her. She accepted them.

Odin spoke, "Tell me of your knowledge and what you see."

She spoke in a chanting monotone, "I see the time before the beginning. I see Ginnungagap. There is Ymir and Audhumla. Then the vile death occurs. His murderers, the sons of Bor and Bestla, raise his body to form the land on which we now stand. But it is all fading and I see the punishment which that early murder has caused. I see an enchanted spear thrown. It holds true to its course and pierces the heart of Baldr."

Odin grew impatient, "Yes, yes, I know all that. What of the future? What is yet to be?"

He moved behind her and placed his hands over her head saying runes which mingled his knowledge with hers. He gained the knowledge he wanted, but she also gained the knowledge he had, for no knowledge is gained without a price.

She spoke, "Angroboda lives in Myrkvyrdr Forest. She sits rearing her strange brood, two children she has had by her son Fenriswulf. They have his form and are named Hati Hrodvitnirsson, sometimes called Skoll, and Mana-Garmr. Soon they will destroy the sun and moon. But now they content themselves with the nourishing flesh of those whom they stumble across in the forest, as well as sucking the marrow from the bones of murderers and adulterers. They have not lacked for food and have grown to be strong and healthy."

Odin returned to Asgardr sorely troubled. He noticed the others in the land seemed less hopeful also. A quiet resignation of things to come had settled over the land and was gradually permeating throughout the Worlds of the Tree. To the east the jotuns were gleeful at the change happening about. They knew their time was coming.

The Fimbulventr

The fall was over and soon winter came to the land. On Midgardr the harsh snows and desperate conditions shortened the tempers of men, and nations were at war against once friendly neighbors. But when spring came and the snows abated so did the conflicts of nations.

A new hopeful mood had settled upon Midgardr. In Asgardr the Æsir looked forward to the approach of summer. But it was not to be. The land did not warm up during spring; summer did not follow after. The snows and blizzards raged more harshly than ever. Instead of long peaceful days under sunlit skies, the days were short, the skies dark and cloudy. And still the snow fell. The drifts piled high as mountains, reaching from Midgardr almost up to Asgardr. The rivers and seas froze solid. Some of the Æsir realized this was no ordinary winter. It was the prophesied Fimbulventr, the winter from which there was no escape. It would be three winters long, with no break of sunshine inbetween. There would be storms and blizzards the likes of which had never before been seen. The winds would blow throughout every nook and cranny of the land. There would be no corner which could provide protection against the icy wind.

Still Jotunheimr rejoiced. The rivers and oceans in Midgardr were frozen solid. Soon the river Ifing, separating their two lands, would be frozen over. Then they could cross into the longed for land of Midgardr and bring about whatever hurt they chose.

As time wore on, those in Midgardr blessed with the ability to see the future began saying the Fimbulventr had come. Its wyrd was upon them.

At first their pronouncements were met with disbelief. But as the second winter began without respite belief spread throughout the land. Many repented of their crimes and changed from doing evil to bringing about good works. Others felt so doomed it didn't matter to them whether their actions were right or just. War broke out again

and continued throughout Midgardr unchecked. Murders, looting, rapes, all became commonplace. Brother killed brother out of common greed. Fathers cheated sons out of property and wife. Incest and sodomy became commonplace; man became the plaything of whoredoms.

Since there was no spring or summer, there had been no crops to harvest. After awhile supplies of food began to run out. Famine spread throughout the land. Even the strongest died of starvation. And with starvation came cannibalism.

No longer fearing humans, animals roamed freely in the cities foraging for food. Outside as animals or humans collapsed and died their carcasses were immediately frozen solid, so those foraging for food, both humans and animals, broke their teeth on the stiff meals. It was survival of the fittest, when even the fittest knew they would not survive.

The waiting in Asgardr continued. The Æsir headed towards their fate with more nobility than those of Midgardr. They made their preparations for battle, listening for the call.

The Sun and Moon are Swallowed Up

One morning a day started as many others had, cold and hopeless. The sun began its journey. It was no longer the warm sun of ages past who had brought the light of day to the land and whose nourishment had helped crops grow. Instead what crossed the sky was a cold faintly shining sun.

In Myrkvyrdr Forest the time had come for the two jotun-wolves, Hati Hrodvitnirsson, or Skoll, and Mana-Garmr, to do their evil. First Hati Hrodvitnirsson let out a howl and leaped up in an attempt to catch the sun. He chased the frightened sun across the sky, and with each leap he became stronger and came a little closer to snatching her from the sky. Towards evening as the sun was sitting and closest to Midgardr he made one final leap, caught the sun between his jaws and swallowed her. The long shadows of the mountains and forests which had been cast across Midgardr suddenly ceased. There was nothing but blackness over the hills as the Æsir watched from high atop Mt. Idavollr in Asgardr.

Next the flat and colorless moon rose and shone full bringing some light and hope to Midgardr as it followed the sun's path across the sky. But now it was the other wolf's turn. Mana-Garmr leaped up as his brother had done. He came close. Everyone watching in Midgardr shuddered as he managed to lick the face of the moon during his second attempt, and with that lick he scooped up Hjuki and Bil the two children Maane had placed on the face of the moon, swallowing them whole. But a third attempt was all which was needed. He swallowed the moon and once again the land was plunged into darkness. The sky seemed drenched in blood as one by one the stars fell from their steadings and disappeared. Soon the sky above was black with no form of light penetrating its inky cover.

The Cocks Crow, The Bonds of Evil Are Loosed

The storms and blizzards hit Midgardr with their full force, raging unabated. Midgardr shook and cities were torn apart by splitting earth. Trees were cast about as if they were twigs. Mountains were moved to new spots as if they were toys being played with by an angry child. Many thought Ymir had been brought back to life and was now trying to get up. Whatever the reasons, everyone knew Ragnarokr had come and time was short.

In the depths of Niflheimr, at the bottom of the root which reached from Yggdrasyll, lay the serpent Nidhoggr entwined and gnawing intently at his desire. Bit by bit he and his sons had chewed through the bark. Now with one final bite the root broke in two. A shiver ran through the Tree frightening those who had made their home in it.

At the same moment Garmr strained at his bonds at the entrance to Niflheimr. They broke as if they had been mere threads, and suddenly he was free. The beautiful purple cock Fiala sitting in Gagalvid in Jotunheimr crowed out the news Garmr was free and the way out of Hela's realm lay open. The entranceway was unguarded, and those trapped in Niflheimr rushed back through it exiting in a stampede which trampled many, but not to death. They were already dead, so they rose as best they could with broken bones and crushed skulls, and slowly went forth.

In Asgardr the Æsir listened. As more bonds were broken other cocks crowed. At Fiala's crowing Heimdallr left his watch on Bifrost and headed to Mimir's Well to retrieve Gjallarhorn so he could call the Æsir and their friends to battle.

In a dark cave in Niflheimr Sigyn had turned to empty the container of poison. A drop fell to Loki's forehead and he writhed in agony. As he twisted and turned his bonds broke and suddenly he was free. He rushed out of the bottomless pit making his own path through the rock. A sooty-red cock perched on Nagrindr Gate crowed out the news that Loki was free, "Loki, Loki, Loki, out of the cave, out of the cave."

On the island of Lyngvi in the lake called Amsvartnir in Niflheimr Fenriswulf stretched and strained at his bonds. Then, they too, broke and once again he was loose. His mouth gaped, held open by Tyr's sword, as he headed off seeking vengeance on the Æsir for having bound him and taken away his freedom. Gullinkambi in Asgardr and Fjalarr, a black cock in Jarnvid Forest in Jotunheimr, shrieked out the news of the freeing of Fenriswulf.

Unstable footing plagued all the lands. Deep holes appeared where mountains had once been. Even those in Jotunheimr were not spared as the jotuns' rock dwellings crumbled to the ground. All fetters were broken. Nor could they be secured again. Evil now ran unchecked throughout all the Worlds of the Tree.

The Gathering for the Last Great Battle on Vigridr Plain

Those in Midgardr ran around helpless with fright. But their time was coming to an end, for with a mighty heave Midgardrsormr rose up out of the sea. First his head, then the curve of his neck, then the fire and poisonous mist from his mouth. He swam towards the nearest land sending out deadly tidal waves with each stroke of his tail. When he reached land he spat out streams of poison into the sky, rending it asunder. Those who had not been drowned were soon overcome by the vile liquid. The waters of Midgardr turned red with the blood of its inhabitants. Having finished his purpose on Midgardr he plunged back into the water and headed to his father's side.

Nastrond Wharf was located in Niflheimr near Hvergelmir Well. Here was moored the ship Naglfar, made from dead men's nails. All the killings on Midgardr during the Fimbulventr had brought about its completion. It was to this spot which Loki had rushed. He boarded the ship and took hold of its rudder. Also on board were his daughter Hela, his brother Byleistr, the dead in Niflheimr who still remained, Surtr and his servants the

Mighty Sons of Muspel. The ship, groaning under the weight of the evil aboard, was launched by a mountain high blood-red wave. Loki smiled as he caught sight of his other son, Midgardrsormr. The party sailed over Myrkvyrdr Forest which was engulfed in water, on their way to Vigridr Plain.

Edgar, the rusty-yellow eagle roosting in the topmost bough of Yggdrasyll, saw the ship and flew off towards Vigridr Plain, eager with anticipation of the carrion which would soon litter the battlefield, and the meals he would be able to pluck and devour.

Heimdallr returned to Bifrost and raised Gjallarhorn to his lips. He blew as loudly as he could. The single trembling tone echoed throughout all the Worlds of the Tree calling all of the friends of the Æsir to Vigridr Plain for the last battle.

In his hall, Valaskjalf, in his watchtower Odin left his throne Hlidskalf, never to return. In on of his last attempts to change Ragnarokr he sent Huginn and Muninn off to seek more knowledge, knowing he would never see them again. In the courtyard he found Sleipnir awaiting him, and mounted. He didn't need to tell Sleipnir where to go. The mighty stead ran as fast as he could to Mimir's Well so Odin could seek some final advice on the best strategy to lead the attack being mounted against their enemies. As he neared the well he saw the three Norns sitting beneath Yggdrasyll. They were dressed in black and veiled and no longer wove at their precious tapestry which was rolled up and propped against Yggdrasyll. A few tattered threads lay on the ground. Their work was finished. Odin dismounted, walked over and attempted to talk to them, but they refused to speak and one-by-one turned their backs to him. Odin realized what the outcome of the battle would be and did not ask Mimir for help. Instead he bent over and whispered a final secret to the head. Another blast from Gjallarhorn sounded. Odin mounted Sleipnir to ride back to Asgardr. He glanced back in horror to see Fenriswulf rush over to Mimir, flip the head in the air with his snout and as it somersaulted back down, Fenriswulf caught and swallow it in his open mouth. Odin watched Mimir's horror-filled eyes staring back at him. Then, the head and its waist-length beard disappeared down the wolf's throat in a single gulp.

Shaken, Odin rode back to Asgardr to gather the Æsir together and lead them to Vigridr Plain. All the Æsir, all the Vanir, the ljosalfar followed Odin's lead.

The last to leave Asgardr was Tyr who looked around at the empty streets and halls. All the magnificent dwellings, no longer shining in the sun, because there was no more sun. He saw an overturned Fidchel set. The king had not been protected. The game had been lost. And over near Baldr's he saw the field stained with Baldr's blood. That bright shining golden Æsir who had been so good and blessed, and had been taken so young.

Idunn's orchard was no longer recognizable. It was overgrown with vines. Rotted fruit lay on the ground. He listened but Bragi's songs could no longer be heard there. Bragi was long gone to be with Idunn.

A dull whoosh of wind swept through the empty streets where once there had been the Æsir going about their lives, planning evening banquets, filling the streets with laughter. And near Thor's hall and Valhalla there was silence where once the clang of swordplay at practice filled the air all day. Now Tyr wondered if that practice would pay off. Might they win this battle?

Tyr closed and latched the gate behind him. He sealed it with oaths hoping the protection would work. Then he hurried to Vigridr Plain.

In Jotunheimr the eagle Hræsvelg licked at his beak and flapped his wings furiously sending a violent wind southward through what remained of Midgardr. He rose up and soared along on it towards Vigridr Plain.

Naglfar traveled out of Niflheimr through Jotunheimr into Midgardr. There Surtr and the Mighty Sons of Muspel disembarked and went through the land destroying any remaining life. Fenriswulf caught up with the ship there. He swam behind it beside his brother, Midgardrsormr. Loki was now reunited with his children heading into battle to avenge all the wrongs which had been perpetrated on them by the Æsir.

After despoiling what remained of Midgardr, Surtr and his party sailed towards Bifrost. Heimdallr had left the bridge heading towards Vigridr Plain after his second call on Gjallarhorn. Surtr and the Mighty Sons of Muspel being of fire, easily walked through the protective burning fire at the foot of the bridge. They pulled the fire into them leaving Bifrost free of flames, and open to all.

They reaching Asgardr's gates at the end of Bifrost. Thor's two goats, Tanngnjostr and Tanngrisnir, were at the bars trying to get out to follow Thor to battle. Surtr's flaming arms reached through the bars, grabbed both goats by their necks, and pulled them through the bars. Soon they were just smoking cinders. Surtr then tried to open the gates, but Tyr's enchantments held. Surtr and the Mighty Sons of Muspel tried to storm the sacred city. Bifrost did its last act of protection for Asgardr. It heaved up to protect itself and Asgardr, trying to throw off the usurpers. They held their footing, so the bridge sacrificed itself, crumbled and fell to Midgardr making it impossible for anyone to ever again enter Asgardr via that route.

Meanwhile, Odin led his side wearing a golden winged helmet and a shining silver war coat. He held Notung in one hand and Gungnir in the other ready to throw it to start the battle. To his left was beloved son Thor. He was walking to the battle, having left his chariot and goats in Asgardr for their protection not knowing that at that moment Surtr and his minions were killing them. Then behind him followed Heimdallr and Freyr. In the next line marched the rest of the Æsir and Vanir.

Bringing up the rear were the warriors from Thrudvangar and Folkvangar. Behind them were the noble Einherjar of Valhalla, marching hundreds of thousands strong forming a line long enough those in the rear could see in the distance Bifrost crumbling back to Midgardr. But they didn't stop to think about the terrible sight they'd seen. They continued marching shoulder-to-shoulder towards Vigridr Plain. This was the battle they had trained for every day. They were worried, and, yes, they were excited. They were warriors off to war. The greatest war ever to be fought. And they were part of it.

Some of the Einherjar were overcome with battle-frenzy and attacked as berserkers in the guise of ulfhednar, frenzied warriors who wore wolfskins to battle.

Vigridr Plain

Vigridr Plain on Oskopnir island was a barren stretch of land two-hundred rosts long in all directions. It was here little-by-little all the factions met. If there had been a sun a new day would just have been dawning. Instead sides were meeting for the final battle. The only light came from the flashing lightning caused by Thor's hammer, and golden animals and treasures and weapons which gave off their own glow.

Naglfar carrying its ghostly crew of dead arrived out of the east, followed by Midgardrsormr and Fenriswulf. Also coming from the east was Hrymr holding aloft a shining shield, leading bands of hrymthursar, rock jotuns and fire jotuns, along with many trolls and dvergar. At first this group looked unreal approaching through the shimmering fog, but soon enough they were found to be quite real.

Surtr and the Mighty Sons of Muspel had plunged into the river beneath Bifrost when it crumbled, turning the water to steam. Those remaining who had not been killed in the fall, or had not drowned, made their way to the battlefield from the south. Along the way Surtr had wielded his flaming sword, med sviga lævi, flinging balls of fire before and after him burning everything in his path. He and the Mighty Sons of Muspel arrived cutting through the sky in their flaming armor.

Fenriswulf frightened many when he appeared. His mouth stretched so wide the tip of it reached the sky while his lower jaw scraped the ground. Flames shot forth from his eyes and nostrils. He was fearsome to look at and many turned to look at something else. But what they saw in other directions gave them little comfort. One horrible sight they could see before them was Midgardrsormr spitting out clouds of poison in their direction.

For a brief moment all was quiet. Still. Everyone was tense and ready for action. The moment foretold so often had finally come. Odin hurled Gungnir at the other side. The battle commenced.

Odin and Thor went forward together for a short distance. Then Odin dug his heels into Sleipnir's side. They darted off towards Fenriswulf. Thor didn't have to wait long before he was engaged in battle with his enemy of old, Midgardrsormr.

During his battle with Fenriswulf Odin let loose with a mighty blow at the wolf's head, dislodging the sword from the beast's mouth. Slowly the jaws closed into a grin as he approached Odin. Swiftly he bit Odin, injuring him mortally. Odin's son, Vidarr the Silent, looked over and saw his father fall. He yelled out the only sound he had ever made, "FATHER!" and rushed to aid him, but was too late. Fenriswulf quickly swallowed the fallen leader. Now it was up to Vidarr to avenge his father's death.

On his right foot he wore a special boot which had been in the making since the beginning of time. It had been cobbled from the snippets of leather which had been left over when the toes and heels had been cut away from a shoe pattern. Also pressed into it were the remnants of worn out leather shoes which had been cast away. It was very tough and allowed him the protection he needed.

He planted his right foot inside Fenriswulf's lower jaw and yelled at his father's slayer. "Your orlog is known you foul son of Hvedrungr." As Fenriswulf began to bite down on him he caught hold of the wolf's upper jaw. Bracing himself against the lower jaw he ripped the two sections apart. Fenriswulf fell back in pain. Vidarr ran around to the side of the foul creature and plunged his sword into him up to the hilt and pierced clean through his heart. His father's death was avenged. Plunging his sword in a second time he cut open Fenriswulf's belly and pulled out the lifeless form of his father. Soon the cries of help from the battlefield penetrated his grief and he stumbled away to help others.

Meanwhile, Thor was engaged in a fierce combat against Midgardrsormr. Thor flung Mjolnir at the head of the serpent who fell over mortally wounded. For the first time Mjolnir failed to return to him. Thor knew he was victorious and went up to the body to retrieve Mjolnir which was embedded in the serpent's side. But with one last dying gasp Midgardrsormr let out a stream of poison which engulfed the thundergod. He stumbled backwards nine steps and fell upon some Einherjar who had already been slain. Midgardrsormr's death preceded Thor's by only seconds.

Loki had with him his magic sword lævateinn, which had been carved with runes by him beneath Nagrindr Gate in ages past. This was the only sword with magic enough to slay the cock Vidofnir who sat on a branch of Yggdrasyll crowing out encouragement to the Æsir. Loki was angered by this and strode up to the Tree and furiously whacked the bird in two, breaking many tree branches in the process. As the tree branches fell to the ground one could almost feel worlds collapsing.

Heimdallr came upon Loki and caught him unawares. As Loki turned around and before he could raise a blow against his old enemy his head was severed by Heimdallr's sword. Heimdallr yelled in triumph, "Finally Brokkr has won his bet." But the joy of that death was soon saddened by Heimdallr's own. While Loki had been bound his hair and beard had grown long and become matted by the poison which had fallen on him, so both beard and hair were stiff and sharp like knifes. As Heimdallr reached over to pick up his enemy's head in triumph a point of the beard cut his arm. The poison was released into him, travelling quickly through his body. Heimdallr collapsed and died next to Loki.

The Mighty Sons of Muspel attacked Yggdrasyll. Soon it was engulfed in flames, creaking and whistling as the flames ate at it. Finally enough of its base was burned away so it first rocked back and forth swaying further and further until it fell on the battlefield with a great grinding, groaning crash killing many who were trapped both in it's branches and under it.

Hrymr signaled for the hrymthursar to attack. One of them, Gymir, rushed towards Skirnir. Skirnir was ready for the battle and prepared to defend himself with Freyr's magical sword. But they were both evenly matched and slew each other evenly.

Garmr and Tyr sought each other out and slew one another. Old enemies were finalizing what had been denied them previously.

The battle now reached its zenith. Jotuns fought against the Æsir, and also against themselves when they couldn't find any enemies. Monsters and trolls found others to conquer. The alfs were doing their best to fight against the dvergar. Vigridr Plain was covered with streams of blood. Warriors stumbled over hacked off limbs and dodged out of the way of falling bodies.

In the midst of this two warriors forgot all others. Freyr and Surtr approached one another. The only weapon Freyr had was a stag's horn, having relinquished his sword to Skirnir many years ago for the love of Gerdr. He knew he was doomed against Surtr's powerful fiery sword, med sviga lævi. The uneven fight was over quickly.

Surtr strove to the middle of Vigridr Plain. He looked at all the destruction around him and cast med sviga lævi up into the sky. Its flames shot away throughout all the Worlds of the Tree, engulfing everything. The fire flickered up to the heavens and ate at the sky. Streams of fire snaked their way to the edge of Midgardr until all four dvergues holding aloft Ymir's skull were consumed in flames. With no further support the skull came crashing down. Asgardr, Jotunheimr, Niflheimr, all the Worlds of the Tree were engulfed in the purifying flames. Then black and scarred the worlds sank beneath the sea.

Silence prevailed. There was nothing. All had been destroyed, sun, moon, stars, Asgardr, Niflheimr, Jotunheimr, Æsir, Vanir, monsters, hrymthursars, jotuns, dvergues, alfs, everything. All were gone. There was nothing but a wide gulf, as in the beginning. This then was the end of the beginning – Ragnarokr.

Chapter 28

Rebirth

As the creation had begun, it also ended with fire and water. Now an eerie colorless light shone over a calm sea. This was Ragnarokr, the twilight of the gods.

Eons passed. Eons of nothing but a sea and a strange light. All the while the Alfadir kept watch over the Ginnungagap, waiting for the right moment to begin again.

Then slowly, almost in discernibly at first, there was another light. But it grew in luminescence. Its red color cast its glow across the water. This was the new sun, a daughter of Alfrothul, the old sun. After her birth she had hidden herself away to await a time after Ragnarokr. She didn't have the imperfections of her parent. She was a calming sun at all times and wasn't so ardent as to cause blistering. Nor did she need a shield to be placed under her. As she grew in brightness the other light which had been lighting the heavens disappeared.

The light from the young sun penetrated through the sea warming it. Its radiance filled the sky with hope. At the end of the first day it sank in the west and was replaced by a new darkness. This darkness was not eerie and desolate as the other had been. It was gentle and peaceful. And on the first night one by one the stars reappeared in the sky. Then a new day dawned followed by another calm night. Eventually this calm ordered return of day and night had a tranquilizing effect on the ocean. It changed to a beautiful deep satin blue color.

Early in he morning the light would play on the mist forming one rainbow after another. Sometimes two rainbows would even double into a circle.

Gradually tips of mountains could be seen rising up through the sea. Then there were islands and large continents. Waterfalls cascaded into lakes. The lakes were seen to have fish playfully swimming in them. Off in the distance an eagle was soaring overhead hunting for food. Grass began to fill the landscape. And though no field had been sown, crops began coming up. Flowers came into bloom in all corners of the land. The chirping of birds could be heard off in the distance as all forms of life began to populate the world again.

One day Baldr walked out of the forest, more beautiful than he had ever been. Following him was his brother Hodr, along with Nanna. Soon they met Hœnir, Vidarr

and Vali. They were all alive and whole with no imperfections. Hœnir had become exceptionally wise and had gained the gift of prophecy. They all agreed he should be their spiritual leader and advisor. He took some twigs and bits of bark which had once been used in sacrifices and read the future from them. It was good, there was no evil.

As they continued walking along exploring the new land they came upon Idunn who was picking wildflowers in a meadow. Then they heard Bragi's sweet voice. He was sitting in a tree looking out over the land and singing of all the beauty he saw.

They recognized some of the landmarks. In the distance they saw Mt. Idavollr and decided to build their halls on the foundation of old Asgardr.

They sat and talked of Thor and Odin and the other old Æsir. As they spoke Thor's two sons, Modr and Magni, arrived. Modr carried Mjolnir with him and vowed to use the hammer only for blessings and not for harm. Magni was several steps behind his brother and stumbled over something in the tall grass. He brought it to the assemblage. It was toflur, the chess set and table which had been lost during the first golden age.

Everyone set about building their halls, although they found some were still standing from before. This time the halls they built were not as ornate as before, yet they seemed more comfortable. Hodr, Baldr and Nanna, and Bragi and Idunn, shared a hall in Hropt's Hills and called it Hropt's battle hall since it was set on the site where Valhalla had been.

Baldr and Hodr's sons shared a hall near their parents' abodes.

One of the halls still standing from before was Gimle. Though it was set a distance from Asgardr, its red-gold roof could be seen shining in the sun.

Another hall was Brimir standing in Okolnir, which meant the uncold. There was no longer a chilly wind being sent through the land, which previously had been piled high with snow. This was the home of the jotuns who had survived. The hall became known for its mead and good times. Here everyone met, no longer enemies but friends, to relax and enjoy things, as well as to reminisce with tales and funny stories about the past.

Then there was Sindri, also made of red gold, which stood in Nidafjoll to the north of the Nida Mountains. This was a place where all who were good and pure dwelt. Many dvergar also dwelt there. Both races, jotuns and dvergar, which had caused the Æsir so much trouble, were forgiven of their sins, since their evil had not been perpetrated with free will, but had been fated.

Off in the distance where the Mimirsbrunnr Well stood came Lifthraser and Lif. When Surtr had set fire to the worlds they had sought refuge in Hoddmimir's Holt. There they had slept during Ragnarokr dreaming the dreams of children. They were the only mortals of Midgardr to have escaped the destruction. Their thoughts were pure and innocent, devoid of all harm or sin. As they emerged from Hoddmimir's Holt they drank of the morning dew and their youthfulness returned to them. They set about creating a new life for themselves in Odainsaker, Mimir's former land, hoping to bring forth children who would love the land and appreciate the goodness in life.

To the south the Alfadir had created another heavenly land called Andlangr, and further off a third known as Vidblain over Gimil's Cave. Many of the surviving Æsir and Vanir lived in these lands and were happy.

Throughout all the lands there were fields of self-sown corn. Vines were overgrown with grapes, and orchards of fruit grew without attendance. Animals grazed in the pastures.

There were beautiful snakes of all colors who slid harmlessly through the grass. Yet a later search of the land would reveal the sons of Fenriswulf had not survived. No one in this new land had any enemies.

One day Baldr and Hœnir sat talking of the past. As they spoke they both glanced to the same spot in the sky. There they saw Nidhoggr flying up from Nidafjoll over the Nida Mountains bearing corpses on his wings. He flew out of sight purging the lands of all the evil from old times. But where did evil serpent go? No one could answer that question.

From that moment on there was peace and rest. And when the Æsir and Vanir met for council the Alfadir watched over them and spoke. He solved their quarrels and established peace amongst Æsir, Vanir, jotuns, humans, other survivors, and animals forever.

In the new Midgardr the men and women would occasionally stare up to Mt. Idavollr for assurance all was well. And it was. It was often said amongst the mortals that the old Æsir and Vanir now lived in Vindheimr, which meant home of the wind. And that was true, since their stories lived on carried by the wind to all corners of the new world.

The unattainable quality that the gods of old had striven for had finally been reached. There was calm and love. There was finally kindness and peace.

Glossary

Glossary

Abundantia (Abundia): Another name for Freyja.

Adal (Aðal, Athal) [offspring]: Son of Jarl the Earl and Erna. He rode Slongvir.

Ægir (Ægir, Æger, Æge, Œgir, Eagor) [destruction]: Sometimes known as Hler. Ruled the sea with his wife Ran. They were also brother and sister. They had two other brothers, Logi and Kari. Their father was Fornjotr. They had nine wave-maiden daughters (Himinglæva, Dufa, Blodughadda, Hefring, Udr, Hronn, Beylgja, Drofn, Kolga). Both were frequent visitors to Asgardr. He had a long flowing white beard, green hair, and was tall and gaunt. He and Ran's hall was on an island in the Kattigut also known as Hlessey. He owned a giant kettle for brewing mead that had been fetched from the jotun Hymir for him by Thor and Tyr.

Ægishjalmr (Ægishjálmar, Ægishjálmr): Ægir's terrifying dark helmet.

Æsir (Æsir, Asar, Anses, Ásas, Asa-folk): The name for the group of gods known for their power rather than fecundity.

Afi: Another name for Gaffer.

Agnar: He and his younger brother Geirrodr were wrecked in a storm and taught on an island by Grimnir (Odin) and his wife (Frigg). He was later cheated out of his inheritance of Reid-Gothland by his brother. He eventually married a jotun and had lots of children. His nephew is also named Agnar.

Agnar: Geirrodr's son and Agnar's nephew. He succeeded his father to the throne of Reid-Gothland.

Ai (Ái) [great-grandfather]: A farmer who was married to Edda. They were visited by Rigr (Heimdallr), and subsequently a son was born to them whom they named Thræl.

Ai (Ái): A rock dvergar. One of Dvalin's Hosts. His horse was Hrafn. He lived in Juravale's Marsh.

Ajo (Ago, Agio, Aio): One of the leaders of the Vinnilers, along with Ibor.

Aku-Thor (Ake-Thor, Auka-Thor, Auku-Thor, Oku-þorr) [Charioteer-Thor]: An ekename for Thor. See Oku-Thor.

Alda Bergr (Defense of Man): An ekename for Thor.

Aldar Rok (Aldar Rǫk [fate of mankind]: The history of mankind through Ragnarokr.

Alf (álf) [elf]: A rock dvergar. One of Dvalin's Hosts. Lived in Juravale's Marsh.

Alfadir (Alföðr, Allföð, Alföðar, Allföðr, Allföð, Alfaðir, Allfaðir, Aldafǫdr, Aldafaðir, Aldafoðr, Alfǫðr, Alfadur) [Allfather]: Guiding spirit of creation.

Alfar (álfr): Alfs. Two kinds, ljosalfar [light alfs] and dokkalfar [dark alfs].

Alf-blot (Alfablôt) [elf-blood]: The name of the sacrifice to the elves. It was held at the beginning of winter.

Alfheimr (Álfheimr, Álfheim, Álfheimar, Alfheim, Alvheim, Elfheim) [elf land]: Home of the ljosalfar. Situated midway between Asgardr and Midgardr. Given to Freyr as a tooth gift.

Alfrig (Alfrigg): A dvergar who was the brother of Dvalin, Berling and Grer. Helped forge Brisingamen and sold it to Freyja in exchange for her sleeping one night with each of them.

Alfrothul (Alfroðul, Álfröðull, Álfrǫðul, Alfrǫðull) [blessed of the elves, elf-beam]: The name of the sun swallowed by the wolf Hati Hrodvitnirsson. Before she was swallowed she had a daughter who became the new son after Ragnarokr.

Alfs [elfs]: Another name for the elfs or elves. Also known as Alfen or Elfen.

Alf the Old: Instein's father. His father was Ulf. Related to Ottar the Simple.

Algrœn Island (Algrœn Island, Algron Island) [All Green Island]: The island where Harbardr lived for five winters and fought Fjolvar.

Alsvidr (Alsviðr, Alsvið, Alsvider, Alsvith) [all-swift]: Maane's horse. Sometimes known as Fjosvartnir. Runes were carved on his hoof.

Alsvin (Alsvinn) [the swift one]: One of two horses pulling Sol's chariot. The other was Arvakr.

Al-Thing (Al-Thingi, Al-þing): A meeting held ten weeks after the first day of summer. Usually to discuss events for the coming harvest and the rest of the year.

Althjofr (Althjófr, Althiofr, Althjóf) [mighty thief]: An earth dvergar.

Alvaldi (Alvald): An ekename for Ymir.

Alviss (Alvíss, Alvis) [all-wise]: A cunning rock dvergar who went to Asgardr while Thor was regaining Mjolnir from Thrymr. He tried to trick the Æsir into giving him Freyja. Instead he was tricked and became a victim of uppr dagr.

Ambatt (Ambat, Ambott) [servant]: One of the daughters of Thræl and Thir.

Ambri: One of the leaders of the Vandals, along with Assi.

Amma [grandmother]: An ekename for Gammer.

Amr (Ámr, Am): A jotun.

Amsvartnir (Ámsvartnir, Åmsvartne, Amsvartner) [gloomy, black]: A lake in Niflheimr near Nastrond, formed by water from the river Slidr. The island Lyngvi was on this lake. Nidafjoll was on the other side of the lake.

An: An earth dvergar.

Anar (Ánnar, Annaver, Ánnarr, Ánar, Anarr, Anaar, Ónarr, Ónar) [second]: An earth dvergar who was Nott's second husband. Their daughter was Jordr. He was also known as Fjorgyn.

Andhrimnir (Andhrímnir, Andhrimner, Andrimner, Andrimne) [sooty-face]: The cook in Valhalla.

Andlangr (Audlang) [far reaching]: This is a wonderful land existing to the south and upward from Asgardr after Ragnarokr. It was above Vidblainn.

Andr-dis (Andr-dís) [goddess of skis]: An ekename for Skadi.

Andvari (Andvare): A rock dvergar Odin, Loki, and Hœnir once caught using Ran's net. His hoard started the saga of the Niebelungenlied. One of Dvalin's Hosts. He lived in Juravale's Marsh.

Angantyr: One of Arngrim and Eyfura's twelve berserker sons. His brothers were Hadding, Hervard, Hjorvard, Hrani, Bui, Brami, Barri, Reifnir, Tind, and Tyrfing. Related to Ottar the Simple.

Angantyr: He had a dispute with Ottar the Simple about an inheritance.

Angeyja (Augeia, Aurgeia, Aurgiafa, Anheyja, Egia) [whelmer]: One of Heimdallr's nine wave-maiden mothers.

Angroboda (Angrboða, Angroboða, Angerbode, Augerbode, Aurboða, Angur-boda, Angurboda, Angurbodi, Angrbotha, Angerboda, Örboða, Órboða, Orbod, Orboð, Órboðr) [boder of grief, arrow-bidder]: A witch from Jotunheimr who lived in the Myrkvyrdr Forest. She was the daughter of Hrimnir. Her uncle was Egther. Her brother was Hrasthjofi. She sometimes wore the disguise of Heidr. Loki ate her heart and subsequently bore three children, Fenriswulf, Midgardrsormr (Jormungandr), and Hela. She was married to the hrymthursar Gymir and had a daughter named Gerdr, and a son named Beli by him in the more conventional way.

Apples of Idunn: These were eleven golden apples which Idunn kept in an ashwood casket. When she handed them out to the Æsir to eat their wounds were healed and they regained their youth. Idunn tended Brunnakr Grove to renew her supply of apples. They were sometimes called Ellifu and Epli Elliyfa.

Arfi (Arvi) [heir]: A son of Jarl the Earl and Erna.

Arinnefja [hearth nose]: A daughter of Thræl and Thir.

Armenn (Ármenn): Another name for the landvættir. The protective spirits that guarded the shores of settlements. The vikings carved frightful heads on the bows of their ships in order to frighten the landvættir away so they could land if they were venturing into strange lands.

Arngrim: Married to Eyfura. Their sons were twelve berserkers named Hadding, Hadding, Hervard, Hjorvard, Hrani, Angantyr, Bui, Brami, Barri, Reifnir, Tind, and Tyrfing. Related to Ottar the Simple.

Arnhofdi (Arnhöfði, Arnhǫfði) [eagle-hooded]: An ekename for Odin.

Arvakr (Árvakr, Aarvak, Árvak, Arwakr) [early waker]: One of the two horses pulling Sol's chariot. Runes were carved on his ear. The other horse pulling the chariot was Alsvin.

Asa-folk: See Æsir.

Asaheimr (Ásaheimr, Asaheim, Ásaland, Asenheim): The land where the Æsir lived. The chief city was Asgardr.

Asa-Loki (Ása-Loki, Asa-Loke): A name sometimes used to distinguish Loki from Utgardr-Loki.

Asa-Thor (Ása-Thor, Ása-þôrr, Asa-þórr): An ekename for Thor.

Asbru (Ásbrú, Asabru, Asa-bridge) [bridge of the Æsir]: An ekename for Bifrost.

Asgardr (Ásgarðr, Ásgarth, Ásgarð, Asgard): The city in Asaheimr atop Mt. Idavollr that was the home of the Æsir.

Asgardreia: An ekename for the Wild Hunt led by Odin.

Askr (Äsk, Askur, Aske) [ash]: The name of the first man. He was fashioned from a piece of driftwood by Odin, Vili, and Ve.

Asmegen (ásmegin) [divine strength]: The name for the increased strength Thor had when he wore Megingjardr.

Asmund: Odin went to his hall in the guise of Jalkr. Nothing further is known of the story.

Ass (Áss, Ás, Asen, Asa, Anse race): A singular form for a member of the Æsir.

Assi: One of the leaders of the Vandals, along with Ambri.

Asvinr (Ásvinr): A jotun.

Asynje (Ásynja, Asynior, Âsynjor): A singular name for a female of the Æsir.

Asynjes (Ásynjur, Asyniur, Ásynja, Asynjer, Asinges): The plural name for all the female members of the Æsir.

Atla [fury]: One of Geirrodr's daughters, and one of the nine mothers of Heimdallr.

Atridr (Atríðr, Atríð, Atrith, Atridi) [rider]: An ekename for Odin.

Audhumla (Auðhumbla, Auðhumla, Auðumbla, Auðumla) [hornless cow, nourisher]: The cow sculpted out of ice by Ymir in Niflheimr and given life by the heat of Muspelheimr. Her bitter milk fed Ymir. She licked the rimestones to form Buri. She drowned during the flood caused by the death of Ymir.

Audi: An ekename for Odin.

Audr (Auðr, Aud, Audi) [space, desolate]: The first son of Nott by her first husband Naglifari.

Aud the Profound: She was the daughter of Ivar. She was married to Hrorek the Ring Giver. Their son was Harald War Tooth. She also had a son with Rathbard. His name was Randver. Related to Ottar the Simple.

Aurgelmir (Aurgelmer, Aurgelmr, Örgelmir, Œrgelmir) [mud seether]: The jotuns' name for Ymir.

Aurkonungr (Aur-Konung, Aurkonung) [marsh king]: An ekename for Hœnir.

Aurr (aur) [loose clay]: The substance brought from Uppsah Spring by the Norns and spread on Yggdrasyll to stave off decay. Also known as hvitr aurr (hvítr aurr: white clay).

Aurvandil (Örvandill, Aurvandill, Orvandel, Orvandell, Örvandil, Ǫrvandil, Orfandel) [the brave, arrow-worker]: Married to Groa. Sometimes "the wise" or "the brave" was added to his name. One of Thjassi's brothers. During an adventure with Thor, while Thor was carrying him hidden in a basket across the river Elivagar his toe broke through and was frostbitten. Thor broke it off and tossed it into the sky where it became a star known as Aurvandil's Toe. Ullr was his and Sif's son.

Aurvandil's Toe (Orvandill's Toe, Orfandel's Toe): The star formed when Thor tossed Aurvandil's frostbitten toe into the heavens.

Aurvangur (Aurvang): A rock dvergar. One of Durinn's Kin.

Austri (Austre, Estri, Estre) [east]: One of four earth dvergues helping hold up Ymir's skull.

Bafurr (Báfurr, Bofur, Bávor): An earth dvergar.

Baldr (Baldur, Balldr, Balder): He was bright and shining and had white eyebrows. Also known as the god of tears. Runes were carved on his tongue. He and Hodr were twins. Before the birth of Vali the Avenger they were Odin's youngest sons. Their mother was Frigg. Baldr's wife was Nanna Nepsdottir. Their sons were Forseti and

Brono. Their closest friends in Asgardr were Bragi and Idunn. Their estate was called Breidablik, while the main hall on the estate was called Feikstaf. Baldr was slain by his blind twin brother Hodr as a result of Loki's trickery. The candles on a Christmas tree are lit to honor Baldr. Nanna died of grief and a pyre was built beside Baldr for her. They both journeyed to Niflheimr together. They survived Ragnarokr and after the new beginning shared a hall in Hropt's Hills with Hodr, Bragi, and Idunn.

Baldr's Bra (Balderbrå, Baldrsbrá, Baldrsbrá, Balder's Braa, Balderblom, Balder's eyelid [Baldr's Brow, Baldr's bloom]: The camomile flower (sometimes the may week, sometimes the ox-eye daisy) was known by this name. It grows in abundance on Baldr's estate Breidablik.

Baldr's Draumar (Baldr's Dream): Baldr's dreams of foreboding about his death.

Baleygr (Báleygr, Báleyg) [flaming-eyed]: An ekename for Odin.

Bara (Bára): One of Ægir and Ran's wavemaiden daughters.

Bari (Bare): An alf.

Barn [child]: Son of Jarl the Earl and Erna.

Barr (Bur, Burr) [son]: Eldest son of Jarl the Earl and Erna. He was the first king of Denmark.

Barri (Barr, Barrey, Barey, Burri, Burr-wood, Bar-Isle) [needle-isle, the leafy]: The name of the grove where Freyr and Gerdr met and were married.

Barri: One of Arngrim and Eyfura's twelve berserker sons. His brothers were Hadding, Hervard, Hjorvard, Hrani, Angantyr, Bui, Brami, Reifnir, Tind, and Tyrfing. Related to Ottar the Simple.

Baugi (Bauge): Son of Gillingr, brother of Suttungr. He hired Bolverkr (Odin) as a fieldhand. The payment for Bolverk's services was to help Bolverkr gain a taste of the Precious Mead from Suttungr.

Baugreginn [king of the gold rings]: An ekename for Mimir.

Beli (Bele) [bellower]: Gerdr's brother, son of Gymir and Angroboda. He was killed in a battle with Freyr.

Bergelmir (Bergelmer, Bergellmer, Berglemer, Berggelmer) [old one of the mountain]: First born son of Thrudgelmir. An hrymthursar who survived the great flood with his wife by scrambling on a mill called Ludr. Their son was Farbauti who was Loki's father.

Berglrui: A rock dweller.

Bergrisar (Berg-risar, Bergthursar) [mountain jotun]: The name for the rock jotuns. They were known to cause land slips and earthquakes.

Berling: A dvergar. Brother of Dvalin, Alfrig, and Grer. Helped forge Brisingamen and sold it to Freyja in exchange for her sleeping one night with each of them.

Berserkers (Berserkir, Berserks) [bare sarks, without shirts, without armor]: Warriors who were so filled with the ecstasy of battle that they wore neither armor nor any other form of protection. They fought in a frenzy usually with the strength of a madman brought on by a lack of fear and caution. They didn't care if they were hacked up or killed in the process. Their mood was so euphoric they felt no pain when they were injured. They were known as ulfhednar (wolf-skinned) when they howled like wolves to frighten their opponents in their frenzy.

Bestla (Besla, Beyzla, Belsta, Beistla): Daughter of Bolthorn. She was Mimir's sister and was married to Bor. Their sons, Odin, Vili, and Ve, were the first of the Æsir. She

drowned in the great flood. But before that she and Bor were able to plant the seed which grew to be the mighty world tree Yggdrasyll.

Beyggiver (Byggvir, Bygver, Beygver): Freyr's valet. Freyr's other servant was Beyggiver's sister Beyla.

Beyla: Freyr's maidservants. Freyr's other servant was Beyla's brother Beyggiver.

Beylgja (Bylgja) [billow]: One of Ægir and Ran's daughters.

Biflindi (Bifliði, Biflindr, Biblindi): An ekename for Odin.

Bifrost (Bifröst, Bifrǫst, Bifraust, Bivrost, Bilrúst, Bilóst, Bilöst, Bilrǫst, Birfr, Birfrost) [trembling way]: Also called Asbru and the Rainbow Bridge. It connected Midgardr to Asgardr. The colors in the bridge came from the different elements—red from fire, blue from air, and green from the sea. The bridge was guarded by Heimdallr. The golden gate at the top had a diamond lock. The only key that could open the lock was held by Heimdallr. The sound it makes when it opens was both sad and happy, like the dripping of leaves after it rains. Thor was too heavy to cross it and had to wade through the rivers under it.

Bifurr (Bívor): An earth dvergar.

Bil: Daughter of Vidfinnr, sister of Hjiuki. She, along with her brother, was forced to fetch water from the well Byvgir. But she and her brother were rescued by Maane, and scooped up to become the faces on the face of the moon.

Bildur (Bíldur): A rock dvergar. One of Durinn's Kin.

Bileygr (Bileyg) [one with sneaky eyes]: An ekename for Odin.

Billing: A rock dvergar. One of Durinn's Kin.

Billingr: King of the Ruthenes (Varns), father of Princess Rindr.

Bilskirnir (Bilskirner, Bilskirne) [storm-serene, lightning]: Thor's hall in Thrudheimr (or Thrudvangar). The outside of it was studded with shields which glowed red. The inside was a gleaming purple. It had 540 rooms which made it the equal to Valhalla in size. Warriors lived here too, as in Valhalla.

Bjarki [bear]: An ekename for Odin.

Bjarr: An ekename for Odin. In this guise he rode the horse Kertr.

Bjorn (Björn, Bjorn) [bear]: An ekename for Odin. In this guise he rode the horse Blakkr.

Blainn, (Bláinn, Bláin) [black one]: An ekename for Ymir.

Blakkr [black]: A horse ridden by Thegn or Bjorn.

Blindr (Blindi, Blinði) [blind]: An ekename for Odin.

Blodorn rista (Blóðorn rísta) [blood eagle]: The form of punishment in which an incision was made in the back, the ribs were then separated and the lungs were drawn out of the body, usually while the person was still alive. This practice was known as cutting the blood eagle.

Blodughadda (Blódughadda) [bloody hair]: One of Ægir and Ran's wavemaiden daughters.

Blodughofi (Blóðughófi, Blodug-hofi, Blodinghofi) [bloody-hoof]: Freyr's horse who could understand speech.

Blotgodar: The name given to Freyja and Freyr as the sacrificial priests of the Æsir.

Boandi (Bóandi, Bondi) [yeoman]: Son of Karl the Yeoman and Snœr.

Boddi [farmholder]: Son of Karl the yeoman and Snœr.

Bodn (Boðn, Boden, Bohn) [offering]: One of the vats that held part of the Precious Mead. The other was Son along with the bronze kettle Odrærir.

Boga ass (boga áss, Bogaáss) [god of the bow]: An ekename for Ullr.

Bolmso [Bolmsö]: The island where the twelve berserker relatives of Ottar the Simple were born.

Bolthorn (Bölþorn, Bælthorn, Bœlthorn, Bóthor, Bölthór, Bölthórr, Bölthori, Bölthórn, Bolthorn, Bolþorn) [evil thorn]: Another son of Thrudgelmir's. He was the father of Bestla and Mimir.

Bolverkr (Bölverk, Bölverkr, Bolvork, Bölwerk, Bolwerk) [baleworker, evil worker, mischief-maker]: The identity and ekename assumed by Odin when he worked as a fieldhand for Baugi, Suttungr's brother. Baugi promised to help Bolverkr get a drink of the Precious Mead as payment for working for him.

Bomburr (Bómburr, Bömbur, Bömbör): An earth dvergar.

Bor (Bur, Buri, Börr, Bör, Bori) [born]: A son of Buri, married to Bestla. Their sons, Odin, Vili, and Ve, were the first of the Æsir. He died in the flood. But before that he and Bestla were able to plant the seed which grew to be the mighty Yggdrasyll.

Bragi (Brage): The son who was the result of Odin sleeping with Gunnlod, Suttungr's daughter, in order to win the Precious Mead. Odin carved magic runes on his tongue. Bragi sang songs and spoke poetry. He was married to Idunn. They both wore white. He went on frequent walking tours throughout Midgardr singing songs of the adventures of the Æsir. When Idunn left Asgardr to live in Yggdrasyll he followed her and sang songs to her. When she fell into Niflheimr he followed her there and stayed with her until Ragnarokr. He and Idunn were Baldr and Nanna's closest friends. He and Idunn both survived Ragnarokr, and shared a hall in Hropt's Hills with Baldr, Nanna, and Hodr.

Brami: One of Arngrim and Eyfura's twelve berserker sons. His brothers were Hadding, Hervard, Hjorvard, Hrani, Angantyr, Bui, Barri, Reifnir, Tind, and Tyrfing. Related to Ottar the Simple.

Brattskeggr (Brattskegg) [high beard]: Son of Karl the Yeoman and Snœr.

Breidablik (Breiðablik, Breidablick, Breithablik) [broad gleaming, broad splendor]: Baldr's estate in Asgardr. His hall was Feikstaf.

Breidr (Breiðr, Breid, Breith) [the broad-shouldered]: Son of Jarl the Yeoman and Snœr.

Brimir (Brimír, Brimer): A hall in Okolnir near Nidavellir. During the beginning it was named after the jotun who lived in the hall. It was also used by Midvitnir as his mead hall. It existed after Ragnarokr, and was known for always having plenty of mead and good times. The Æsir could meet here, relax and talk about the old times.

Brimir (Brimír, Brimer): A ekename for Ymir.

Brisingamen Necklace (Brísíngamen Necklace, Brísinga Necklace, Brínga-men, Brîníga-Men, Brísing belt, Necklace of the Brísings, Brísing Necklace): The necklace forged by the four dvergar brothers Dvalin, Alfrig, Berling, and Grer. It was sold to Freyja in exchange for her sleeping one night with each of them, and was stolen by Loki but recovered by Heimdallr. Freyja was forced to wear it as a reminder of her unfaithfulness. That unfaithfulness caused Odr, her husband, to leave and wander in Midgardr. She would go in search of him crying bitter tears of gold along the way.

Brokkr (Brokker, Brokkur, Brokur, Brok, Brokk, Brock, Brökk): A rock dvergar. Brother of Sindri. He wagered Loki for his head that his brother was the finest artisan in the world. In order to win the wager Sindri forged Draupnir, Gullinbursti, and Mjolnir.

Brono [daylight]: Baldr and Nanna's son. His brother was Forseti.

Brudr (Brúðr, Brud, Bruth) [bride]: Daughter of Karl the Yeoman and Snœr.

Bruni (Brúni): A rock dvergar. One of Durinn's Kin.

Brunnakr Grove (Brunnaker Grove): A grove of apple trees that became the home of Idunn and Bragi. It was located near the southern ridge of Asgardr near Gladsheimr and the gold-thatched hall, Gimle. The grove was also known as Glasir.

Buchi: A famous archer who traveled with Thorkill and King Gormr to find Geirrodr's Garth.

Bui (Búi) [house owner]: Son of Karl the Yeoman and Snœr.

Bui: One of Arngrim and Eyfura's twelve berserker sons. His brothers were Hadding, Hervard, Hjorvard, Hrani, Angantyr, Brami, Barri, Reifnir, Tind, and Tyrfing. Related to Ottar the Simple.

Bumburr: A dvergar.

Bundinskeggi [trimbeard]: Son of Karl the Yeoman and Snœr.

Buri (Búri, Bure, Búr, Burr, Burí, Bori, Borr, Bors) [created]: The jotun formed by Audhumla when she was licking the rimestones in Niflheimr. His son was Bor. Buri was killed by Ymir.

Buri: A rock dvergar. One of Durinn's Kin.

Burr [son]: A son of Jarl and Erna.

Buseyra (Búseyra): Someone who was slain by Thor.

Byleistr (Býleist, Býleist, Býleiptr, Býleipt, Beyleipt) [whirlwind from the east, trampler of towns]: Loki's brother. Their other brother was Helblindi.

Byrgir (Byrger, Byrgvi, Byrgi): Well from which Hjiuki and Bil fetched water for the jotun Vidfinnr. It gave the drinker youthfulness.

Cup of Penance: The cup Thor drank so heartily from in Utgardr. One end extended into the ocean on Midgardr. Thor drank so much that he lowered the ocean level on Midgardr and thus caused the ebb and neap of the tides.

Dagr (Dag) [dag]: Son of Nott and Dellingr. He guided the moon around Midgardr. The horses pulling his chariot were Gladr and Skinfaxi, although he sometimes borrowed Drosull from Dellinger to give one of his horses a rest.

Dain: One of the dvergar who helped make Freyja's boar Hilksuin. The other dvergar was Nabbi.

Dain (Dáinn, Dáin, Daain) [one at rest]: An earth dvergar who with Thrain, was sought by Huginn to find out where Idunn was. The two were also sent for to interpret Baldr's dreams. He and Thrain were dvergues of sleep and dreams. They had both drunk mead from Mimirsbrunnr Well. Dain made Tyrfing and taught runes to elves and dvergues.

Dainn (Dáinn, Dáin, Daain): One of four harts grazing beneath Yggdrasyll at Urdarbrunnr Well. Dvallinn, Duneyrr, and Durathorr were the other three.

Danish Zealand (Danish Sealand, Danish Seeland, Danish Selund): The land Gefjun carved from Gylfi's kingdom in Sweden, leaving behind a hole which filled up to form Lake Logrin (also known as Lake Malar).

Dansleif: The name of a magical sword made by the dvergues. Once drawn it could not be put away until it had tasted blood.

Danpr (Danp, Danr, Dan): The son of Kon.

Dark elves: See dokkalfar.

Dellingr (Dellinger, Delling) [dayspring, the shining one]: Nott's third husband. Their son was Dagr. His world was on the eastern border of the lower world. His horse, Drosull, was sometimes lent to Dagr for use in helping pull his chariot so he could give either Skinfaxi or Gladr a rest.

Digraldi [fat]: One of Thræl and Thir's sons.

Dis (Dís, Dîs): Plural of Disir. They are attendant spirits or guardian angels. This term could also be used to signify any female deity.

Disablot (Dísablót, Dîsablot): The sacrifice to the Disir consisting of heavy drinking and celebrating. Usually held in Autumn, although it was not uncommon to also hold a Disablot in the winter. The house in which it was held was called a horgr or Disarsalr.

Disir (Dísir, Dîsir): The plural of Dis.

Dokkalfar (døkkálfar, døkálfar, Døkk-alfar) [dark elves]: Another name for the dvergues.

Dolgthoari (Dólgthoari): A dvergar.

Dolgthrasir (Dólgthrasir, Dólgþrasir): A dvergar. One of Dvalin's Hosts. Lived in Juravale's Marsh.

Dolgthvari (Dólgthvari, Dólgthvar) [battle stock]: A rock dvergar.

Doomstead: The place for giving final judgement at a Thing.

Dori (Dóri, Dore): A rock dvergar. One of Dvalin's Hosts. He also worked for Dellingr and Durinn. Lived in Juravale's Marsh.

Draugr (Draugar): A zombie.

Draupnir (Draupner, Draupne) [dropper, dripper]: The red-golden arm ring forged by Sindri and his brother Brokkr and given to Odin as part of the three gifts given to the Æsir to win a wager against Loki. Draupnir was shaped like a snake holding its tail in its mouth. Every nine days it magically produced nine more arm rings equally as valuable.

Draupnir: A rock dvergar. One of Dvalin's Hosts. Lived in Juravale's Marsh.

Drengr (Dreng) [strong, warrior]: A son of Karl the Yeoman and Snœr.

Drifa [snow storm]: A jotun descendant of the hrymthursar Kari.

Drofn (Dröfn) [wave]: One of Ægir and Ran's wavemaiden daughters.

Dromi (Drómi, Drome, Droma, Drone): The second chain forged by Thor in Asgardr for use in binding Fenriswulf. Lædingr was the first. Dromi was twice as strong, but also failed in binding Fenriswulf. The third chain was Gleipnir which succeeded in binding Fenriswulf.

Drosull (Drösull) [roamer]: The name of the horse belonging to Dellingr. It was sometimes used by Dagr to pull his chariot in order to give either Gladr or Skinfaxi a rest.

Drottr (Dröttr, Drott) [lazy, sluggard]: Son of Thræl and Thir.

Drumba [log]: Daughter of Thræl and Thir.

Drumbr (Drumb) [log]: Son of Thræl and Thir.

Duer (Dúer): A dvergar.

Duf (Dúf): A rock dvergar.

Dufa (Dúfa, Duva) [one who dives]: One of Ægir and Ran's daughters.

Dufur: A rock dvergar. One of Dvalin's Hosts. Lived in Juravale's Marsh.

Duneyrr (Dunéyrr, Dunneyr, Duneyr): One of four harts grazing at Urdarbrunnr Well. Dainn, Dvalinn, and Durathorr were the other three.

Durathorr (Duraþrór, Duraþrórr, Dyrathrór, Durathor) [light sleep]: One of four harts grazing at Urdarbrunnar Well. Dainn, Dvalinn, and Duneyrr were the other three.

Durinn (Durin): A dvergar created by Modsognir. He was the second dvergar created. He in turn created many other dvergues, and was thought of as the king of the dvergues. Many dvergues were especially loyal to him and were known as either Durinn's Kin or Durinn's Folk.

Durinn's Folk: See Durinn's Kin.

Durinn's Kin: Dvergues created by Durinn who were especially loyal to him. Usually they lived in rocks. Also known as Durinn's Folk.

Dvalin [one in a trance]: An earth dvergar. One of Ivaldi's sons who helped forge Sif's hair, Odin's spear Gungnir, and Freyr's ship Skidbladnir. He forged the Brisingamen Necklace with his three brothers, Alfrig, Berling, and Grer, and sold it to Freyja in exchange for her sleeping one night with each of them.

Dvalinn (Dvalin): One of four harts grazing at Urdarbrunnr Well. Dainn, Duneyrr, and Durathorr were the other three.

Dvalin's Doom: An expression for the sun. Dvergues, the sons of Dvalin, had to beware of uppr dagr, being dayed up. This meant if they were hit by the rays of the sun they would be turned to stone unless they were wearing a red tarnkappe which made the wearer invisible so the sun's rays could not see the wearer and therefore could not turn the wearer to stone.

Dvalin's Leika [playmate of Dvalin]: The dvergues bitter ekename for the sun, since seeing the son would turn them to stone.

Dvergar (Dvergr): Another name for the dvergues. The first dvergar was Modsognir. He and the others were created from the maggots crawling in and out of Ymir's decomposing body. They collected gold, other precious metals and gems and hid them away in the ground. Their hoards were used to fashion magical weapons and jewelry. They were masters of runes and magic songs. Other names for them included brownies, trolls, goblins, pucks, gremlins, Huldra folk, and kobolds. The dvergues from Svartalfheimr were particularly mischievous. Many wore red caps called tarnkappes, which made the wearer invisible to those on Midgardr, including the sun, so they wouldn't be turned to stone in the daylight, giving them more time to do their mischief.

Dvergues [dwarves]: Plural of dvergar.

Dwarf: See dvergar.

Dwarves: See dvergues.

Dwerg-mal (dwerg-mál, dwerg-mála) [dwarf talk]: An echo, supposedly caused by dvergues mischievously repeating the ends of words and sentences spoken by those on Midgardr in order to try and confuse them.

Edda [great-grandmother]: Her husband was Ai. They were the first couple Rigr the Walker (Heimdallr) came upon in his travels to populate Midgardr with warriors. They worked with the land. She was the mother of Thræl (Rigr was the father).

Edgar (Egðir, Egdir, Egder, Egder) [wise beyond all-knowing]: The satin eagle, rusty-yellow in color who roosted on the topmost bough of Yggdrasyll. The hawk Vedrfolnir sits in his view.

Egil (Egill): He was a farmer of Midgardr whose cottage was on the banks of the river Ifing. He often took care of Thor's goats and chariot when the thundergod journeyed to Jotunheimr or Utgardr. His children, Thjalfi and Roskva, were Thor's servants.

Egther (Eggther, Eggthur) [sword guardian]: An hrymthursar. He was the brother of Hrimnir. His niece was Angroboda, his nephew was Hrasthjofi.

Eigandi Fressa [owner of cats]: An ekename for Freyja representative of the fact she owned a cat-driven chariot.

Eikin (Ekin, Ækin) [oaken]: A river flowing out of Hvergelmir through Asgardr and on into Midgardr.

Eikinskjaldi (Eikinskiald) [having an oak shield]: A rock dvergar. One of Dvalin's Hosts. Lived in Juravale's Marsh.

Eikintjasna [oak peg]: Daughter of Thræl and Thir.

Eikthrynir (Eikthyrner, Eikthyrnir, Eikthyrni, Eikthyrner, Eikþyrnir) [oak antlers]: The name of the hart standing on the shield-roof of Valhalla eating the leaves off Yggdrasyll. Water dripping from his antlers formed several rivers flowing to Midgardr. They included Sid, Vid, Sokin, Eikin, Svol, Gunnthra, Fjorm, Fimbulthul, Gipul, Gopul, Gomel, and Geirvimul.

Eild: A name by which fire was known in Asgardr.

Einhendr Asa: An ekename for Tyr.

Einherjar (Einheriar, Einherjes): The collective name for the dead (valr) chosen for Valhalla. The singular was Einherje.

Einherje (Einheri): A single warrior fighting in Valhalla. The plural was Einherjar.

Einmyria [ashes]: One of Loki's two daughters by Glut. The other was Eisa.

Einridi: An ekename for Thor.

Eir (Eira, Eyra) [peace, clemency]: She was one of Menglod's attendants and was considered the healer of the Æsir. She was the goddess of medicine and the best of all physicians.

Eisa [embers]: One of Loki's two daughters by Glut. The other was Einmyria.

Eistla (Eistlæ, Aistla) [foamer]: One of Heimdallr's nine wavemaiden mothers.

Ekename: An alternate name, epithet, nickname.

Eldhrimnir (Eldhrimner) [soot-covered from fire]: The name of the kettle in Valhalla in which Sæhrimnir was boiled.

Eldir (Elder, Eld, Elde) [person of fire]: Ægir and Ran's cook.

Elgr [elk]: An ekename for Odin.

Elidner [Éljúðnir, Elvidnir, Elvidner, Eliudnir] [home of storms]: The name of Hela's hall in Niflhel. Its doors face north so there is never a chance of any sunlight hitting it. There are serpents entwined around each other covering the walls.

Elivagar River (Elivagur, Élivágar, Elivågar, Eliwagar, Elivog) [stormy waves]: A river in Niflheimr that was the source of Hvergelmir Well. Eleven other rivers branched from it. They were Svoll, Gunthra, Fjorm, Fimbulthul, Slidr, Hridr, Sylgr, Ylgr, Vid, Leiptr, and Gjoll.

Ellewomen (elle-maidens): Servant women. They had no heart and pitied no one. Their backs were hollow. They grinned continuously and were not to be trusted. The jotun Thjassi had used them as servants in his castle. They would turn around if one made the sign of Thor's hammer (the sign of the cross). If you were uncertain whether or

not a woman was an ellewoman then you would make the sign and cause them to turn around and show their hollow backs.

Elli (Ellie, Elle) [old age]: Thor fought against her in Utgardr, but she won when she brought him to one knee.

Embla [elm]: The piece of driftwood found by Odin, Vili, and Ve and fashioned into the form of a woman.

Epli Ellifu (Eppli Ellifo) [eleven apples]: Another name for the Eleven Apples of Idunn. Also known as Epli Elliyfs.

Epli Elliyfs [apples of old-age medicine]: Another name for the Eleven Apples of Idunn. Also known as Epli Ellifu.

Ergi: The name given to the practices used to perform seidr. Used derogatorily to refer to homosexuality.

Erlkonig [King of the elves]: An ekename for Freyr.

Ermt (Örmt): Another name for the river Ormt.

Erna: The daughter of Hersir who married Jarl the Earl. Their sons were Adal, Arfi, Barr, Barn, Jod, Kon, Kundr, Mogr, Nidr, Nidjungr, Sonr, Sveinn.

Ettin (Etin): A jotun.

Eyfura: Married to Arngrim. Their sons were twelve berserkers named Hadding, Hadding, Hervard, Hjorvard, Hrani, Angantyr, Bui, Brami, Barri, Reifnir, Tind, and Tyrfing. Related to Ottar the Simple.

Eylimi: A king of the Othling clan. His daughter was Hjordis. Related to Ottar the Simple.

Eyrgjafa (Eyrhjafr) [maker of sandbanks]: One of Heimdallr's nine wavemaiden mothers.

Fadir (Faðir, Fathir) [father]: Husband of Modir. Their son (actually Modir and Rigr's son) was Jarl the Earl.

Fafnir: A dragon who was slain by Sigurdr, who ever after was called Sigurdr Fafnirsbani.

Fakr (Fákr) [jade]: The name of the horse ridden by Haki.

Falhofnir (Falhófnir, Falhóni, Falhofner) [barrel hoof, hollow hoof]: One of the horses of the Æsir.

Falkeham: Another name for valsharmr, Freyja's falcon-guise. See Fiadrhamr.

Falr (Fal): A rock dvergar.

Farbauti (Fårbaute, Fárbauti) [destroyer of ships, danger dunts]: A storm jotun married to Laufey. Their sons were Loki, Byleistr, and Helblindi.

Farmagud (Farmaguð, Farma-gud) [god of cargoes]: An ekename for Odin. Same as Farmatyr.

Farmatyr (Farmatýr) [god of cargoes]: An ekename for Odin. Same as Farmagud.

Farœ Island (Farve Island): The island where Rogner lived with his parents. Odin, Hœnir, and Loki visited them and saved Rogner from the jotun Skrymali.

Fegjafi (Fégjafi) [giver of good]: An ekename for Freyr.

Feikstaf (Feiknastafr): Baldr's hall on his estate Breidablik. It had a silver roof and gold pillars.

Feima [bashful]: A daughter of Karl the Yeoman and Snœr.

Fengari: Another name for the moon.

Fengr (Feng): An ekename for Odin.

Fenriswulf (Fenriswolf, Fenris-wolf, Fenriwúlfr, Fenrir, Fenrer): A wolf cub that Loki bore after eating the evil Angroboda's heart. He was brother to Midgardrsormr and

Hela. The Æsir finally bound him on their third attempt using the chain Gleipnir in Niflheimr on the island Lyngvi in the lake Amsvartnir. He bit off Tyr's hand while being bound. They were enemies ever after. He swallowed Mimir's head at Ragnarokr. he also killed Odin at the final battle. But Odin's death was avenged by Vidarr the Silent who successfully slew Fenriswulf. He was also known as Vanargandr and Hrodvitnir. His sons by Angroboda were Hati Hditnirsson and Managarmr.

Fensalir (Fensalar, Fensale, Fensala, Fensal) [water hall]: Frigg's hall. It was gold and silver, encrusted with pearls and situated near the sea. Some of those who drown go to this hall rather than to Ægir and Ran's hall. This hall was preferable since Frigg was much nicer than Ægir and Ran.

Fiadrhamr (Fiaðrhamr): Another name for valsharmr, Freyja's falcon-guise. See Falkeham.

Fiala (Fjalarr, Fjalar, Fialar): The purple cock in Gagalvid in Jotunheimr.

Fidr (Fiðr, Fidr, Fið, Fid): A rock dvergar.

Fili (Fíli): An earth dvergar.

Fimafengr (Fimafeng, Fimaffenger, Funafengr, Funfeng) [quick, nimble]: Ægir's personal servant. He was struck and killed by Loki at Ægir and Ran's last feast for the Æsir.

Fimbulfambi (Fimbulfambe) [mighty fool]: A derogatory term for a foolish person.

Fimbulthul (Fimbulþul, Fimbuþulr) [heavenly river]: One of the eleven rivers flowing from Elivagar.

Fimbultyr (Fimbultýr) [mighty god]: An ekename for Odin.

Fimbulventr (Fimbulvetr, Fimbul-vetr, Fimbul-vetre, Fimbul-winter) [mighty winter]: The harsh winter that was three winters long during which the sun and moon were swallowed. It immediately preceded Ragnarokr. Starvation, greed, and murders plagued Midgardr during this time.

Finnr (Finn): A dvergar. One of Dvalin's Hosts. Lived in Juravale's Marsh.

Fiolsvidr (Fiölsvidr, Fiölsvider): Guardian of Menglod's.

Fitjung: An ekename for Midgardr.

Fitjung's Sons: An ekename for those in Midgardr.

Fjalarr (Fjalar, Fialarr, Fialar, Fiala) [very wise]: He and Galarr were rock dvergues, and Durinn's Kin. They killed Kvasir and made the Precious Mead from his blood. They also killed Gillingr and his wife.

Fjolnir (Fjölnir, Fjolner, Fiölnir, Fiolnir) [many-shaped]: An ekename for Odin.

Fjolnir (Fjölnir, Fjolner, Fiölnir, Fiolnir) [many-shaped]: The name of Freyr and Gerdr's son.

Fjolsvidr (Fjölsviðr, Fjolsvið, Fjolsvith) [one having great wisdom]: An ekename for Odin.

Fjolvar: He loved on Algrœn Island where Harbardr battled him and made love to his seven jotun daughters.

Fjorgvin (Fjörgvin, Fiorgune): Frigg's daughter.

Fjorgyn (Fjorgyn, Fjorgynr, Fjúorgyn, Fjörgyn, Fjörgvin, Fiörgyn, Fiorgyna): The masculine form of Fjorgyn. The name of Frigg's father. An ekename sometimes used by Odin. Anar was sometimes known by this name, also.

Fjorgynn (Fjorgynn, Fjorgynnr, Fjúorgynn, Fjörgynn, Fjörgvinn, Fiörgynn): Another name for Jord, Thor's mother.

Fjorm (Fjörm, Fjorn) [noisy bubbling]: One of the eleven rivers that flow from Elivagar.

Fjosnir (Fjósnir) [herd, cattle]: One of Thræl and Thir's sons.

Fjosvartnir (Fjósvartnir, Fjösvartnir, Fjosvartner) [black life]: Another name for Alsvidr, Maane's horse.

Fljod (Fljóð, Fljoð, Fljoth) [good woman]: A daughter of Karl the Yeoman and Snœr.

Flytting: A question and answer contest between two people in order to decide an issue.

Folkvaldi goda (folkvaldi goða) [ruler of plain folk]: An ekename for Freyr.

Folkvangar (Folkvangr, Folkvangr, Folkvangar, Folkvangur, Fólkvangr, Fólkvangar, Folkvang, Folkvanger) [land of warriors, people's plain]: Freyja's estate. Her hall was Sessrumnir. She received a portion of the slain for her hall.

Folkvir (Fölkvir): A horse ridden by Haraldr.

Fonn [dense snow]: A jotun descendant of the hrymthursar Kari.

Fordæda (fordæða): A term meaning witch.

Forn: An ekename for Freyja.

Fornbogi: A dvergar.

Fornjotr (Fornjótr, Fornjot, Fornjotnr, Forniot): An ancient jotun, possibly an ekename for Ymir. He was the father of Ægir or Hler – ruler of the ocean, Logi – ruler of flame or fire, Kari – the wind, and Ran – also the ruler of the ocean. These divinities do not, for the most part, have much to do with Norse mythology, but were probably influences from Finnish and Celtic cults.

Forseti (Forsetti, Forsete) [presiding one, president]: Baldr's and Nanna's son. His hall was Glitner. He was well-known for being able to solve problems and was often brought in to mediate situations. He was regarded as the lawgiver of the Æsir. His brother was Brono.

Foundation of Poetry: An ekename for the Precious Mead.

Fragr (Frægr, Frag, Fræg, Frægur): A rock dvergar. One of Durinn's Kin.

Franangr Falls (Franângr Falls, Franângr Falls, Frananger Falls, Franangrsfors, Frânangrs-Fors, Fraananger-Force, Fránangr Falls, Fránang Falls, Fraananger Falls) [shining water]: Loki built a house next to this river after he fled Ægir and Ran's last feast for the Æsir. Loki would hide in the falls during the day in the form of a salmon. He was captured here by the Æsir.

Frar (Frár): A rock dvergar. One of Durinn's Kin.

Fravitnir: Another name for Nidhoggr.

Freki (Freke, Feki, Feke) [gobble-up]: One of Odin's wolves. The other was Geri.

Freyja (Freya, Freija, Frija, Freia, Frea) [lady]: One of the Vanir. Daughter of Njordr and Nerthus, twin sister of Freyr. She came to the Æsir as a hostage and then stayed of her own free will. Her estate was Folkvangar, her hall was Sessrumnir. She was married to the handsome Æsir Odr. They had two daughters, Hnoss and Gersemi. She and Odin were lovers. She slept with four dvergues to buy the Brisingamen Necklace. Odr left her to wander in Midgardr when he found out. She went in search of him crying tears of bitter gold along the way. Odin forced her to wear Brisingamen as a reminder of her unfaithfulness. She owned a golden boar named Hilksuin, which glowed in the dark. Pigs and boars were sacred to her, as were cats. She owned a cat-drawn chariot and was thus known as the eigandi fress (owner of cats) because of her love of them.

She practiced two forms of magic, gladr and seidr, and taught the latter to Odin. She could change her form and owned the falcon-guise valsharmr.

Freyr (Frey, Fro, Ingvi-Freyr, Yngvi-Freyr, Ingunaryr, Yngvi, Yngve, Yng, Ing, Ingîngar, Ingvîngar) [lord]: ᚠ was the rune called Freyr. One of the Vanir. Son of Njordr and Nerthus, twin brother of Freyja. He came to the Æsir as a hostage and then stayed of his own free will. His valet was Byggvir, while Beyla was his maidservant. He lived in Uppsala. He fell in love with Gerdr and gave his magical sword Gambanteinn, also known as Tamsvondr, to Skirnir, his best friend, for the wooing and winning of Gerdr, whom he eventually married, but not before killing her brother Beli on the way to the ceremony. He was slain by Surtr at Ragnarokr. He had no weapons to defend himself with since he had given them to Skirnir.

Friaut: The mother of Hledis. Her mother was Hildigun. Related to Ottar the Simple.

Frigg (Frigga, Friga, Fricca) [love]: Fjorgyn's daughter. Odin's consort. Their twin sons were Baldr and Hodr. Her hall was Fensalir.

Friggjar Rock: The name of the constellation in the sky that represents Frigg spinning at her distaff. It was located near Orion's belt.

Froblod (Fröblod): The sacrifice to Freyr.

Frodi: King Frodi was the father of Hledis and Kari. Related to Ottar the Simple.

Frœgr (Froegr): A dvergar.

Frosti: A rock dvergar. One of Durinn's Kin. Lived in Juravale's Marsh.

Frosti [iceberg]: A jotun descendant of the hrymthursar Kari. He was also known as Jokull. He married Mioll, the daughter of King Snar of Finland.

Fulla (Fulla, Full) [fullness]: A goddess of the Æsir. She was Frigg's attendant and took care of her toilette, clothes and slippers. She was a virgin. Nanna sent her a finger ring from Niflheimr. She wore her hair flowing over her shoulders.

Fulminum: The name given to the thunderbolts that shot forth from Mjolnir.

Fulnir (Fúlnir) [stinker]: A son of Thræl and Thir.

Fundinn (Fundin) [found one]: An earth dvergar.

Fylgja (fylgie): The singular form of fylgjur.

Fylgjur (fulgiur): The plural form representing the lesser goddesses who acted as individual guardian spirits for those on Midgardr. Each person had his or her own fylgja.

Gaffer [grandfather]: Husband of Gammer. Also known as Afi. He and his wife were the second couple visited by Rigr the Walker (Heimdallr). Their son (actually the son of Gammer and Rigr) was Karl the Yeoman.

Gagalvid: The place where the purple cock Fiala sits in Jotunheimr.

Galarr (Galar, Galor): He and Fjalarr were rock dvergues and Durinn's Kin. They killed Kvasir and made the Precious Mead from his blood. They also killed Gillingr and his wife.

Galdr (Galðr): A type of magic.

Galdrsfadir (galdrsfaðir) [father of magic]: An ekename for Odin.

Galgatyr (Galgatýr): An ekename for Odin.

Gambanteinn (Gambantein): Freyr's magical sword. It could fight of its own accord. Its name was changed to Tamsvondr (taming wand) after Skirnir carved runes on it three times and threatened Gerdr with it.

Gambantrim: Odin's runic staff. Odin lent it to Hermodr to use against Hrossthjofi.

Gambara: The mother of Ibor and Ajo, the leaders of the Vinilers. She was a favorite of Frigg's.

Gammer (Gammar) [grandmother]: Wife of Gaffer. Also known as Amma. Second couple visited by Rigr the Walker (Heimdallr). Their son (actually the son of Gammer and Rigr) was Karl the Yeoman.

Gammleid (Gammleið): An ekename for Loki.

Gandalfr (Ganndálf, Gandálf): An earth dvergar.

Ganglati (Ganglat) [lazy]: Hela's manservant.

Gangleri (Gangleri, Ganglere, Gangler) [way weary]: An ekename for Odin.

Gangleri (Ganglêri, Ganglere, Gangler) [way weary]: The name used by King Gylfi when he visited Asgardr.

Ganglot (Ganglöt) [slow]: Hela's maidservant.

Gangr (Gângr, Gang): One of the sons of Olvaldi. He was storm jotun. His two brothers were Idi and Thjassi. his niece was Skadi.

Gangraaf (Gagnráðe, Gagnráðr, Gagnrad, Gagnráth, Gagnráðe, Gagnraad, Gagnrad, Gagnrath, Gangráðr, Gangraad, Gangradur) [the one who gives good advice]: The name Odin assumed on his journey to gain knowledge from the jotun Vafthrudnir.

Gardrofa (Garðrofa, Gaarðrofa) [fence breaker]: The goddess Gna had a horse named Hofvarpnir. The horses' sire was Hamskerpir. Gardrofa was its dam.

Garmr (Garmar, Garm): The wolf chained at the entrance to Gnipahellir Cave by the Gjoll River guarding the entrance there. The offering of a hel-cake calmed him down so you could pass on to Helgrindr Gate. Garmr and Tyr slew each other at Ragnarokr.

Gastrofnir: The name of Asgardr's gate. Its movement was regulated by chains which raised and lowered it to allow or deny passage into Asgardr. It could trap or kill anyone who tried to tamper with it.

Gautatyr (Gautatýr, Gauta-tayr) [god of the gauts]: An ekename for Odin.

Gautr (Gauti, Gaut) [father]: An ekename for Odin.

Gefjun (Gefjún, Gefjon, Gefion, Gefione, Gefn, Geujon, Gafn) [giver]: A goddess of the Æsir. She visited King Gylfi of Sweden and cut out the land from his kingdom that became known as Danish Zealand. All those who died virgins became her maidservants. She was present at Ægir's feast. Odin said she knew men's destinies as well as he did. She married Skjold, and together they lived in the city of Hleidra. A noble line of kings and warriors descended from them.

Geirahod (Geirahöð, Geirahöð): A valkyrie.

Geiravor (Geiravǫr): A valkyrie.

Geirdriful: A valkyrie.

Geironul (Geirönul, Geirölul) [spearbearer]: A valkyrie.

Geirrodr (Geirrodr, Geirrøðr, Geirrøð, Geirrøth, Geirröðr, Geirröd, Geirröðr, Geirröðr, Gerrad, Geirrodur, Geirraudr, Gerriöd, Geirrøðr, Geirrœd, Geirrœth, Geyruth): An hrymthursar. His land was called Geirrodr's Garth. His daughters were Gjalp, Greip, Eistla, Eyrgjafa, Ulfrun, Angeyja, Imdr, Atla and Jarnsaxa. His grandson was Thjassi. Greip's son captured Loki at Geirrodr's command and in exchange for his freedom Loki had to persuade Thor to come to the castle unarmed. Thor, however, armed himself before his arrival and destroyed Geirrodr and his household.

Geirrodr (Geirrod, Geirrøðr, Geirrøð, Geirrøth, Geirröðr, Geirröð, Geirroðr, Geirróðr, Gerrad, Geirrodur, Geirraudr, Gerriöd, Geirrøðr, Geirrœd, Geirrœth, Geyruth): He and his older brother, Agnar, were wrecked in a storm and taught on an island by Grimnir (Odin) and his wife (Frigg). He later cheated his brother out of the crown of Reid-Gothland.

Geirrodr's Garth (Geirröðargardar, Geirrodr's Gardr, Geirrodsgard, Geirödhsgard, Geirróðr's Garth): The home of the hrymthursar Geirrodr. The river Vimur flowed near here.

Geirskogul (Geirskögul, Geir-Skogul, Geir-Skaugul, Giruskogul): A valkyrie.

Geirvimul: The name of a river in Asgardr flowing to Midgardr.

Gelgja (Gelgia): A chain attached to Gleipnir to help bind Fenriswulf.

Gerdr (Gerd, Gerðr, Gerdur, Gerð, Gerda, Gerth) [field]: The daughter of the hrymthursar Gymir and Angroboda. Freyr saw her and fell in love with her. Her brother was Beli. She was threatened by Skirnir with having to marry the three-headed hrymthursar Hrimnir if she didn't agree to marry Freyr. She agreed to marry Freyr. Freyr killed her brother Beli on the way to the ceremony. Freyr and Gerdr's son was Fjolnir.

Geri (Gjere, Gere) [hunger, greedy-guts]: One of Odin's two wolves. The other was Freki.

Gering [gleaming]: A horse in Asgardr.

Gersemi (Gersime, Gerseme, Gem) [valuable thing]: She and her sister Hnoss were the daughters of Freyja and Odr.

Gillingr (Gilling): The jotun killed, along with his wife, by the dvergues Fjallar and Galarr. His son Suttungr avenges his death. Their other son was Baugi.

Gimils Cave: After Ragnarokr the land to the south of Andlangr was called Vidblain. It was located over Gimils Cave.

Gimle (Gimli, Gîmle, Gimlé, Gimill, Gimlir, Gimil) [heaven]: The name of a gold-thatched hall in the southern part of Asgardr near Brunnakr Grove. Only the most righteous and good dwelt there. It stood after Ragnarokr.

Ginnarr (Ginnar) [enticer]: A rock dvergar. One of Dvalin's Hosts. Lived in Juravale's Marsh.

Ginnungagap (Ginungagap, Ginnunga-Gap, Ginunga-Gap, Ghinmendegap) [yawning void]: The Yawning Gulf that existed at the beginning of creation.

Giottunagard: The name of the mare's heart used in Mokkurkalfi.

Gipul (Gípul): A river flowing in Asgardr.

Gisl (Gísl) [sunbeam]: The name of a horse in Asgardr.

Gizur (Gizurr) [god of war]: An ekename for Odin.

Gjallarbru (Gjallarbrú, Gjallar-bridge, Gjallarbro, Giallar-bridge, Gjöll Bridge) [echoing bridge]: The Echoing Bridge roofed with burning gold was in Gnipahellir Cave. It was held in place by a single strand of hair. The dead were so light (their blood having been drained into Gjoll as a toll) that one strand was all that was needed to hold the bridge up. It was guarded by Modgudr who exacted the toll of blood before any were allowed to cross over.

Gjallarhorn (Giallar Horn, Gjallar-horn, Gjallarhorn, Gillarhorn, Gillar-horn) [echoing horn]: Heimdallr's crescent-shaped horn which summoned the Æsir to the last battle. It was hidden in Mimirsbrunnr next to Odin's eye until it was needed.

Gjalp (Gjálp, Gialp, Gjǫlp, Gjölp, Gjalph) [yeller, shouter]: The daughter of the hrymthursar Geirrodr. Her sister was Greip, her nephew was Thjassi, and her uncle was Gudmundr. Thor broke Gjalp and Greip's backs during his visit to Geirrodr's Garth. She is one of the nine jotun sisters seduced by Odin. They simultaneously bore Heimdallr.

Gjoll River (Gjöll, Gjol, Giöll, Giallar, Giöl, Gyoll): One of the eleven rivers of Elivagar. It was a stagnant black stream flowing into Gnipahellir Cave.

Gladr (Glaðr, Glad, Glath) [clear, bright, shining]: One of two horses pulling Dagr's chariot. The other was Skinfaxi.

Gladr (Glaðr, Glad, Glath) [clear, bright]: A form of good magic practiced only by a woman or a man in the form of a woman. Odin learned it from Freyja and changed himself into the form of a woman to practice it.

Gladsheimr (Gladsheim, Glads-heim, Glaðsheim, Glaðsheimr, Glathsheim) [Place of Joy]: The first hall built in Asgardr. It was made of gold throughout. There were twelve thronefs in it with one higher than the others for Odin. General meetings and council took place here.

Gladsvidr (Gladsvidr, Gladsvith): An ekename for Odin.

Glæsisvellir (Glæsisvellir, Glæsisvoll) [Glittering Plains]: A section of Jotunheimr passed through by Thorkill, King Gormr and his men on their journey to find Geirrodr's Garth. Glittering, the tallest mountain in Jotunheimr was here. This was also where Geirrodr's nine daughters lived.

Glapp: The servant child sent by the jotun Geirrodr to fetch Loki. He was Greip's son.

Glapsvidr (Glapsviðr, Glapsvi∂, Glapvith) [swift in deceit]: An ekename for Odin.

Glasir (Glaser): The red-gilt leafed grove near Gladsheimr and Valhalla. This was where Idunn grew her apples. See also Brunnakr Grove.

Gleipnir (Gleipner): The third chain used to bind Fenriswulf. The first two, Lædingr and Dromi, were unsuccessful. They had been forged by Thor. Gleipnir was forged by the Sons of Ivaldi, and was successful in binding Fenriswulf. It was made from a cat's footfall, the beard of a woman, the spittle of a bird, the roots of a mountain, the breath of a fish, and the sinews and nerves of a bear. Gleipnir was attached to the chain Gelgja and then bound around Fenriswulf.

Glenr (Glener, Glen) [gleam]: Married to Sol. One of Surtr's sons.

Glenr (Glener, Glen) [gleam]: The name of one of the horses in Asgardr.

Gler (Glær) [shining]: The name of one of the horses in Asgardr.

Glitnir (Glitner) [glittering]: Forseti's hall which was built of gold and roofed with silver.

Glittering: The name of the tallest mountain in Utgardr and Jotunheimr.

Gloi: A rock dvergar. One of Dvalin's Hosts. Lived in Juravale's Marsh.

Gloinn (Glóinn, Glói n, Gloinn): A rock dvergar. One of Durinn's Kin.

Glut [glow]: Loki's first wife. They had two daughters, Eisa and Einmyria before Loki deserted her.

Gmir: Hymir's 900-headed mother.

Gna (Gná, Gnaa): The goddess who was Frigg's messenger. Frigg sent her into the various worlds on errands, usually of love. Her horse was called Hofvarpner.

Gnipahellir Cave (Gnípahellir Cave, Gnipahelleren, Gnipa-Cave, Gnipa's-Cave, Gnypahall, Gnipahall) [cliff cave]: The entrance to Niflheimr. The Gjoll River flowed into here. The wolf Garmr was chained here to guard the entrance.

Godblodi (Goðbloði): The sacrifice to the gods.

Godheimr (Godheim) [God land]: Another name for Asgardr.

God of the Gallows: An ekename for Odin, referencing the fact that he sacrificed himself to himself by hanging on Yggdrasyll for nine days and nights in order to gain the knowledge of the dead.

Godul (Gödul): A valkyrie.

Goinn (Góinn, Góin, Goin): A son of Nidhoggr's eating away at the Niflheimr root of Yggdrasyll.

Golden Age: The period after the building of Asgardr and before the coming of the three Norns out of the east.

Gollr (Göll, Gol, Gǫll) [screaming]: A valkyrie.

Gomul (Gömul): A river in Asgardr.

Gondlir (Göndlir) [owner of the magic wand]: An ekename for Odin.

Gondul (Göndul, Göndol, Gaundul) [warrior]: A valkyrie.

Gonul (Gönul): A valkyrie.

Gopul (Göpul): A river in Asgardr flowing to Midgardr.

Gormr (Gorm): The king of Denmark who commissioned Thorkill to lead him and some of his men on an expedition to find Geirrodr's Garth.

Goti: Gunnr's horse.

Grabakr (Grábakr, Grábak, Graabak) [gray back]: A son of Nidhoggr's eating away at the Niflheimr root to Yggdrasyll.

Grad (Gráð, Gráth, Graad, Grod, Groth): A river in Asgardr flowing to Midgardr.

Grafvitnir (Grafvitner) [gnawing wolf]: His sons were pulling twigs off Yggdrasyll at the Urdarbrunnr root.

Grafvolludr (Grafvölluðr, Grafvollud, Grafvolluth) [field gnawer]: A son of Nidhoggr eating away at the Niflheimr root of Yggdrasyll.

Greip [one who grasps]: The daughter of the hrymthursar Geirrodr. Her sister was Gjalp, her nephew was Thjassi, and her uncle is Gudmundr. Her son, Glapp, captured Loki for Geirrodr. Thor broke both sister's backs during his visit to Geirrodr's Garth.

Grendel: A sea jotun descendant of the hrymthursar Kari.

Grer (Grerr): A dvergar. His brothers were Dvalin, Alfrig, and Berling. He helped forge the Brisingamen necklace and sold it to Freyja in exchange for her sleeping one night in turn with each of them.

Gridarvolr (Gríðarvölr, Gríðarvǫlr, Gríðarvöllr, Gridarvold) [Gridr's wand]: Gridr's magic staff which she lent to Thor when he journeyed to Geirrodr's Garth.

Gridastadr (Griðastadr) [sacred place]: The name given to any sacred place where blood may not be shed (Asgardr, Breidablik, etc.).

Gridr (Gríðr, Grîðr, Gríth, Gríð, Grid, Griða, Grydur): She was a jotun who lived in the Jarnvidr Forest. She and Odin were lovers. Their son was Vidarr the Silent. She lent Thor her girdle of strength, iron gloves, and magic staff called Gridarvolr when she found out he was journeying unarmed to Geirrodr's Garth.

Grimnir (Grímnir, Grîmnir, Grimner) [the hooded one]: An ekename for Odin. It was also a type of hood or cowl worn to cover the upper part of the face.

Grimr (Grímr, Grím) [hooded]: An ekename for Odin.

Griseldis [all golden]: Tyr's mother, Gymir's wife. She was one of the Æsir.

Grjotanagardr (Grjottungard, Grjótúnagarðar, Grjótúnagarðr, Grjótúnngardr, Grjollon, Grjottungard, Grjóttangard, Grjóttunagarðar, Griottunagardr) [stone fence house]: The name of Hrungr's mountainous home.

Groa (Gróa, Grôa): Groa was the volva whom Thor sought out after his battle with the jotun Hrungr. A flintstone had lodged in his head and no one had been able to loose it. She succeeded in loosening it but was so overcome with joy hearing that her husband Aurvandill was returning that she forgot the rest of her spells and was unable to finish the job. She was also known as Olgefn.

Grund: The name of Gudmundr's hall.

Gudheimr (Guðheimr, Guðheim, Guthheim, Godheim) [god land]: Another name for Asaheimr.

Gudmundr (Guðmunðr, Gudmond, Godmond): The brother of Geirrodr and uncle of Gjalp and Greip. His hall was called Grund. He tried to trick Thorkill, King Gormr, and King Gormr's men. He had twelve sons and many daughters.

Gudr (Guðr, Guð, Gôð, Guth) [conflict]: A valkyrie.

Gullfaxi (Gullifaxi, Gulfaxi, Goldfax) [gold mane]: The horse belonging to the jotun Hrungr. After Hrungr was killed it was given to Magni, Thor's son.

Gullinbursti (Gullinbürste, Gullin-bursti, Gullinbusti, Gyllenbuste, Gullinbörst, Gullinborste) [golden-bristled]: Also known as Slidrugtanni. A red-golden boar forged by Sindri in order to help win his brother Brokkr's bet against Loki. It was given to Freyr as a present. It could run equally as fast on land, air, or water and was so brilliant it could light up the sky at night so one could easily find one's way.

Gullinkambi (Gullinkambe, Gullin-kambi, Gollinkambi, Gyllenkambe) [golden-combed]: The crow that crows to awaken the Einherjar in Valhalla every morning. He was also called Salgofnir.

Gullintanni (Gullintanne, Gullin-tani) [golden-teethed]: An ekename for Heimdallr.

Gulltoppr (Gultopr, Gulltopp. Golltoppr) [gold top]: The name of Heimdallr's golden-maned horse.

Gullveig (Gulveig, Gullveg, Göllveig, Gollveig) [gold drink, gold thirst]: The name and form Freyja assumed when she was disguised as a witch and visited Asgardr to corrupt the Æsir.

Gungnir (Gungner, Gûngnir, Gungne, Gugner): Odin's spear forged by the Sons of Ivaldi. It was tossed at the beginning of a battle to signify the start of the conflict. It never failed to hit its mark.

Gunnlod (Gunnlöð, Gunnlad, Gunlad, Gunnlödd, Gunlöde, Gunnlödh, Gunnlödhe, Gunnloth, Gunnlaug): Suttungr's daughter whom he imprisoned in his treasure chamber in Hnitbjorg to guard the Precious Mead. Baugi was her son by Odin.

Gunnr (Gunn, Gunnarr) [war]: A valkyrie. Her horse was named Goti.

Gunthra (Gunnthrá, Gunnthró, Gunnþrá): One of the eleven rivers which flowed from the river Elivagar.

Gylgien: A female jotun living in Jotunheimr.

Gylfi (Gylfe, Gyive, Gylphi, Gylphe): A king of Sweden (Svithiod) who visited Asgardr disguised as Gangleri. Part of his kingdom was carved out and pulled away by Gefjun.

Gyllir (Gyller) [golden]: The name of a horse in Asgardr.

Gymir (Gýmir, Gýmer, Gymer): An hrymthursar married to Angroboda. His land was Gymirsgardr. His daughter and son were named Gerdr and Beli. He and Skirnir slew each other at Ragnarokr.

Gymirsgardr (Gymirsgarðr, Gymirsgard, Gymirsgard, Gymirsgarth): The land belonging to the hrymthursar Gymir. Gerdr, his daughter, lived there. The land was surrounded and protected by a flickering fire called myrkvan vafrloga.

Habrok (Hábrók, Hobrok) [high-leg]: A great hawk in Jotunheimr.

Hadding: Two of Arngrim and Eyfura's twelve berserker sons were both named Hadding. Their brothers were Hervard, Hjorvard, Hrani, Angantyr, Bui, Brami, Barri, Reifnir, Tind, and Tyrfing. Related to Ottar the Simple.

Hæn (Hæn): An ekename for Freyja.

Hafeti (Háfeti) [high hoof]: A horse in Asgardr.

Hafr drottinn (Hafra dróttínn) [lord of goats]: An ekename for Thor.

Hafra njotr (hafra njótr) [goat user]: An ekename for Thor.

Haki: He rode Fakr. A great warrior whose father was Hjorvard, one of the twelve berserker sons of Arngrim and Eyfura. His sister was Hvedna. Related to Ottar the Simple.

Halr (Hal) [man]: First son of Karl the Yeoman and Snœr.

Hallinskidi (Hallinskíði, Hallinskîði, Hallinskid, Hallinskide, Hallinskeide) [ram]: An ekename for Heimdallr.

Hamingja: The term representing a guardian spirit. The plural was Haminjes.

Haminjes: The plural of Hamingja.

Hamskerpir (Hamskerper) [hide-hardener]: A horse, the sire of Hofvarpnir, Gna's horse.

Hanar: An earth dvergar.

Hangagud (Hangaguð, Hanga-gud, Hangagoð) [god of the hanged]: An ekename for Odin.

Hangatyr (Hangatýr, Hangatǫr) [god of the hanged]: An ekename for Odin.

Hangi [the hanged]: An ekename for Odin.

Hanar (Hanarr, Hannar): A rock dvergar.

Haptagud (Haptaguð, Hapta-gud, Haptagod) [god of the gods, god of chains]: An ekename for Odin.

Haraldr: Rides Folkvir.

Harald War Tooth: The son of Hrorek the Ring Giver and Aud the Profound. His Half-brother was Randver. Related to Ottar the Simple.

Harbardr (Hárbarðr, Hårbard, Hárbarth, Hárbarð) [grey beard]: This was the name and form assumed by Odin in disguise as the ferryman who taunted Thor and Tyr on their return from slaying the jotun Hymir. He told Thor his master was the jotun Hildwolf who lived in Rathsey Sound. He fought Fjolvar on Algrœn Island and made love to the jotun's seven jotun daughters. He also battled the jotun Hlebard and won his magic wand. Fought in Valland.

Harfjoter: A valkyrie.

Harr (Hárr, Hár, Hâr, Har, Haar, Hor) [high one, tall one]: An ekename for Odin. Used by him when Gylfi visited Asgardr. See Jafnharr and Thridi.

Harr (Hárr, Hár, Hâr, Har, Haar, Hor) [high one, tall one]: One of Odin's halls. The witch Gullveig was burnt here.

Harr (Hárr, Hár, Har, Hâar, Haar, Hor) [high one, tall one]: A rock dvergar. One of Dvalin's Hosts. Lived in Juravale's Marsh.

Hati Hrodvitnirsson (Háti Hróðvitnírsson, Háti Hróðvitnísson, Hati Hrodvitneson, Hati Hrôðvitnis, Hate Hroðvitneson) [Hati the son of the mighty wolf]: Also known as Skoll. One of the two wolves (the other was his brother Mana-Garmr) chasing Nott's chariot. He swallows the sun at Ragnarokr. He and his brother were raised in the Jarnvidr Forest by their mother Angroboda. Their father was Angroboda's son Fenriswulf.

Haugspori: A rock dvergar. One of Dvalin's Hosts. Lived in Juravale's Marsh.

Haugstari: A dvergar.

Haur: A rock dvergar.

Havi (Hávi): An ekename for Odin.

Hefring [swelling]: One of Ægir and Ran's daughters.

Hefti: An earth dvergar.

Heidr (Heiðr, Heið, Heid, Heidur, Heith, Heidi, Haid) [bright shining one]: The form and name assumed by Angroboda when she went in disguise to Asgardr after Gullveig (Freyja) had been brunt as a witch. She too was spitted and burnt in Harr Hall. She was reborn and lived on Midgardr spreading her evil. Odin visited her before Ragnarokr seeking to gain knowledge from her. Her father was Hrimnir. Her brother was Hrossthjofi.

Heiddraupnir's Skull (Héiðraupnir's Skull, Heiddraupner's Skull) [clear dripper's skull]: The name of one of the containers in which Midvitner kept the Precious Mead after he had stolen it from the Æsir. It was also known as Hoddropnir's Horn.

Heidrun (Heiðrúnr, Heiðrún, Heithrún) [bright-running]: The nannygoat nibbling at Læradr in Valhalla. Mead from her teats fed the Einherjar. Her urine dripped down and fed those doomed in Elidner, Hela's hall in Niflhel.

Heimdallr (Heimdal, Heimdáll, Heimdall, Haimdallar, Heimdalr, Heimðallar, Heimðallr, Heimdali, Heimdǫllr, Heim-Dellinger, Heimdellinger, Heimdäglingr) [world bow]: The son of Odin and nine wavemaidens, the daughters of the jotun Geirrodr. He was the watcher of the Æsir. At the command of his father, Odin, he traveled through Midgardr under the name of Rigr the Walker creating the different classes of mankind. His hall was Himinbjorg, his sword was Hofud, and his horse was Gulltoppr. He owned a crescent-shaped horn called Gjallarhorn. He wore white armor (and was known as the hviti ass, white god, because of this) and had shining golden teeth (which gained him the nickname of Gullintanni). He needed less sleep than a bird and always kept one eye open. He was blessed with keen eyesight and sharp hearing. He traded one ear to Mimir for increased hearing in the other. He fought Loki in the forms of a rain cloud, polar bear, and seal by the rocks of Vagasker and Singasteinn to regain the Brisingamen Necklace for Freyja. He and Loki slew each other at Ragnarokr.

Heiteitr [host glad]: An ekename for Odin.

Hel: One of the worst regions in Niflheimr.

Hela (Hel): She was the half-dead, half-living daughter Loki bore after eating Angroboda's heart. Her brothers were Fenriswulf and Midgardrsormr (Jormungandr). After she was cast down to the depths of Nilfheimr she became ruler of the dead there. Her hall was called Elidnir.

Helblindi (Helblinde, Helblinder, Hel-Blinder) [death blind]: An ekename for Odin.

Helblindi (Helblinde, Helbinder, Hel-Blinder) [death blind]: The name of one of Loki's brothers. The other was Byleistr.

Hel-cake: The treat given to Garmr by those hoping to calm him so they could escape Niflheimr. Only those who had given bread to one in need while they were alive would be given one when they were dead.

Helgrindr Gate (Helgrind, Helgate) [death gate, hel gate]: There were several gates containing the dead in various lands. The gate leading into Helheimr was called Helgrindr Gate. It was inside Gnipahellir Cave. Flowing outside the cave was the Gjoll River. Gnipahellir Cave and Helgrindr Gate were guarded by the hel-hound Garmr who could be calmed down enough to pass by if you gave him a hel-cake. Once inside you would come to the Gjallarbru (Echoing Bridge) guarded over by the skeleden maiden Modgudr who exacted a toll of blood before letting anyone cross over her bridge. Only the dead could cross over because the bridge was held up by a single strand of hair. A living person would break the bridge. The Gjoll River flowed into the cave and was the river flowing under the Gjallarbru Bridge. The sooty-red cock who crowed at Ragnarokr and the hrymthursar Hrimgrimnir lived inbetween Helgrindr Gate and Nagrindr Gate. One other gate was Valgrindr Gate.

Helheimr (Helheim): The deepest of the nine regions of Niflheimr and where Hela had her hall, Elidnir.

Helskor (Helskór) [death shoes]: The deathshoes made of lead put on the dead at their funeral so the dead person would have steady footing against the raging current and be protected from the poisonous water in the river Slidr which had to be crossed during the journey to Niflheimr.

Helveg (Hel way): The name given to the road leading to Hel.

Hemra: Another name for the river Vimur.

Hengjankjapta: Slain by Thor.

Heptifili (Heptifili, Hepti): A rock dvergar. One of Durinn's Kin.

Herblindi [host blind]: An ekename for Odin.

Herfajodr (Herfajódr) [father of hosts]: An ekename for Odin.

Herfjotur (Herfjötur, Herfjöturr, Herfjotur, Herfjǫturr, Herfjoter, Herfiötr) [one who chains an army]: A valkyrie who caused a form of panic to come over warriors in battle so their terror caused them to be unable to fight.

Herfodr (Herföðr, Herfaðir, Herjaföðr, Herjafather, Herfather) [warrior father]: An ekename for Odin.

Heri: A dvergar.

Herja [warrior]: A valkyrie.

Herjan (Herjann) [warrior, ruler]: An ekename for Odin.

Herjan's Disir: An ekename for the Valkyries, since Herjan was an ekename for Odin and he commanded the disir.

Herlathing: Another name for the Wild Hunt.

Hermodr (Hermóðr, Hermôðr, Hermodur, Hermóð, Hermod) [courage of hosts]: One of Odin and Frigg's sons. His brothers were Hodr and Baldr. He was one of the greeters, along with Bragi, at the gates to Valhalla, welcoming the warriors as they arrived. He was the messenger of the Æsir and in that capacity journeyed to Niflheimr to try and persuade Hela to let Baldr and Nanna return to the living. He also journeyed to northern Midgardr to seek out Hrossthjofi and find out knowledge about Rindr. He owned the sword Gambantein at one time.

Hersir [lord]: Erna's father. Erna married Jarl the Earl (Rigr).

Herteitr (Herteit) [glad of battle]: An ekename for Odin.

Herthrumu gautr [Herþrumu gautr) [thunder god]: An ekename for Thor.

Hervard: One of Arngrim and Eyfura's twelve berserker sons. His brothers were Hadding, Hjorvard, Hrani, Angantyr, Bui, Brami, Barri, Reifnir, Tind, and Tyrfing. Related to Ottar the Simple.

Heyrn (hearing): The sense given to Askr and Embla by Ve.

Hild: The father of Hoalf. Related to Ottar the Simple.

Hildigun: The mother of Friaut. She was the daughter of Svava and Sækonung. She married the noble warrior Ketil. Related to Ottar the Simple.

Hildr (Hildur, Hilda, Hildi, Hild) [battle warrior]: One of the leaders of the valkyries. She was also known as Skeggold.

Hildwolf (Hildolf, Hildov) [battle wolf]: The jotun of Rathsey Sound who Harbardr claimed was his master.

Hilksuin (Hildisvín, Hildisvíni, Hildisvín, Hildisvíni, Hildesvine, Hilksuin, Hildisvini) [battle pig, battle boar]: The golden boar belonging to Freyja. It glowed in the dark. Forged by the dvergar Dain and Nabbi.

Himinbjorg (Himinbjörg, Himinbjǫrg, Himinbiörg, Himinbiord, Himinbjörg, Himinbrjodr, Himmelbjerg, Himmelbierg, Himmelbjeig, Himmelbjeig) [mount of heaven, heaven cliffs]: The name of Heimdallr's hall at the keystone of Bifrost. The eighth hall in Asgardr.

Himinhrjodr (Himinbrjótr, Himinbrjoter, Himinbrjot, Himinbrjóðr, Himinbjoter, Himinbrioter, Himinbriotr, Himinhrjot) [heaven-breaker]: A coal black bull who was the most prized of the jotun Hymir's stock. He was used as bait by Thor when he went fishing for Midgardrsormr.

Himinglæva (Himinglœfa, Himinglœva, Himinglæfa) [heaving glittering, clear heavens]: One of Ægir and Ran's wavemaiden daughters.

Hinn almattki ass (hinn almáttri áss) [all-powerful god]: An ekename for Thor.

Hinn dyri mjodr (Hinn ðyri mjoðr): An ekename for the Precious Mead.

Hinn einhendi ass (Hinn einhendi áss) [one-handed god]: An ekename for Tyr.

Hinn thogli ass (hinn þögli áss) [silent god]: An ekename for Vidarr.

Hjalmberi (Hjálmberi) [helmet bearer]: An ekename for Odin.

Hjalmther (Hjálmthér): A horse in Asgardr.

Hjalmthrimul (Hjalmþrimul): A valkyrie.

Hjiuki (Hjúki, Hjuke, Hiuki): He and Bil were Vidfinnr's son and daughter. They were forced to fetch water from the well Byrgir.

Hjor (Hjör): A valkyrie.

Hjordis: She was the daughter of King Eylimi. Grandmother of Sigurdr Fafnirsbani. One of the Hraudungs. Related to Ottar the Simple.

Hjorthrimul (Hjörþrimul, Hjǫþrimul): A valkyrie.

Hjorvard: One of Arngrim and Eyfura's twelve berserker sons. His brothers were Hadding, Hervard, Hrani, Angantyr, Bui, Brami, Barri, Reifnir, Tind, and Tyrfing. His daughter was Hvedna. Related to Ottar the Simple.

Hlævangr (Hlævangr, Hlévang): A dvergar. One of Durinn's Kin.

Hlaka: A valkyrie.

Hlebard (Hlébarð, Hlébarth, Lebard, Lebord): He battled Harbardr and lost his magic wand to him.

Hledis: Ottar the Simple's Mother. She was the daughter of King Frodi. Her sister was Kari. Her equally noble mother was Friaut. She was married to Instein. Related to Ottar the Simple.

Hledjolfr (Hleðjólfr, Hleðjólf): A rock dvergar.

Hler (Hlér, Hlêr) [the shelterer]: An ekename for Ægir.

Hlessey (Hlésey, Hlêssey, Læsö, Læsøy, Læssø, Lässœ, Lessöe): The island where Ægir and Ran had their hall. Also known as Læsso in the Kattigat, the island of Lessœ or the island of Hler.

Hleidra (Lethra, Leire): The city in Danish Zealand where Gefjun and Skjold settled.

Hlevangur (Hlévangur): A rock dvergar. One of Dvalinn's Hosts. Lived in Juravale's Marsh.

Hlidolfr: A dvergar.

Hlidskjalf (Hliðskjálf, Hliðskialf, Hliðsciâlf, Lidskialf, Lidskjalf, Hlithskjolf, Hlithskjalf) [hill opening, battle shelf, heaven's crag]: The name of Odin's throne in his watchtower in his hall, Valaskjalf. Anyone sitting on this throne could see out over all the Worlds of the Tree.

Hlin (Hlin, Hlín, Hlyn): Also known as Lin. One of Frigg's attendants whom she sometimes sent to Midgardr to protect her favorites. Frigg also used this name on occasion.

Hlodyn (Hlóðyn, Hlöðyn, Hlǫdyn, Hlóthun, Hlóthyn, Hlôðyn, Hlopthyn): Another name for Jordr, Thor's mother.

Hlodynjar (Hlôðynjar) [Thor son of earth]: An ekename for Thor.

Hlokk (Hlök, Hlǫkk, Hlok, Hlöck) [clammer of battle, shrieking]: A valkyrie.

Hlor (Hlóra, Hlodune): Thor's foster-mother. Her husband was Vingnir. Thor was sent to live with them after he became too much for Frigg to handle.

Hlorridi (Hlóridi, Hloride, Hlórriði, Hlorriði, Hlorride, Hlorrid, Hlórrithi, Hlorrithi, Lorride, Lorridi) [heat bringer]: An ekename for Thor referencing the fact one of his foster-parents was Hlor.

Hlynir (Hlýnir): Heaven

Hnikarr (Hnikar, Hnikuder, Hnikuðr, Nikarr, Nikuz) [spear thruster]: An ekename for Odin.

Hnikudr (Hnikuðr, Hnikuð, Hnikudr, Hnikuder, Hnikuth) [over thrower]: An ekename for Odin.

Hnitbjorg (Hnitbjörg, Hnitbergen) [lock rock]: The name of Suttungr's treasure chamber in which his daughter Gunnlod guarded the Precious Mead.

Hnoss (Hnos, Hnossa) [jewel]: She and her sister Gersemi were the two daughters of Freyja and Odr.

Hoalf: The son of Hild. Related to Ottar the Simple.

Hoarfrost: A type of frost that gives the appearance of intersecting ice needles.

Hoddmimir's Holt (Hoddmímisholt, Hoddmímir's Holt, Hodd-Mímir's Holt, Hodd-mímir's Holt, Hoddmimir's Holt, Hodmimir's Holt, Hoddmimishold, Hoddmímis Holt, Hodmimer's Holt, Hodmimer's Grove, Hodmimer's Wood) [Mimir of the treasure's wood]: The place where Lif and Lifthraser hid to survive the darkness of Ragnarokr.

Hoddrofnir (Hodd-dropnir) [treasurer opener]: An ekename for Mimir.

Hoddropnir's Horn (Hoddropner's Horn) [treasure-opener's horn]: Another name for Heiddraupnir's Skull.

Hodr (Höðr, Hǫdr, Höð, Hodúr, Höður, Höðer, Hoth, Hoder, Hödur, Höð, Hœdur) [war, battle]: Baldr's blind twin brother. Until the birth of Vali the Avenger they were Odin's youngest sons. Their mother was Frigg. Loki gave him a spear and aimed his arm. He tossed it at Baldr and killed his brother. After his brother's death he took refuge in the forest on Baldr's estate until he was killed and thus Baldr's death was avenged by Vali the Avenger. Then he joined Baldr and Nanna in Niflheimr and was forgiven by them for his act. The troll Mimring forged several magic gifts for him to use while he was hiding out on Baldr's estate. They included a shield of darkness, a magic shirt that could render him invisible, and a magic sword. Hodr understood the language of birds. He survived Ragnarokr and shared a hall in Hropt's Hills with Baldr, Nanna, Bragi, and Idunn. It was at this time his blindness was cured.

Hœfir (Hoefir) [meat]: One of Gefjun's four oxen. The other three were Hyrr, Raudr, and Rekinni. They were actually her sons by a jotun.

Hœnir (Hoenir, Hönir, Hœner, Høne, Hænir, Hahnir): The member of the Æsir sent to the Vanir with Mimir as a hostage in exchange for Njordr, Freyr, and Freyja, at the conclusion of the War Between the Æsir and Vanir. He was also known as the Aurkonungr (the marsh king). In Vanaheimr he was made their leader because of his noble bearing. Unfortunately, he wasn't very intelligent. When his stupidity was discovered he was sent back to the Æsir carrying Mimir's decapitated head. He survived Ragnarokr and was known for his silence after the Rebirth. He was a frequent traveling companion of Odin and Loki's.

Hofud (Höfud, Höffud, Höfud) [head]: The name of the sickle-shaped sword owned by Heimdallr.

Hofvarpnir (Hófvarpnir, Hofvarpner) [hoof-thrower]: Gna's horse. His sire was Hamskerpir, his dam was Gardrofa. He could run through air and water.

Hogni (Högni): Rode Holvir.

Holdr (Höldr, Hold, Holdâ, Holth) [farmer]: Son of Karl the Yeoman and Snœr.

Hall (Höll, Hol): A river flowing from Asgardr to Midgardr.

Hollar vœttir (Hollar voettir) [kind spirits]: Guardian spirits of good will.

Holmgang (Hólmganga): A battle between two opponents which takes place within a defined area with a specific set of rules. Usually used to solve arguments. Instead of two armies battling each other, frequently a warrior from each side would meet in a holmgang to decide the conflict.

Holvir (Hölvir): A horse ridden by Hognir.

Horn (Hörn, Hœrn, Horn, Hern): The asynje of flax. One of Frigg's attendants.

Hornbori: A rock dvergar.

Horr (Hörr): A dvergar.

Hoslur (Hoslur) [poles]: The poles marking off the area of a holmgang.

Hosvir (Hösvir) [grey]: A son of Thræl and Thir.

Hottr (Höttr) [hat]: An ekename for Odin.

Hræda (Hræda): The rope used to hold the chain Gleipnir to the mountain Gjoll.

Hræsvelg (Hræsvelg, Hræsvelgr, Hræsvelgr, Ræsvelg, Ralsveg, Hræsvelger, Hresvelgr, Hræsvelgur) [eater of corpses]: The hrymthusar who sat in the north in the form of an eagle flapping his wings causing a bitter north wind hoping to freeze the river Ifing and those in Midgardr. Then the jotuns would be able to enter and conquer Midgardr.

Hrafn [raven]: A horse ridden by the dvergar Ai.

Hrafnass (Hrafnáss) [raven god]: An ekename for Odin.

Hrafnblots godi (Hrafnblóts goði) [priest of the raven sacrifice]: An ekename for Odin.

Hrafngud (Hrafnaguð) [raven god]: An ekename for Odin.

Hraki: The name of the spittle that sealed the peace between the Æsir and Vanir. It was formed into Kvasir and given life.

Hrani: One of Arngrim and Eyfura's twelve berserker sons. His brothers were Hadding, Hervard, Hjorvard, Angantyr, Bui, Brami, Barri, Reifnir, Tind, and Tyrfing. Related to Ottar the Simple.

Hraudgrani (Raudgrani) [red beard]: An ekename for Odin.

Hrauding (Hrauðungr, Hraudungr, Hraudung, Hradung, Hrauthung, Hrodung, Raudung): A king of Reid-Gothland. His sons were Geirrodr and Agnar.

Hridr (Hriðr, Hríð, Hrith) [storming]: One of the eleven rivers flowing out of Elivagar.

Hrimfaxi (Hrímfaxi, Hrímfaxe, Hrimfaxi, Hrymfaxe, Rimefax, Rimfaxi, Rimfakse) [frost maned]: The name of the horse who pulled Nott's chariot. The drool from his bit formed the dew present in the morning on Midgardr.

Hrimnir (Hrímnir, Hrímgrímnir, Hrimgrimir, Hrimgrimnir) [frost hooded]: The three-headed hrymthursar who was the father of Angrboda and Hrosthjof. His brother was Egther. Skirnir threatened Gerdr with having to live with him if she didn't consent to marry Freyr.

Hrimr (Hreim, Hreimr) [shouter]: One of the sons of Thræl and Thir.

Hringhornr (Hringhorni, Hringhorn, Hringthorn, Hringham, Hringhaune, Ringhorni, Ringhorn) [curved prow]: The name of Baldr's ship which was used as his funeral pyre.

Hrist [shaker]: A valkyrie. She and Mist serve Odin his mead in Valhalla.

Hrodvitnir (Hroðvitnir, Hrodvitner, Hróthvitnir, Hritvitnir) [mighty wolf]: The wolf father of Hati Hrodvitnirsson. An ekename for Fenriswulf.

Hronn (Hrönn, Hrön, Hrǫnn, Ronn) [billow, rising wave]: One of Ægir and Ran's daughters.

Hronn (Hrönn, Hrön, Hrǫnn, Ronn) [billow, rising wave]: A river flowing from Asgardr to Midgardr to Hel.

Hroptatyr (Hroptatýr, Hrôptatýr, Roptatyr) [god of gods]: An ekename for Odin.

Hroptr (Hropt) [the sage, the wise one]: An ekename for Odin.

Hropt's Hills: The area where Hodr, Baldr and Nanna, Bragi and Idunn share a hall after Ragnarokr.

Hrorek the Ring Giver: He was married to Aud the Profound. Their son was Harald War Tooth.

Hrossharsgrani (Hrosshársgrani) [horse-hair bearded]: An ekename for Odin.

Hrossthjofi (Hrossþjófr, Hrassþjófr, Hrasthjof, Hrosthjof, Hrassþjófi, Hrossþiofri, Hrossthiofr, Rossthiof, Rosthiof, Rostioph) [horse thief]: A wizard who lived in a green castle in the northern part of Midgardr. Hermodr was sent to find him and learn about Rindr from him. He was Heidr's brother. Their father was Hrimnir.

Hrothr (Hróthr): An ekename for Fenris.

Hrund: A valkyrie.

Hrungr (Hrungnir, Hrungner, Hrunger, Hrûngni, Grungner, Rungir, Runger, Rungrnir, Rungne): The largest rock jotun in Jotunheimr. He once raped Thor's daughter. The mountainous land he lived in was called Grjotanagardr. Odin lured him to Asgardr in a horse race. his horse was Gullfaxi. His shield was named randarr iss, but it didn't help in his fight with Thor, who slew him. Gullfaxi was then given to Thor's son, Magni.

Hrungr's Heart: The runic character Ψ Hrungr had a triangle-shaped heart of stone. The runic character was carved on Hrungr's shield, and the rest of his weapons for protection.

Hrutr (Hrútr): An ekename for Heimdallr.

Hrymr (Hrym, Ryme, Rymer, Rym): The frost jotun who leads many of the jotuns at Ragnarokr.

Hrymthursar (hrímþursar, hrimthursar, hrímþursar, hrímþörsar, hrimthursen, hrîmþurses, hrim-thurs, hrim-thursar, rhimthursar, rhimthursar, rhimthurs, reimthursen, rime-giants) [frost giant]: The frost jotuns. They caused avalanches and made glaciers.

Hugi (Huge, Hugin) [thought]: The messenger Thjalfi raced and lost against in Utgardr.

Huginn (Hugin, Hunin) [mind]: One of the two ravens who sit on Odin's shoulders. They fly throughout the worlds during the day for knowledge and then sit on Odin's shoulders during dinner in Valhalla and whisper all they've heard in his ears. They were a gift to Odin from Hulda.

Hugo: A dvergar.

Hugstari: A rock dvergar.

Huldr (Hulda, Huldra, Hulla, Huldre): A valkyrie who gave the two ravens Huginn and Muninn to Odin. Her two daughters were Irpa and Thorgerdr. She was sometimes called Skeggjold.

Hvedna: Her father was Hjorvard, one of the twelve berserker sons of Arngrim and Eyfura. Her brother was the great warrior Haki. Related to Ottar the Simple.

Hvedrungr (Hveðrungr, Hveðrung, Hvethrung) [the roarer]: An ekename for Loki.

Hvedrungr's Son (Hveðrungr's Son, Hveðrung's Son): The name given to Fenriswulf when Vidarr slays him at Ragnarokr to avenge Odin's death.

Hveralungr (Hveralundr, Hveralund, Hveralundi) [the grove of roaring hot springs]: The place in Niflheimr where Loki was bound.

Hvergelmir Well (Hvergelmer Well, Hvengelmir, Hveigilmer, Hvergelmin, Hvergelmen, Hwergelmr, Kvergjelme, Vergelmir) [bubbling kettle]: The well towards the center of Niflheimr from whence the river Elivagar flowed. Hvergelmir Well, Mimirsbrunnr Well, and Urdarbrunnr Well were the wells that nourished Yggdrasyll.

Hviti ass (hvíti áss, hvítti áss, hvîta âss) [white god]: An ekename for Heimdallr.

Hymir (Hýmir, Hymer, Hyme, Hrymer): The foster-father of Tyr. He was married to Griseldis, Tyr's mother. His giant kettle was stolen by Thor and Tyr and given to Ægir and Ran. His mother, Gmir, had 900 heads. He went fishing with Thor and was nearly scared to death when Thor hooked Midgardrsormr. His most prized oxen was a black bull named Himinhrjodr which was used by Thor as bait for Midgardrsormr. Hymir was slain by Thor.

Hyndla: A jotun who recited the lineage of Ottar the Simple to Freyja, and thereby helped Ottar the Simple gain great fortune.

Hyrr (Hýrr) [burnt]: One of Gefjun's four oxen. The other three were Hœfir, Raudr, and Rekinni. They were actually her sons.

Hyrrokkin (Hyrrokin, Hyrrokkinn, Hyrroken, Hyrrockin, Hirrokin) [one who was burned]: The storm jotun sent for to launch Hringhorni, Baldr and Nanna's funeral ship.

Ibor: One of the leaders of the Vinnilers, along with Ajo.

Iki: One of the sons of Olvaldi. His brothers were Gangr and Thjassi. His niece was Skadi.

Idunn (Iðunn, Iduna, Iðun, Ithun, Ydun) [one who renews]: A daughter of the light elf Ivaldi. She was married to Bragi. She owned and tended to her apples which she passed out to the Æsir. When they ate them their wounds were healed and they regained their youth. She and Bragi both wore white. They were Baldr and Nanna's closest friends, and were affected greatly by Baldr's death. Just before Ragnarokr Idunn left Asgardr to live in Yggdrasyll. Bragi would visit her and sing to her. Eventually she fell to Niflheimr and stayed with Bragi, who followed her there. She and Bragi survived Ragnarokr and lived in a hall in Hropt's Hills with Nanna, Baldr, and Hodr.

Ifing (Iving): The river to the east between Midgardr and Jotunheimr. The unique thing about it was that it would not freeze over, thus keeping the Jotun's in Jotunheimr.

Imdr (Imðr, Imð, Imth) [dusk]: One of Heimdallr's nine jotun mothers.

Imr (Im) [doubt]: A son of the jotun Vafthrudnir. His sister was Modgudr.

Ingi: A rock dvergar.

Ingunar-Freyr (Ingung's Frey): An ekename for Freyr.

Instein: Ottar the Simple's father. He was the son of Alf the Old. He was married to Hledis. Related to Ottar the Simple.

Iri (Ire): An elf.

Irmin: An ekename for Heimdallr.

Irpa: One of the Æsir. Her sister is Thorgerd. They were both virgins. Their mother was Huldr.

Isarnkol (Ísarnkol): The iron-cooling substance placed under Arvakr and Alsvin's withers to protect them from the sun which was carried in the chariot they were pulling.

Isle of Samsey: The island where Odin, in the form of a woman, practiced seidr, the black magic taught to him by Freyja.

Isulf: One of the sons of Skurhold and Olmod. His brother was Osulf. Related to Ottar the Simple.

Ivaldi (Ívaldi, Ivald, Ivalde, Ivallðr, Ivallda, Invaldi, Allvaldi, Auðvaldi, Ölvali, Yvaldr): An elf who was progenitor of many elves.

Ivaldi's Sons (Ívaldi's Sons, Ivald's Sons): An ekename for elves. They forged Sif's hair, Odin's spear Gungnir, and Freyr's ship Skidbladnir for Loki. They also forged the chain Gleipnir for the Æsir to be used in binding Fenriswulf.

Ivar: He was the father of Aud the Profound. Related to Ottar the Simple.

Jafnhar (Jafnhár, Jafnhárr, Jafnhor, Jafenhar, Jafnhaar, Jafuhar, Iafnhar, Iafn-har) [equally as high]: An ekename Odin used when Gylfi visited Asgardr. See Harr and Thridi.

Jari: A rock dvergar. One of Durinn's Kin.

Jalkr (Jálkr, Jalki, Jalk, Iâlkr) [gelding]: The name Odin used when he visited Asmund's hall.

Jarl the Earl: A son of Rigr (Heimdallr) and Modir. Heimdallr gave him the name of Rigr and the lands of Udal after he reached adulthood. He married Erna, the daughter of Hersir. Their sons were Adal, Arfi, Barr, Barn, Jod, Kon, Kundr, Mogr, Nidr, Nidjungr, Sonr, and Sveinn.

Jarngreiper (Jarn-greiper, Iarn-greiper) [iron gripper]: The name of Thor's iron gauntlets which when worn gave him enough wrist strength so he could hold and throw Mjolnir.

Jarnvidr Forest (Járnviðr Forest, Járviðr Forest, Járnviður Forest, Jarnvidiur Forest, Jarnvidi Forest, Jarnved Forest, Jarnrid Forest, Forest of the Jarvids, Jarnveld Forest, Jernvidi Forest, Gaglviðr Forest, Galgviðr Forest) [ironwood forest]: A forest in Jotunheimr. A group of female jotuns called Jarnvids lived there. This was also the home of Thor's mistress Jarnsaxa. Odin's mistress Gridr also lived here, as well as witches and sorcerers who changed themselves into wolves.

Jarnsaxa (Járnsaxa, Iarnsaxa) [iron chopper]: Thor's jotun mistress who lived in the Jarnvidr Forest. She was one of Heimdallr's nine mothers by Odin, as well as the mother of Magni and Modr by Thor.

Jod (Joð, Joth) [youth]: A son of Jarl the Earl and Erna.

Jokull: An ekename for Frosti.

Jol (Jól) [yule]: An ekename for Odin.

Jolnir (Jölnir, Jölnar): An ekename for Odin.

Jor (Jör): A horse in Asgardr.

Jordr (Jorðr, Jörðr, Jörd, Jördh, Jorth, Iörd, Fjörgyn, Erda) [earth]: The daughter of Anar and Nott. She was the mother of Thor by by Odin. Also known as Fjorgynn. She lived in Verland.

Jormungandr (Jörmungandr, Jörmungand, Jörmungander, Jörmungandur, Iörmungandr): Another name for Midgardrsormr.

Jormunr (Jörmunr, Iörmunr): An ekename for Odin.

Jormunrekkr: A kinsman to Ottar the Simple cited by Hyndla. He was also related to Sigurdr Fafnirsbani.

Jotuls: Mountain-sized spirits.

Jotunheimr (Jötunheimr, Jötunheim, Jötunheimar, Jotunheim, Jötunheimar, Jetunheimr, Iötunheim) [giant land]: The land to the east of Midgardr, across the river Ifing, known for its vast distances and giant inhabitants. It was also known as Utgardr.

Jotuns (Jötuns, Jötunn, Jótunn, Jetunn, Jötnar, Júte, Iötunn) [giant]: The giant beings living in Jotunheimr. There were many types such as rock and hill jotuns (bergthursars), fire jotuns (the Mighty Sons of Muspel), and frost jotuns (hrymthursar). Many had multiple heads and hands. If they became angry their true shape was revealed and often their strength would double.

Jotun-wolves (Jötun-wolves): The wolves chasing Sol and Maane.

Juravale's Marsh: The land where many dvergues, known as Dvalin's Hosts, lived.

Kari (Kâri, Kaare): A son of Fornjotr, brother of Logi, Ægir, and Ran. His descendants included Frosti, Fonn, Grendel, and Drifa.

Kari (Kâri, Kaare): Her father was was King Frodi. Her sister was Kari. Related to Ottar the Simple.

Karl the Yeoman: The son of Gammer and Rigr (Heimdallr). His wife was Snœr. Their sons were Boandi, Boddi, Brattskeggr, Breidr, Bui, Bundingkeggi, Drengr, Halr, Holdr, Seggr, Smidr, and Thegn. Their daughters were Brudr, Feima, Fljod, Ristill, Snot, Sprakki, Sprund, Svanni, Svarri, and Vif.

Kattigat (Kattegat, Kattigut, Cattegat, Catte grat): The island where Ægir and Ran's hall was. Also known as Hlessey.

Kefsir [whore-master]: The son of Thræl and Thir.

Keila: Fought Thor and was killed by him.

Kerlaug (Kerlaugar, Kerlaung, Kerlögar): The name given to the two rivers under Bifrost. A poisonous mist arose from them.

Kertr [candle]: Bjarr's horse.

Ketil: A noble warrior who was married to Hildigun. Related to Ottar the Simple.

Kili (Kíli): An earth dvergar.

Kjalarr (Kjalar) [keel]: An ekename for Odin.

Kjallandi: Fought Thor and was killed by him.

Kleggi (Kreggi) [horsefly]: A son of Thræl and Thir.

Klurr (Klúrr, Klur) [coarse]: A son of Thræl and Thir.

Kolga [raging sea, the coal-black]: One of Ægir and Ran's wavemaiden daughters.

Kon (Konur) [king]: The youngest son of Jarl the Earl and Erna. He changed his name to Rigr after his father Jarl the Earl died. He understood the speech of birds.

Kormt (Körmt): One of two rivers flowing through the clouds to Asgardr (the other was Ormt). A poisonous mist arose from the two rivers.

Kumba [stupid]: A daughter of Thræl and Thir.

Kundr (Kund) [kinsman]: Son of Jarl the Earl and Erna.

Kvad galdra (Kvað galdra, val galdrar): The mystical songs sung to raise the dead in order to gain their knowledge.

Kvasir (Kvásir, Kvaser, Kvase, Quaser, Qvâsir): The man formed from the spittle which was the peace offering called Hraki which sealed the peace between the Æsir and the Vanir at the conclusion of the war between the two. He was very wise and walked through all the lands sharing his knowledge with others. He as murdered by the

dvergues Fjalarr and Galarr who took his blood, mixed it with honey and rum to brew the Precious Mead.

Kvasir's Blood: Another name for the Precious Mead.

La (Lá) [warmth]: The warmth given to Askr and Embla.

Laga: An ekename for Saga, also known as Sage.

Lædingr (Lædingr, Læding, Leding, Lœðingr, Lädine, Lœding, Lœdingr, Leuthing): The first adamantine chain forged by Thor in Asgardr to use to bind Fenriswulf. It failed. The other two chains were Dromi (forged by Thor, it also failed) and Gleipnir (forged by dvergues, it succeeded).

Læradr (Læraðr, Læra ð, Lædr, Lærðr, Lærath, Læradi, Lärad, Lera ð, Lerad, Leradur, Leding) [giving protection]: The name of the pine tree growing in the center of Valhalla.

Lævateinn (Lævateinn) [devious twig, guileful twig]: The name of Loki's magic sword. Carved by Loki with runes beneath Nagrindr Gate. It was the only sword with magic enough to slay the cock Vidofnir.

Land-ass (land áss) [land god]: An ekename for Odin.

Landvættir (landvættir): The guardian spirits who roamed the shores of Midgardr protecting an area. Ships had vicious faces carved on their bow hoping to scare away the landvættir when they landed.

Landvidi (Landví ði, Landvithi, Landvide): Vidarr the Silent's abode. No one else lived in this secluded forest.

Langbardr (Langbar ðr) [long-beard]: An ekename for Odin.

Laufey (Laufeia, Laufia, Laufeya) [leafy]: She married Farbauti, also known as Bergelmir. Her son was Loki. She was also known as Nal.

Laugardagr (Laugardag) [wash day]: Saturday. The day usually reserved for bathing.

La ok litr (Lá ok litr) [blood and healthy hue]: The gift given to Askr and Embla by Ve.

Leggjaldi [huge legs]: A son of Thræl and Thir.

Leidi: A jotun slain by Thor.

Leikn (Leikin): A jotun. Thor fought and broke her leg.

Leiptr (Leipter, Leipt, Leift) [quick as lightning]: One of the eleven rivers of Elivagar. It was in Niflheimr near the Gjoll River. Solemn oaths were sworn by it.

Lerbrimr (Lerbrimer) [Ymir's limbs]: The base on which Asgardr's wall was built.

Lettfeti (Léttfeti, Letfet) [light-foot]: The name of a horse in Asgardr.

Lidskjalfr (Lidscialfr): An elf.

Lif (Lif, Lief) [life]: She hid in Hoddmimir's Holt with Lifthraser. They were the only two in Midgardr to survive Ragnarokr and repopulate the world after the Rebirth. They ate the dew of the morning for nourishment.

Lifthrasir (Lifthraser, Lífþrasir, Liiþrasir, Leifthraser, Leifþrasir, Livthraser) [anxious for life]: He hid in Hoddmimir's Holt with Lif. They were the only two in Midgardr to survive Ragnarokr and repopulate the world after the Rebirth. They ate the dew of the morning for nourishment.

Light Alfs: See ljosalfar.

Lin (Hlin, Hlín, Hlyn): One of Frigg's attendants whom she sometimes sent to Midgardr to protect her favorites. Frigg also used this name on occasion.

Litr (Liter, Lit, Litur, Littur) [color, complexion]: An earth dvergar whom Thor in his anger kicked onto Baldr and Nanna's funeral pyre. He subsequently accompanied them to Nilfheimr and waited on them as a servant.

Litu goda (litu góða, lá ok litu góða) [good countenance]: The good countenance given to Askr and Embla by Ve.

Ljosalfar (ljósálfar, Ljósalfar, liosalfar, ljusalfersa) [light alfs]: Odin created them from the maggots crawling in and out of Ymir's body, along with the svartalfheimr. They differ, though, from the dokkalfar in that they were fair, good, and useful. They were friends of the Æsir. Their homes were in Alfheimr, a land given to Freyr as a tooth gift. They looked upon Freyr as their best friend in Asgardr.

Ljosalfrheimr (Ljósálfrheimr, ljosalfaheim, ljosalfheim): Another name for Alfheimr.

Loddfafnir (Loddfáfnir, Lodfafner): A man who was given words of wisdom by Odin.

Lodurr (Lóðurr, Löður, Loder, Loðr, Lodr, Lodur, Lóthur, Lother): One of the Æsir. In many legends he was a brother of Odin and along with Odin and Hœnir one of the creators of Askr and Embla.

Lofar: A dvergar. One of Durinn's Kin.

Lofn (Lofna): One of the Asynjes. Frigg and Odin gave her the power to bring together those on Midgardr who had been forbidden to marry if they petitioned her for permission.

Logi (Loge) [wildfire]: The "cook" Loki ate against, and lost to, in a food eating contest in Utgardr. A son of Fornjotr, brother of Logi, Ægir, and Ran.

Logrinn (Lögrinn, Lögrin, Löer, Lör, Logrinn): The lake formed when Danish Zealand was carved from Sweden by Gefjun. Also called Lake Malar.

Loki Laufeyjarsonr (Loke, Lok, Lokki, Loki Laufeyjarson, Loki Laufeyarson) [fire]: His brothers were Byleistr and Helblindi. Their parents were Farbauti and Laufey. He was Odin's cousin, and in times past they had sworn blood brotherhood together. He was first married to Glut. They had two daughters, Eisa and Einmyria. He changed himself into a mare and had the eight-legged horse Sleipnir by Svadilfari. After swallowing Angroboda's heart he also had three more children, Fenriswulf, Midgardrsormr (also known as Jormungandr), and Hela. He was always getting into mischief and causing trouble for the Æsir. He stole the Brisingamen Necklace from Freyja and fought and lost to Heimdallr in the forms of fire, a polar bear, and a seal by the rocks Vagasker and Singasteinn for possession of it. Loki had a magic sword called Lævateinn which he had carved with runes beneath Nagrindr Gate. He used this sword at Ragnarokr to slay the cock Vidofnir. He also had shoes that gave him the ability to run on air and sea to get away from those chasing him (who wer many). His eldest two sons were Vali and Narfi. Their mother was Sigyn, his loyal second wife. Eventually the Æsir became fed up with him and bound him with Vali and Narfi's intestines near a bottomless pit in Niflheimr. There was a poisonous serpent hung overhead dripping poisonous venom on him. Sigyn caught as much of it as she could in a conch. When she turned to empty it the poison would hit Loki causing him pain. His writhing in agony caused earthquakes on Midgardr. He broke free at Ragnarokr and slew Heimdallr at the last great battle.

Lokk: A valkyrie.

Longobards: The name adopted by the Vinnilers after Frigg helped them gain a victory over the Vandals. The name eventually evolved to Lombards.

Loni (Lóni): A rock dvergar. One of Durinn's Kin.

Loptr (Lopter, Loptur, Lopt, Lopta): An ekename for Loki.

Lora (Lorride, Hlora) [heat]: One of Thor and Sif's two daughters. The other was Thrudr.

Ludr (Lüðr): The name of the mill Bergelmir and his wife scrambled onto in order to save themselves during the great flood. They continued the race of Jotuns.

Lungr: A horse in Asgardr.

Lutefisk (Norwegian), Lutfisk (Swedish) [lye fish]: A Northern delicacy made with cod soaked in water-lye-water for a couple of weeks until it's rancid (but not quite turned into soap). It is pretty much a smelly jelly texture by the time it's cooked – either baked, fried/steamed, or parboiled. No silver cooking utensils are used since the lye-soaked cod will destroy the silver. After all of this, for some unknown reason, people actually sit down together and eat it. It's best to eat it with company so there's someone to rush you to the hospital. Cooking utensils and plates are cleaned immediately because it's almost impossible to get the lutefisk off if you let it set. Just think what it must be doing to your insides? Loki craved lutefisk when he was pregnant with Midgardrsormr, Fenriswulf, and Hela. This may be the reason they turned out to be such monster children.

Lutr (Lútr, Lút, Lut) [bent]: A son of Thræl and Thir.

Lyfjaberg [hill of healing]: The hill where Menglod lived.

Lyngvi (Lyngve) [rocky island]: An island on lake Amsvartnir in Niflheimr.

Lytir (Lýtir): A member of the Æsir. He was worshiped primarily by the Swedes.

Maane (Máni, Mâni, Måne, Mone) [moon]: The son of Mundilfari and brother of Sol. He was snatched away by the Æsir to help guide Nott on her journey. His horse was named Alsvidr.

Magni (Magne) [might, strength]: Thor's son by his jotun mistress Jarnsaxa. Magni's brother was Modr. Thor gave him Hrungr's horse Gullfaxi as a gift. It was a reward for Magni having lifted the jotun's leg off of Thor. Magni survived Ragnarokr with his brother Modr, and found the chess set that had been lost at the end of the Golden Age.

Malar (Mälar, Mælar, Mälaren): See Logrinn.

Malit [speech]: The power of speech given to Askr and Embla by Ve.

Managarmr (Mánagarmr, Mána-garm, Mánagarm, Mana-garm, Mânagarmr, Maanegarm, Maana-Garm, Mána-Garmr, Mánagarm, Manigarm, Moongarm) [moon-swallower, moon hound]: One of two wolves from the Jarnvidr Forest following Nott's chariot. The other was his brother Hati Hrodvitnirsson (also known as Skoll), who swallowed the sun. Managarmr swallowed the moon. Their parents were Angroboda and her son Fenriswulf.

Manavegr (Mánavegr) [moon way]: The path the moon travelled through the sky.

Mannheim (Mana-heim, Manheim, Manheimr, Manheimar, Mannaheim): Another name for Midgardr.

Mardoll (Mardöll, Mardal, Marþöll, Marþǫll, Mardǫll, Mardallar, Mardel, Marthaul): The name assumed by Freyja when she traveled in Midgardr in search of Odr.

Mardallr Gratr (Mardallr Grátr, Mardallar Grátr, Mardaller Grátr) [tears of Mardal, tears of gold]: The gold tears that fell when Mardoll cried.

287

Mead of Inspiration: Another name for the Precious Mead.

Med sviga lævi (med sviga lævi) [consumer of branches, danger to branches]: The fiery sword belonging to Surtr, given to him by Angroboda in Jarnvidr Forest.

Megingardr (Megingjardar, Megingjorðr, Megingjarder, Megingjarðar, Megingjǫrðr, Megingjardir, Megingjord, Megingjǫrð, Megingjǫrðr, Megingiörð, Megingjörð, Megingiardr, Meigingardur): Thor's girdle of strength. The strength derived from it was known as asmegen.

Meili (Meile): One of Odin's sons. Thor's brother.

Meinthjofr (Meinthjófr, Meinþjófr): Rode Mor.

Menglod (Menglöð, Menglad, Menglǫð) [necklace glad]: An attendant of Frigg's. She was the goddess of medicine and lived on Lyfjaberg.

Midgardr (Miðgarðr, Midgard, Midgaard, Midgarth, Mithgarth) [middle land, middle enclosure]: The earth.

Midgardrsormr (Miðgarðrsormr, Miðgarðsormr, Miðgarðsorm, Mithgarthsorm, Mithgarth-worm) [earth serpent]: Also known as Jormungandr. The giant sea serpent child Loki bore after eating the evil Angroboda's heart. His siblings were Fenriswulf and Hela. He was thrown into the sea where he grew and grew until he encircled the land and could catch hold of his tale with his mouth. He would spit out poison when angered, and was a long time enemy of Thor's. Thor went fishing along with the jotun Hymir, and almost captured Midgardrsormr using one of Hymir's prize oxen, Himinbjorg, as bait. Thor and Midgardrsormr destroy each other at Ragnarokr.

Midgardsveor [protector of Midgardr]: An ekename for Thor.

Midvitnir (Miðvitnir, Mithvitnir) [mead wolf]: A jotun who lived in Muspelheimr. He once stole the Precious Mead, but it was recovered by Odin. Odin slew his son Sokkmimir during the recovery.

Mighty Sons of Muspel: The fiery demon subjects of Surtr in Muspelheimr. See Muspels Lydir.

Mimameidr (Mímameiðr, Mimameider, Mímamd, Mímameið) [Mimir's Tree]: A mythic tree, probably another name for Yggdrasyll. It derives its name from Mimir.

Mimir (Mímir, Mîmir, Mímr, Mimer, Mími, Mime, Mím) [memory]: He guarded the Mimirsbrunnr Well at the Jotunheimr root of Yggdrasyll. He was old with a long silvery beard. His sister was Bestla, the mother of Odin, Vili, and Ve, making him their uncle. Both the jotuns and the Æsir went to him to seek knowledge. Usually they had to pay dearly for a drink from his well; Odin gave an eye, Heimdallr gave an ear. he was sent as a hostage to the Vanir along with Hœnir, but his head was cut off when Hœnir's stupidity was discovered. It was sent back to the Æsir and preserved by Odin and kept at Mimer's Well.

Mimirsbrunnr Well (Mimesbrunn Well, Mímisbrunnr Well, Mímisbrunnar Well, Mímis-brunnar Well, Mímis-Brunnr Well, Mimir's Well): One of three wells that helped nourish Yggdrasyll. (Hvergelmir Well and Urdarbrunnr Well were the other two). It was located at the Jotunheimr root, and was a well of memory and knowledge guarded over by Mimir.

Mimring (Miming, Mimingus): A troll who had forged magic gifts for Hodr when he was hiding out on Baldr's estate. The gifts included a shield of darkness, a magic shirt that rendered him invisible, and a magic sword.

Mimung (Mímung): A sword forged by Volund the Smith.

Mioll: The daughter of King Snar of Finland. She married Frosti.

Mist [mist]: A valkyrie. She and Hrist served Odin his mead in Valhalla.

Mistarblindi [one who blinds with mists]: An ekename for Odin.

Mistilteiin (Mistillteinn, Mistilteinn, Misteltein, Mistiltein, Misteltân) [mistletoe]: The name of the mistletoe from which Frigg neglected to extract a promise not to harm Baldr. Loki took the sprig and magically turned it into a weapon which was used by Hodr against Baldr, killing him.

Mithotyn (Mythotyn, Mithridates): An evil sorcerer who deposed Ullr in Asgardr ten years after Odin's banishment. He became a tyrannical dictator and was eventually overthrown by Odin's brothers Vili and Ve.

Mjodvitnir (Mjöðvitnir, Miodvitnir, Mjothvitnir): An earth dvergar.

Mjofvitr (Mjöfviðr) [mead tree]: Another name for Yggdrasyll.

Mjolnir (Mjollnir, Mjǫllnir, Mjolner, Mjölnir, Miölnir, Miöllnir, Mjöllnir, Mjølne, Mjǫllnr) [crusher]: The hammer forged by Sindri so Brokkr, his brother, could win a bet against Loki. It was given to Thor. Its one defect was its short handle, due to Loki's evil machinations. yet it had other wonderful properties. It could be squeezed into a small shape and hidden away, and each time it was thrown it would automatically return to its owner. Usually it was red-hot to the touch. It was used not only to slay jotuns, but also for consecrating sacred events such as weddings, births, funerals, etc. It was also called Mullicrusher, Thrudhammer, and Vigdi. The thunder and lightning which shot from it when Thor hurled it was called Fulminen.

Modir (Moðir, Mothir, Móðir) [mother]: The wife of Fadir. Their son (actually Modir and Rigr's) was Jarl the Earl.

Modgudr (Moðguðr, Modgarðr, Mödgudur, Mœdgud, Modgud, Móðguðr, Mödgud, Modgudur, Modgudhr) [soul in misery]: The skeleton maiden who guards Gjallarbru in Gnipahellir Cave. Her brother was Imr. Their father was Vafthrudnir.

Modnir (Módnir) [spirited]: Dvalin's horse.

Modr (Moðr, Môdr, Môd, Môdi, Mödi, Módi, Mode, Móthi, Mothi) [courage]: One of Thor's sons by his jotun mistress Jarnsaxa. The other was Magni. Both sons survived Ragnarokr.

Modrodnir (Módrödnir) [angry]: A hart.

Modsognir (Móðsognir, Modsogner, Mótsognir, Möðsognur, Mótsognir, Motsugnir) [mead drinker]: The first dvergar created by Odin from the maggots crawling in Ymir's body. Modsognir in turn created Durinn who in turn created the rest of the race of Svartalfheimr.

Mogr (Mögr, Mog) [sonny]: A son of Jarl the Earl and Erna.

Mogthrasir (Mogthrásir, Mogþrásir) [desirous of sons]: A name for humans on Midgardr.

Moinn (Mónn, Móinn, Móin, Moin) [one who lives on a moor]: One of the serpent Nidhoggr's six sons eating away at the Niflheimr root of Yggdrasyll.

Mokkurkalfi (Mokkurkálfi, Mökkurkálfi, Mokkerkalfe, Mökkrkálfi, Mokerkialfi, Möckurkalfi) [cloud calf, mist calf]: The clay jotun built to bolster Hrungr's courage for his battle against Thor. It was nine rosts high and three rosts broad across the chest. It did not have a human heart, since one large enough for it's body couldn't be found. Instead a mare's heart (named Giottunagard) was substituted. The clay jotun was a

coward and proved it when it wet all over itself from fright at the beginning of the battle.

Mor (Mór, Marr): Horse ridden by Meinthjofr.

Morginn: Rode Vakr.

Mt. Idavollr (Mt. Idavöllr, Mt. Idavǫllr, Mt. Idavale, Mt. Idavöld, Mt. Idavöll, Mt. Idavollr, Mt. Idavöller, Mt. Idavollen, Mt. Ithavoll, Mt. Ida-voll, Mt. Idawold, Mt. Ida) [field of deeds, peak of Ida]: The centermost and highest peak in Midgardr. Asgardr was built on top of it.

Mullicrusher: Another name for Mjolnir.

Mundilfari (Mundilfare, Mundilföri, Mundilferi, Mundilfær, Mundilfaxi) [axis swinger]: A jotun who had been presumptuous enough to name his children after the sun and moon (Sol and Maane) because he thought they were more beautiful. This angered the Æsir who then stole his children and put them to work guiding the sun and moon.

Muninn (Munin, Munnin, Mummin) [memory]: One of Odin's ravens who flew throughout the worlds during the day gathering information, and then at dinnertime sat on Odin's shoulder whispering in his ear what he had found out. The other raven was Huninn. Both were gifts to Odin from Huldr.

Muspels Lydir (Múspells Lyðir) [men of Muspell]: The fire jotuns, also known as the Sons of Muspell, who lived in Muspelheimr and were ruled by Surtr.

Muspelheimr (Múspellsheimr, Muspélheimr, Muspelheim, Muspellheim, Muspellsheimr, Musspellsheim) [land of fire]: The land to the south of Ginnungagap. It was the second land created and was ruled over by Surtr who commanded the Mighty Sons of Muspel to do his bidding.

Myrkvan vafrloga [flickering fire]: This was the name given to the flickering fire surrounding and protecting Gymirsgard. Skirnir's horse leapt over it so Skirnir could win Gerdr for Freyr.

Myrkvyrdr Forest (Myrkvidr, Myrkviðar, Myrkvidar, Myrkvith, Myrkwood, Murkwood, Myrkwood Forest, Mirkwood, Mirkvid, Myrkviðr) [The Black Forest]: The Black Forest. Also a forest in Jotunheimr. Its trees had leaves made of black iron. Angroboda lived there. Hermodr passed through here on his way to Niflheimr.

Nabbi: One of the dvergar who helped make Freyja's boar Hilksuin. The other dvergar was Dain.

Naglfar (Naglfare, Nalgfar) [nail-ship]: A ship made from the nails of the dead being constructed at Nastrond near Hvergelmir in Niflheimr. It carried the dead in Niflheimr to the last battle on Vigridr Plain during Ragnarokr.

Naglifari (Naglfare, Nagelfari, Nagelfare) [twilight]: The first husband of Narfi. They had a son named Audr.

Nagrindr Gate (Nágrinðr, Nagrind, Na-gates) [corpse gate]: There were several gates containing the dead in various lands. The gate leading into Niflheimr was called Nagrindr Gate. The sooty-red cock who crowed at Ragnarokr and the hrymthursar Hrimgrimnir lived inbetween Nagrindr Gate and Helgrindr Gate. A third gate was Valgrindr Gate.

Nain (Naínn): An earth dvergar.

Nal (Nál, Ná, Naal) [needle]: Another name for Laufey, Loki's mother.

Nali (Nali, Vali): An earth dvergar.

Nanna: The daughter of Nokkvi. Related to Ottar the Simple.

Nanna Nepsdottir (Nanna Nepsdóttir, Nanda) [blossom, daughter of Nep]: Baldr's wife. Their best friends in Asgardr were Bragi and Idunn. Nanna was overcome with grief at Baldr's funeral and died. A pyre was built beside his and they both were burned and journeyed to Niflheimr together. She survived Ragnarokr with Baldr and shared a hall in Hropt's Hills with Baldr, Hodr, Bragi, and Idunn.

Nar (Nár) [corpse]: An earth dvergar.

Narfi (Narfe, Narvi, Narve, Nari, Nare, Nörfi, Norfi, Nǫrvi, Nörvi, Norvi, Nörve, Norve, Nör, Nor, Nari) [binding]: One of Loki and Sigyn's sons. Vali was the other. Narfi was turned into a wolf by the Æsir, and ate Vali. Then his intestines were turned into the magical chain used to bind Loki.

Narfi (Norve, Nörfi): The first jotun to settle in Jotunheimr after the flood. He was Nott's father.

Nastrond (Náströnd, Náströndr, Nástrond, Nástrond, Ná Strand, Naastrand, Nástrand, Nástrandir, Nastrender, Nâströnd) [shore of corpses]: The wharf near Hvergelmir where the ship Naglfar was moored.

Not (Nöt, Naut): A river flowing from Asgardr through Midgardr to Hel.

Nep (Nepr, Nip) [bud]: A son of Odin's. His daughter was Nanna. Baldr's father-in-law.

Neri: An ekename for Ymir.

Nerthus (Nerþuz, Herthus, Hertha): Njordr's twin sister. She and Njordr were the parents of Freyr and Freyja.

Nidafjoll (Niðafjóll, Niðafjöll, Niðafjhöll, Nidafell, Nida fells, Nithafjoll, Nitha Fields) [hills of darkness]: In the beginning this was one of the worst regions in Niflheimr. It was located to the north of the Nida Mountains. After Ragnarokr only the good and pure dwelled here. The hall, Sindri, stood here. Nidhoggr flew over this area when he was carrying the corpses away from the land, purging it of evil.

Nida Mountains (Nide's Mountains): A mountain range to the north in Niflheimr. The land called Nidafjoll was located near here after Ragnarokr. Only the good and pure dwelled in this area after Ragnarokr. Nidhoggr flew over the Nida Mountains after Ragnarokr carrying corpses away from the land, purging it of evil.

Nidavellir (Niðavellir, Nithavellir) [fields of darkness]: A land where some dvergues lived. It was located near Okolnir.

Nide's Plain: A hall of gleaming gold located at the base of the Nida Mountains within sight of those in Niflheimr. It gave them hope.

Nidhoggr (Níðhöggr, Níðhögg, Niðhǫggr, Nidhogger, Nid Hog, Nidhogg, Nithogg, Nidhug, Nithhogg, Nydhoggur, Nidhögg, Nighogg, Nidhogg) [terrible biter]: The name of a serpent who was entwined around Yggdrasyll at the Niflheimr root. In addition to chewing away at Yggdrasyll's Nilfheimr root, he and his sons also sucked the bodies of the dead and then ate them. His sons were Goinn, Moinn, Grabakr, Grafvolludr, Ofnir, and Svafnir. After Ragnarokr he could be seen flying up from Nidafjoll over the Nida Mountains bearing corpses on his wings. Thus was the land purged of evil.

Nidi (Niði, Nide, Nithi) [lower world]: An earth dvergar. Possibly another name for Mimir.

Nidjungr (Niðjungr, Niðjung, Niojung, Nithjung) [descendant]: A son of Jarl the Earl and Erna.

Nidr (Niðr, Nið, Nid, Nith) [descendant]: A son of Jarl the Earl and Erna.

Niflheimr (Nifelheimr, Nifelheim, Niffelheim, Niflheim, Nifl-heim, Niffl-heim, Nivlheim) [land of mists]: This was the land of cold created to the north of Ginnungagap. It was the first land created. It was eventually given to Hela and became the land of death. It was divided into nine regions, each worse than the next.

Niflhel (Nifhel, Nifelhel): One of the worst regions of Niflheimr. This is where Hela had Elidner, her estate.

Nikarr (Nikar): An ekename for Odin.

Nikudr (Nikud) [striker]: An ekename for Odin.

Nipingr (Nípingr, Nipiner): A dvergar.

Nipung: An earth dvergar.

Njordr (Njörðr, Njǫrðr, Njǫrd, Njorth, Njörð, Njord, Niördr, Niörd): Chief of the Vanir. Father of Freyr and Freyja by his twin sister Nerthus. He wore a sea green tunic and crown of shells. Skadi picked him as her husband, but the marriage didn't work out. His hall was Noatun, by the sea, while Skadi liked her home in the snow-covered mountains.

Njotr (Njótr, Njötr): An ekename for Odin.

Noatun (Nóatún, Nöatun, Nôatûn) [place of ships]: The name of Njordr's home by the sea.

Noinn: A dvergar.

Nokkvi: The father of Nanna. Related to Ottar the Simple.

Nonn (Nönn, Nón) [strong]: A river flowing from Asgardr to Midgardr.

Nor: Nott's mother.

Nordri (Norðri, Norðr, Nordi, Nordre, Northri) [north]: One of the four dvergues helping to hold up Ymir's skull.

Nori (Nóri): An earth dvergar.

Norns (Nornas, Nornies, Nornir) (singular: Norny, Nornie, Norni) [fates]: The three jotun women from the east whose coming heralded the end of the Golden Age. They were Urdr, Verdandi, and Skuld. They wove a tapestry of the history of the world showing things as they were fated to happen. They finished their weaving at Ragnarokr.

Nott (Nótt, Niol, Natt, Nat) [night]: She was the daughter of the jotuns Narfi and Nor. She was born in the dales beneath Yggdrasyll and was swarthy and dusky-haired. Her first husband was Naglifar. Their son was Audr. Her second husband was Anar. Their daughter was Jordr. Her third husband was Dellingr. Their son was Dagr.

Notung: The name of Odin's sword.

Nyi (Nýi, Ny, Næ): An earth dvergar.

Nyr (Nýr) [new one]: An earth dvergar.

Nyradr (Nýrádr, Nyrád, Nýrádur, Nyrath): An earth dvergar.

Nyt (Nýt): A river flowing from Asgardr through Midgardr to Hel.

Odainsaker: Mimir's land and Mimir's grove. Asmegin lived here. Lif and Lifthraser settled here after Ragnarokr.

Odin (Oðin, Óðinn, Oithin, Óthin, Óth): The eldest son of Bor and Bestla. He was tall and looked about fifty years of age. His brothers were Vili and Ve. They were the first

of the Æsir. They killed Ymir and created Midgardr from his body. They also created Askr and Embla to populate the new land. Odin's main hall was Valaskjalf. He was the master of two ravens, Huginn and Muninn, who flew out over the worlds during the day and returned at dinnertime and sat on his shoulders in Valhalla whispering in his ear all they had learned during the day. He also had two wolves, Geri and Freki, whom he fed his food to at the table. His children included Thor, Heimdallr, Hermodr, Hodr, Baldr, Bragi, Vidarr the Silent, and Vali the Avenger. He was slain during Ragnarokr by Fenriswulf. His death was avenged by his son Vidarr the Silent. He had many ekenames including Herjan (the valkyries were known as Herjan's Disir), Bolverkr (the name Odin assumed in quest of the Precious Mead), Gangraaf (the name and disguise Odin assumed on his journey to gain knowledge from the jotun Vafthrudnir whom he eventually bested in a battle of wits), and Vegtamr Valtamssonr (the name Odin used when he raised the Volva from the dead to gain knowledge about Ragnarokr). He owned several valuable weapons including a spear called Gungnir and a sword called Notung. He also carried a shield to battle. His horse was eight-legged Sleipnir.

Odin's Way: Another name for the Milky Way.

Odr (Óðr, Oð, Od, Oder, Oddur, Odur, Odhr, Odurn): The gift of thought given to Askr and Embla by Vili.

Odr (Óðr, Óð, Oder, Oth): One of the Æsir. He was married to Freyja. They had two daughters, Hnoss and Gersemi. He frequently went wandering in Midgardr. When he found out about Freyja's unfaithfulness (she had slept with four dvergues to purchase the Brisingamen Necklace), he went away for a long time. Freyja followed him to Midgardr crying tears of gold along the way while she searched for him. Eventually she found him, was forgiven, and they returned to Asgardr.

Odrærir (Ódrœrir, Odrœrer, Oðrærir, Odrær, Óðrerir, Oðrörir, Othrörir, Óthrœrir, Odhrärir, Odhærir, Od-hrœrir, Odreyrer) [heart-stirrer]: The bronze kettle that held part of the Precious Mead. The other two containers were the vats Son and Bodn.

Odhrœris dreckr (Odhroeris dreckr, Oðhrœris dreckr): Another name for the Precious Mead.

Ofnir (Ófnir, Ofner) [bewilderer]: A son of Nidhoggr eating away at the Nilfheimr root of Yggdrasyll.

Oinn (Óinn, Óin): An earth dvergar.

Okkvainkalfa (Ökkvinkalfa, Økkvinkalfa) [fat legs]: One of the daughters of Thræl and Thir.

Okolnir (Okonir, Ókólnir, Ókólner, Okolnur) [never cold]: The region in Muspellheimr where Midvitnir lived. Brimir was the name of his mead hall. This hall stood after Ragnarokr.

Oku-Thor (Öku-þórr, Ôku-þórr, Oku-þórr, Ökuþôrr, Öku-Thor, Oka-Thor) [driving Thor]: An ekename for Thor based on the fact he drives his chariot fiercely enough to cause thunder and lightning as the wheels roll over the clouds. See Aku-Thor.

Olgefn (Ölgefn, Ölgefion): An ekename for Groa.

Olmod: He was married to Skurhold. Their two sons were Isulf and Osulf.

Olvaldi (Ölvaldi, Alvaldi, Allvaldi): Thjasse, Idi and Gangr's father. Skadi's grandfather.

Omi (Ómi) [the shouter]: An ekename for Odin.

Ond (Önd, Aand): The breath of life given Askr and Embla by Odin.

Ondurdis (Ôndurdís, Ǫndurdís, Öndurdís) [ski-god]: An ekename for Ullr.

Opnir: An ekename for Odin.

Ori (Óri, Ore) [raging one]: An earth dvergar. One of Dvalin's Hosts. He also worked for Dellingr. Lived in Juravale's Marsh.

Orlog: Fate.

Ormt (Ermt, Örmt): One of two rivers flowing through the clouds into Asgardr (the other was Kormt). A poisonous mist arose from the two rivers.

Orne-ham: The eagle-guise owned and used by Thjassi.

Oski (Óski, Oske) [god of wishes]: An ekename for Odin.

Oskopnir (Óskópnir): The island where Vigridr Plain was located.

Osulf: One of the sons of Skurhold and Olmod. His brother was Isulf. Related to Ottar the Simple.

Othlings: One of the warrior families mentioned by Hyndla as being related to Ottar the Simple.

Ottar the Simple: He prayed to Freyja, asking for her help in gaining an inheritance over Angantyr. Also known as Ottar the Young. He was the son of Instein and Hledis.

Ottar the Young: Another name for Ottar the Simple.

Otti jotna (Ôtti iötna, Otti iotna) [giant terror]: An ekename for Thor.

Outgardr: Another name for Utgardr.

Þ: The magic rune which Skirnir carved on Gambanteinn, and then changed its name to Tamsvondr. He used this new sword to threaten Gerdr into agreeing to marry Freyr.

Poetry: Known by the ekenames: Odin's catch, Odin's discovery, Odin's gift, Drink of the Æsir.

Precious Mead (Foundation of Poetry, Mead of Inspiration, Kvasir's Blood, Suttungr's Hoard): This was the drink made by the dvergues Fjalarr and Galarr out of Kvasir's blood. They mixed it with rum and honey. Eventually it became the possession of the jotun Suttungr as weregild for his father, Gillingr, and mother whom the two dvergues had murdered. His daughter Gunnlod guarded it in Suttungr's treasure chamber called Hnitbjorg. But Odin was successful in stealing it from her and took it to Asgardr. It was stolen again by Mitvitnir and guarded by Sokkmimir, but stolen back by Odin. Anyone who drank of it became a poet.

Radgridr (Ráðgríðr, Rágríð, Radgrid, Ráthgrith) [plan-destroyer]: A valkyrie.

Radsvidr (Ráðsviðr, Rásvíð, Rathsvith) [wise in advice]: A rock dvergar.

Rafnagud [raven god]: An ekename for Odin.

Ragnarokr (Ragnarök, Ragnarökr, Ragnarøkr, Ragnarokkr, Ragnarøkkr, Ragna rok, Ragnarǫk, Ragnarokur, Ragnarock) [Ragnarokr = Doom of the gods, Ragnarok = Twilight of the Gods]: The doom of the gods. The period started after Baldr's death and included the Fimbulventr, the swallowing of the sun and moon, and finally culminated into the battle on Vigridr Plain and the conflagration of all the Worlds of the Tree.

Ran (Rán, Rân, Rana, Rœna) [rob, concealer, shelterer]: She ruled the sea with her husband Ægir. They were also brother and sister. Their other brothers included Logi and Kari. They were frequent visitors to Asgardr. Their hall was on the island Hlessey in the Kattigat, also known as Hlessey. They had nine wavemaiden daughters. They owned a giant kettle for brewing mead taken from the jotun Hymir by Tyr and Thor.

Randarr iss (randarr íss): The name of Hrungr's shield.

Randgridr (Randgríðr, Rangríð, Randgrid, Randgrith) [shield destroyer]: A valkyrie.

Randver: The son of Aud the Profound and Rathbard. His half-brother was Harald War Tooth. Related to Ottar the Simple.

Ratatoskr (Ratatöskr, Ratatöskur, Ratatösk, Ratatosk, Rat-tusk) [swift gnawing teeth]: The red squirrel running up and down Yggdrasyll spreading gossip between Nidhoggr and Edgar. Also known as Ratr.

Rathbard: He and Aud the Profound were the parents of Randver. Related to Ottar the Simple.

Rathsey Sound (Ráthsey Sound, Rådøysund): The place where the jotun Hildwolf lives.

Rati (Rate) [the traveller]: The name of the magic auger used by Odin to cut through Hnitbjorg so he could gain entry to Suttungr's treasure chamber so that he could steal the Precious Mead.

Ratr [wanderer]: An ekename for Ratatoskr.

Raudr [red]: The name of one of Gefjun's four oxen. The other three were Hœfir, Hyrr, and Rekinni. They were actually her sons.

Regin: An earth dvergar.

Reginleif [relative of the gods]: A valkyrie.

Reid-Gothland: The land in the gulf of Finland ruled over by King Hrading, his son Geirrodr, and his son Agnar. The Vistula river defined its borders.

Reifnir: One of Arngrim and Eyfura's twelve berserker sons. His brothers were Hadding, Hervard, Hjorvard, Hrani, Angantyr, Bui, Brami, Barri, Reifnir, Tind, and Tyrfing. Related to Ottar the Simple.

Rekinni [driver]: The name of one of Gefjun's four oxen. The other three were Hœfir, Hyrr, and Raudr. They were actually her sons.

Rekkr (Rekk): An earth dvergar.

Rigr (Rígr, Rîgr, Ríg, Rig, Righ, Riger) [the walker]: The ekename used by Heimdallr as he walked in Midgardr fathering the various classifications of humankind. This was also the name given to his son Jarl the Earl. Jarl the Earl's son, Kon, took the name Rigr after Jarl the Earl died.

Rimestone: A stone covered with granular ice crystals.

Rinn (Rín): A river flowing from Asgardr to Midgardr.

Rindr (Rind, Rinda, Rindur, Rinde, Rindus, Wrindr): The daughter of King Billingr (of the Ruthenes, or Varns). Odin slept with her in the guise of Vecka. Their son was Vali the Avenger who avenged Baldr's death.

Rinnandi (Rennandi): A river flowing from Asgardr to Midgardr.

Risar: Another term for jotuns.

Ristill (Ristil) [the graceful]: A daughter of Karl the Yeoman and Snœr.

Rogner (Rognir): A young boy hunted by the jotun Skrymali who intended him as his evening meal. He was hidden by Odin, Hœnir and Loki. Eventually Skrymali was killed and Rogner was finally free from fear.

Roskva (Röskva, Reskva, Roska) [holdfast]: The youngest child of Egil and his wife. She was blond and blue-eyed. Her brother was Thjalfi. They became Thor's servants.

Rosterus (Rosstheow): The name Odin used when he tried to woo Princess Rindr of Ruthenia in the guise of a goldsmith.

Rostgridr (Róstgríðr): A valkyrie.

Rosts: A measure of distance equivalent to 4–5 miles.

Rota (Róta): A valkyrie. One of their leaders, along with Gudr and Skuldr.

Rowan Tree (Reynir): The type of tree Thor grabbed onto when he almost drowned in a river. It was ever after known as Thor's Deliverance.

Rune: The magical letters invented by Odin that were carved on objects in order to gain knowledge, courage, protection, or raise the dead in order to quiz them about their secret knowledge.

Ruthenes [Russians]: The people living in Ruthenia.

Ruthenia (Ruteni) [Russia]: The land where King Billingr ruled. Princess Rindr was his daughter. Same as the land of the Varns. Vali the Avenger was born here. It was only when Nott passed over this land she felt safe from the wolves pursuing her.

Sadr (Saðr, Sað, Sath) [truthful]: An ekename for Odin.

Sæfari: Ulf's father. His father was Svan the Red. Related to Ottar the Simple.

Sæger (Sæger, Sægr, Sœg): The name of the cask which Hjiuki and Bil used to fetch water.

Sæhrimnir (Sæhrímnir, Sæhrimner, Særimne, Sehrimner, Serimnir) [sooty-black]: The name of the boar who was slaughtered daily and fed to the Einherjar in Valhalla and made whole again to be cooked the next day.

Sækonung: The father of Hildigun. He was married to Svava. Related to Ottar the Simple.

Sæming (Sæming, Seming): The son of Odin and Skadi.

Sage (Sága, Sagâ, Sage) [history]: One of the Asynjes and Odin's daughter. She was the goddess of poetry. Her hall was Sokkvabekkr. Also known as Laga.

Salgofnir [house bird, bird of the hall]: The name of the cock sitting over the hall facing the Einherjar in Valhalla. It crows to awaken them each morning. Also known as Gullinkambi.

Samsey: The island where Odin practiced seidr.

Sangridr (Sangriðr, Sangrið, Sangrith): A valkyrie.

Sanngetall (Sanngetal, Sann-getall) [one who guesses]: A somewhat derogatory ekename for Odin.

Seggr (Segg) [man, goodfellow]: A son of Karl the Yeoman and Snœr.

Seidmadr [sorcerer, one who practices seidr, mother of seidr]: An ekename for Odin.

Seidr (Seiðr, Seid, Seith): The magic taught to Odin by Freyja. She also invented it. It could only be practiced by women, so Odin had to change into a woman to practice it. A platform was set up on which the Volva (woman leading the ceremony) sat singing spells until she, and sometimes all who were present, were lulled into a state of ecstasy. In this state the Volva could divine the future.

Sekin: A river flowing from Asgardr to Midgardr.

Sessrumnir (Sessrúmnir, Sessrumner, Sessrymner, Sessrymnir, Sessrumnis) [place with lots of seats]: The name of Freyja's hall on Folkvangr, her estate.

Sid (Sið, Síth): A river flowing from Hvergelmir.

Sidgrani (Siðgrani, Sídgrani, Sithgrani) [long-beard]: An ekename for Odin.

Sidhottr, Síðhöttr, Síðhöttr, Sídhött, Sîðhöttr, Sîðhöttr, Síðhötyr, Sídhotyr, Síthhott, Síðhötr, Sidhatt, Sidhat): An ekename for Odin based on the disguise he wears. It referred to the wide-brimmed hat he wore pulled low over his missing eye.

Sidskjegg (Síðskeggr, Síðskegg, Siðskeggi, Sîðskeggr, Sithskegg, Sidskeg) [long beard]: An ekename for Odin. It was also an ekename sometimes used by Bragi.

Sif (Sif, Sîf, Sifr, Siv) [kin]: One of the Asynjes. She was married to Thor. She had long golden hair which was once cut off by Loki while she slept. He had to have new hair forged by some dvergues. She and Aurvandill had a son named Ullr who was the god of skis and eventually married Skadi. She and Thor had two daughters, Thrudr and Lora.

Sigdir (Sigðir): An ekename for Odin.

Sigfadir (Sigfaðir, Sigföðr, Sigföð, Sigfather) [father of victory]: An ekename for Odin.

Siggautr: An ekename for Odin.

Siglilnin: The hill on the island Lyngvi on the lake Amsvartnir in Nilfheimr where Fenriswulf is bound.

Sigmundr [god of war]: An ekename for Odin.

Sigmundr: A bold warrior of Midgardr mentioned by Hyndla. Related to Ottar the Simple.

Sigrhofundr (Sigrhöfundr) [giver of victory]: An ekename for Odin.

Sigrthjod (Sigrthjoð, Sigrþjoð, Sigrthjoth) [battle-people]: Another name for the Einherjar.

Sigtryggr: An ekename for Odin.

Sigtyr (Sigtýr, Sigtǫr) [god of victory]: An ekename for Odin.

Sigurdr Fafnirsbani: A kinsman to Ottar the Simple cited by Hyndla. He was also related to Jormunrekkr He slew the dragon Fafnir. Two of his grandparents were Volsungr and Hjordis.

Sigyn (Sigyon, Sigryn, Siguna, Synge, Signi): Loki's devoted wife, despite the fact he frequently beat her. They had two children, Vali and Narfi. Narfi was turned into a wolf and ate Vali. His intestines were turned into a magical chain used to bind Loki. Skadi hung a poisonous snake over him. Sigyn stayed at his side and held a conch over his face to catch the poison. When she turned away to empty it the poison would fall on him causing him to twist and turn, resulting in violent earthquakes on Midgardr.

Silfrintoppr (Silfrintopp, Silfrintop, Silfrtoppr) [having a silver forelock]: One of the horses of the Æsir.

Simul (Simul): The name of the pole Hjiuki and Bil used to carry the cask Sæger from the well Byrgir.

Sindri (Sindre): A hall used after Ragnarokr. It stood in Nidafjoll to the north of the Nida Mountains. The good and pure dwelt there after Ragnarokr.

Sindri (Sindre, Eitri, Sindrig): A rock dvergar, Brokkr's brother, who forged Gullinbursti (also known as Slidrugtanni), Draupnir and Mjolnir so Brokkr could win his wager against Loki.

Sindur: One of Heimdallr's nine mothers. Geirrodr was her father.

Singasteinn (Singastein): The place where Loki hid in the form of a seal after stealing the Brisingamen Necklace from Freyja. Vagaskr was a part of the area.

Sinir (Siner) [sinew, strong muscles]: One of the horses of the Æsir.

Sjafni: The term for love taken from the name of the goddess of love, Sjofn.

Sjofn (Sjöfn, Sjǫfn, Siofna, Sniofna, Sjafni, Skjalf): An attendant of Frigg's. She was the goddess of love and eases the way for those with insurmountable problems to fall in love. Love was called Sjafni after her. She was also goddess of sheep.

Sjon: The fit of sight given to Askr and Embla by Ve.

Skadan: The land to the north where the Vinnilers lived and were conquered by the Vandals.

Skadi (Skaði, Skade, Skada, Skadhi, Skathi): The jotun Thjassi's daughter. Her uncles were Idi and Gangr. She and Loki had been lovers. She had also been lovers with Odin and had a son, Sæming, by him. She lived in Thrymheimr. As weregild for the Æsir's killing of her father she was allowed to choose one of the Æsir as her husband. She had to choose him by his feet and chose Njordr thinking it was Baldr. Eventually she married Ullr after the breakup of her marriage to Njordr.

Skafidr (Skafiðr, Skafið, Skavid, Skáfidur, Skafith): A rock dvergar. One of Dvalin's Hosts. Lived in Juravale's Marsh.

Skævadr (Skævadr) [hoof-tosser]: A horse in Asgardr.

Skaldr (Skald): A poet who created verses, usually extemporaneously, about the glory of warriors and battles.

Skald-Fiflahlutr (Skáld-Fíflahlutr): The name given to the fool's portion of the Precious Mead that fell outside the walls of Asgardr.

Skeggjold (Skeggjöld, Skeggǫld, Skeggöld, Skegghold) [axe-time]: One of the chief valkyries. She was also known as Hildr.

Skeidbrimir (Skeiðbrímir, Skeiðbrimer, Skeithbrimir) [fast runner]: The name of a horse in Asgardr.

Skekil: The father of Skurhold. Related to Ottar the Simple.

Skidbladnir (Skíðblaðnir, Skîðblaðnir, Skíðbladdr, Skîðblaðnir, Skidbladner, Skidbladne, Skíthblathnir) [wooden bladed]: A ship forged for Loki by Ivaldi's Sons. It was given to Freyr. It was so large it could hold all of the Æsir, even if they were wearing all of their armor and carrying all of their weapons. Yet it was so compact it could be folded up so it was small enough to be pocketed. It never failed to find a breeze.

Skilfingr (Skilfing, Silving) [shaker]: An ekename for Odin.

Skilfings: One of the warrior families mentioned by Hyndla as being related to Ottar the Simple.

Skinfaxi (Skinfaxe, Skînfaxi, Skinfakse) [shining mane]: One of Dagr's two horses pulling his chariot. The other was Gladr.

Skirfir (Skirvir): A rock dvergar. One of Dvalin's Hosts. Lived in Juravale's Marsh.

Skirnir (Skírnir, Skîrnir, Skirner, Skirne) [bright one]: Freyr's best friend, frequently acting as his messenger. In this capacity he was sent to woo and win Gerdr for Freyr, which he did using threats. In gratitude Freyr gave him his sword Gambanteinn. He and Gymir slew each other at Ragnarokr.

Skjald (Skjold, Skjöl, Skiold, Scyld, Skjoldr): Gefjun's husband.

Skjaldar ass (skjaldar áss) [shield god]: An ekename for Ullr.

Skjoldungs: One of the warrior families mentioned by Hyndla as being related to Ottar the Simple.

Skogul (Skögul, Skogul, Skaugul) [raging]: A valkyrie.

Skoll (Skol, Sköll, Skǫll) [repulsion]: Also known as Hati Hrodvitnirsson. One of two wolves raised in the Jarnvidr Forest. The other was Mana-Garmr. Their parents were Angroboda and her son Fenriswulf. Skoll followed Dagr's chariot hoping to swallow the sun. Mana-Garmr followed Nott's for the same reason.

Skrymali (Skrymsli, Skrimsle): The jotun who tried to find Rogner so he could eat him for his evening meal.

Skrymir (Skrýmir, Skrymer, Skrymner, Skymer, Skryme) [the big fellow]: The jotun who taunted Thor, Loki, Thjalfi, and Roskva on their way to Utgardr. He was also known as Utgardr-Loki.

Skuldr (Skuld, Skulda) [future, shall be]: One of the Norns. Also a Valkyrie. She lived at Urdarbrunnr Well with her sisters, Verdandi and Urdr, the other two Norns. They controlled the fates of everything by weaving a tapestry of destiny. They also tended to the upkeep of Yggdrasyll.

Skurhold: The daughter of Skekil. Related to Ottar the Simple. She married Olmod. Their two sons were Isulf and Osulf.

Sleipnir (Sleipner, Sleipne) [tie slipper]: Odin's swift eight-legged horse. His father was Svadilfari. His mother was Loki who had taken the form of a white mare in order to lure Svadilfari away from his work.

Slidr (Slíðr, Slíð, Slid, Slith) [fearful]: One of the eleven rivers of Elivagar flowing out of the east, near Gjoll and Leiptr. It's waters were filled with swords, knives, and other instruments. The dead on their way to Niflheimr have to wade through it.

Slidrugtanni (Slíðrugtanni, Slidrugtanne, Slíðrugtaoi) [sharp-toothed]: Another name for Freyr's boar Gullinbursti.

Slongvir (Slöngvir) [slinger]: Adal's horse.

Smidr (Smiðr, Smith) [craft maker]: A son of Karl the Yeoman and Snœr.

Snar: King of Finland. His daughter was Mioll who married Frosti.

Snœr (Snoer, Snör, Snør) [daughter-in-law]: The wife of Karl the Yeoman. Their sons were Boandi, Bœdi, Brattskeggr, Breidr, Bui, Bundinskeggi, Drengr, Halr, Holdr, Seggr, Smidr, and Thegn. Their daughters were Brudr, Feima, Fljod, Ristill, Snot, Sprakki, Sprund, Svanni, Svarri, and Vif.

Snor [snow]: A jotun descendant of the hrymthursar Kari.

Snot (Snót) [good woman]: A daughter of Karl the Yeoman and Snœr.

Snotra (Snotr) [neat]: One of the Asynjes in Asgardr.

Sokin (Søkin, Sökin, Sækin, Sœkin, Sekin): A river flowing from Hvergelmir.

Sokkmimir (Sökkmímir, Sokmimer, Sökk-Mímir, Sunk-Mimir) [Mimir of the deep]: Midvitnir's son who guarded the Precious Mead after it had been stolen from the Æsir by his father and hidden away in Okolnir in Muspelheimr. It was stolen back for the Æsir by Odin. Sokkmimir's head was hacked off by Odin using Surtr's fiery sword, med sviga lævi. Not much in the way of detail is known of the legend.

Sokkvabekkr (Sökkvabekkr, Søkkabekkr, Sökwabek, Sökkvabekk, Sokvabek, Sœquabeck, Soequabkeck, Soquabeck) [sunken hall, singing floor, singing stream]: The name of Saga's hall by the sea. It was a crystal hall with waves breaking all around.

Sol (Sól, Söl, Sœl, Sôl) [sun]: The daughter of Mundilfari. Her brother was Maane. They were snatched away from him by the Æsir to help guide Dagr. She was married to Glenr. Her two horses were Arvakr and Alsvin.

Solblindi (Solbinde): The son of Valgrindr and Thrymgjoll. He was hired by the Æsir to fashion a gate for Asgardr's wall.

Son (Sonr, Són, Sohn) [blood]: One of the vats that held part of the Precious Mead. The other was Bodn. The bronze kettle Odrærir held the rest.

Sonr [son]: A son of Jarl the Earl and Erna.

Soti (Sóti) [soot-colored]: One of the horses in Asgardr.

Spamadr (Spámaðr, Spæ-man): Male form. A prophet gifted with second sight.

Spæ wife: Female form. A Volva gifted with second sight.

Sprakki [the fair]: A daughter of Karl the Yeoman and Snœr.

Sprund [the proud and vain]: A daughter of Karl the Yeoman and Snœr.

Sterkoddr: A jotun with six arms.

Strond: A river flowing from Midgardr to Hel.

Stufr (Stófr) [stump]: A horse ridden by Vifill.

Sudri (Suðri, Sudre, Suthri) [south]: One of the four earth dvergues holding up Ymir's skull. The other three were Nordri, Vestri, and Austri.

Summer: An old god before the Æsir. He was the son of Vindsval who was the son of Vasudr.

Surtr (Surt, Surti, Surtur, Surter) [blackened by fire]: The Liege of Muspelheimr. He was the owner of a fiery sword called med sviga lævi. His son was Glenr who was married to Sol. At the final battle on Vigridr Plain he slew Freyr and then flung his sword so everything was engulfed in flames.

Suttungr (Suttung) [to drink]: The jotun Gillingr's son. His brother was Baugi. He obtained the Precious Mead as weregild from Fjalarr and Galarr, the two dvergues who had killed his parents. His daughter Gunnlod guarded the Precious Mead in his treasure chamber in Hnitbjorg. Even so, it was still stolen by Odin.

Suttungr's Hoard: Another name for the Precious Mead.

Svadilfari (Svaðilfari, Svaðilfœri, Svadilfare, Svathilfari, Svadilföri): The horse used to help build Asgardr's walls. He was the sire of Odin's eighty-legged horse Sleipnir. The dam was Loki.

Svafnir (Sváfnir, Svafner, Svafnir) [he who charms to sleep]: One of Nidhoggr's sons chewing away at the Niflheimr root of Yggdrasyll.

Svafnir (Sváfnir, Svafner, Svafnir) [he who charms to sleep]: An ekename for Odin.

Svalin (Svalinn, Valin) [cooler]: The shield hung at the back of Arvakr and Alsvin to protect Sol and her horses from Skinfaxi and Gladr and the sun's brilliance. It also protected everything on Midgardr from being burned to a crisp.

Svanni [the slender]: A daughter of Karl the Yeoman and Snœr.

Svan the Red: Sæfari's father. Related to Ottar the Simple.

Svarangr (Svårang, Svárang, Svarang): His sons once threw mountains at Thor while he was guarding the river Ifing. Thor fought and defeated them.

Svarri [the proud]: A daughter of Karl the Yeoman and Snœr.

Svartalfar (Svart-alfar) [black alf]: The name of the dokkalfar living in Svartalfheimr.

Svartalfheimr (Svartalfheim, Svartálfaheimr, Svartálfaheim, Svarttalf-heimr, Svart-alfa-heim, Svartheim) [dusk alf land]: The land of the dark alfs.

Svasudr (Svásuðr, Svasud, Svásuth, Suasuthur, Svosödur) [delightful, the mild one]: The name of a jotun. He was the father of the sun.

Svava: The mother of Hildigun. She was married to Sækonung. Related to Ottar the Simple.

Sveinn (Svein) [boy]: A son of Jarl the Earl and Erna.

Sviarr (Svíarr, Svíar): A rock dvergar. One of Durinn's Kin.

Svidrir (Sviðrir, Sviðirr, Sviðurr, Svithrir, Svithur) [the wise one]: The name Odin used when he stole the Precious Mead from Midvitnir.

Svigdir (Svigðir, Svigðiri, Svigár, Svegðir, Svigðir) [changing]: An ekename for Odin.

Sviorr: A dvergar.

Svipall (Svípall, Svipal) [changing]: An ekename for Odin.

Svipul: A valkyrie.

Svithiod (Svithod, Swithiod, Svitjod): Gylfi's kingdom. Now known as Sweden.

Sviur (Svíur): A rock dvergar.

Svivor (Svívör): Slain by Thor.

Svoll (Svöll, Svöl, Sval) [cool]: One of the eleven rivers flowing from Elivagar.

Svolner: Groa's first husband. He died.

Swan Maidens: Another name for the Valkyries.

Sylgr (Sylg) [wide]: One of the eleven rivers flowing from Elivagar.

Syn (Sýn, Sin) [prudent, justice]: One of the Asynje in Asgardr. She was called upon when one wants to guard their door against entry by undesirables. She was also called upon during trials as the defending counsel to refute charges.

Syr (Sýr) [sow]: An ekename for Freyja.

Tamsvondr (Tarmsvöndr) [taming wand]: Freyr's magical sword, also known as Gambanteinn. It could fight of its own accord. Its name was changed from Gambanteinn to Tamsvondr after Skirnir carved runes on it three times and threatened Gerdr with it. Because of these threats she agreed to marry Freyr. Freyr was so grateful he gave the sword to Skirnir, an action which caused his defeat at Ragnarokr since he was left weaponless.

Tanngnjostr (Tanngnjost, Tanngnistr, Tanngnost, Tanngniostr) [the tooth cracker]: One of Thor's two male goats. The other was Tanngrisnir. They were bridled with silver reins.

Tanngrisnir (Tanngrisnr, Tanngrisni, Tanngrisne, Tanngrisner) [gap toothed, tooth gnasher]: One of Thor's two male goats. The other was Tanngnjostr. They were bridled with silver reins.

Tarnkappe: The red cap worn by some dvergues so they would be invisible and thus the sun's rays could not find them and turn them to stone.

Thegn (Þegn) [freeman]: A son of Karl the Yeoman and Snœr. His horse was Blakkr.

Thekkr (Thekkur, Thekk, Þekkr) [welcome one]: An ekename for Odin.

Thekkr (Thekkur, Thekk, Þekkr) [welcome one]: An earth dvergar.

Thing (Þing): A council or meeting to try and come up with a group solution to a problem affecting the group. Also known as the doomstead.

Thir (Thír, Þír, Thyr) [bondwoman]: She was married to Thræl. Their sons were Digraldi, Drottr, Drumbr, Fjosnir, Fulnir, Hosvir, Hrimr, Kefsir, Kleggi, Klurr, Leggjaldi, and Lutr. Their daughters were Ambatt, Arinnefja, Drumba, Eikintjasna, Kulba, Okkvainkalfa, Totrughypja, Tronubeina, and Ysja.

Thirvald: An ekename for Ymir.

Thjalfi (Thjálfi, Thjalfe, Tjalve, Þjálafi, Thialfi, Tialf) [the swift]: The eldest child of Egil and his wife. His sister was Roskva. They both were blond and blue-eyed. They became Thor's servants and traveled with him to see Utgardr-Loki.

Thjassi (Thiassi, Thjasse, Thjazi, Thjatsi, Tjasse, Tjatse, Thiazi, Þjázi, Þjassi, Þjazzi) [the storming]: The storm jotun who kidnapped Idunn and stole her apples. His brothers were Idi and Gangr, one of whom was the master mason who built Asgardr's walls. Their father and mother were Olvaldi and Greip. His daughter was Skadi. They lived in Thrymhymr. After his death in Asgardr Odin took his eyes and threw them up into the sky to form a constellation.

Thjodnuma (Thjóduma, Thjódnuma, Thjóthuma, Thjothnuma) [sweeping people away]: A river flowing from Midgardr to Asgardr.

Thjodreyrir (Thjothrörir, Thodrœrer) [waker of the people]: A dvergar who lived near Dellingr's house.

Thjodvitnir's Fish (Thjodvitnir's Fish, Thjóthvitnir's Fish, Þjódvitnir's Fish) [the great wolf's fish]: A term used to represent the fish swimming in the river Thund.

Thogn (Þogn): A valkyrie.

Thokk (Thok, Thökk, Thök, Thökt, Thöck, Thaukt, Thökt, Tokk, Þökk, Þokk, Þokkr, Þökk) [darkness]: An old hag. The form Loki took when he visited Frigg and found out the sprig of mistletoe had not made a promise to protect Baldr. He also took this form when he refused to weep for Baldr.

Tholl (Thöll, Thol): A flowing from Asgardr to Midgardr.

Thor (Þórr, Thór, Thórr, Thôrr, Thôr, Tôr, Thór): The eldest son of Odin and Jordr. His beard was fiery red, which matched his long red curly hair. Soon after his birth he became too much for Jordr to handle so he went to live with two foster-parents, Vingnir and Hlor. In honor of them he sometimes used the ekenames Vingthor and Hlorridi. His estate in Asgardr was called Thrudheimr, while his hall was called Bilskirnir. It was the equal of Valhalla in size. Thor received a portion of the dead in battle for his hall. His greatest enemy was Midgardrsormr. They slew each other at Ragnarokr. He had two daughters, Lora and Thrudr, and two sons Magni and Modr. He owned the hammer Mjolnir which he wielded with his right hand. He was too heavy to ride a horse, so he either walked or rode in his goat-driven chariot. His armor, like many of the Æsir was made of copper.

Thorgerdr (Thorgerðr): One of the Æsir. Her mother was Huldr. Her sister was Irpa. They were both virgins.

Thorinn (Thorin): An earth dvergar.

Thorkill (Thôrkîll, Thorkil Þorkill, Þorkil): A Danish explorer who went in search of Geirrodr with King Gormr. He also searched for and found the bound Loki. Most of his crew were killed during both of these expeditions.

Thor's Deliverance: An ekename for the Rowan tree. A type of tree which Thor once grabbed onto when he almost drowned in a river.

Thræl (Thræl, Þræll, Träl) [thrall]: A son of Ai (actually Rigr) and Edda. He married Thir. He and Thir worked the land as did most of their descendants. Their sons were Digraldi, Drottr, Drumbr, Fjosnir, Fulnir, Hosvir, Hrimr, Kefsir, Kleggi, Klurr, Leggjaldi, and Lutr. Their daughters were Ambatt, Arinnefja, Drumba, Eikintjasna, Kumba, Okkvainkalfa, Totrughypja, Tronubeina, and Ysja.

Thrainn (Thráin, Thróinn, Thróin) [the swift]: One of the earth dvergues, along with Dain, who was visited by Huginn to find out where Idunn had been taken. The two were also sent for to interpret Baldr's dreams.

Thrar: A dvergar.

Thridi (Thridi, Thriðe, Thride, Thrithi, Þriði) [the third]: An ekename for Odin. In this form his personality was actually split into three. Thridi (the third), Har (high), and Jafnhar (twice as high). This guise was used when Gylfi visited Asgardr.

Thrigeitr: An ekename for Ymir.

Thrimu (Þrimu): A valkyrie.

Thrimul (Þrimul): A valkyrie.

Thrivaldi (Thrívaldi, Þrívaldi): A jotun with nine heads who was defeated by Thor.

Throk: An earth dvergar.

Thror (Thrór, Þrór) [inciter of strife]: An ekename for Odin.

Thror (Thrór, Þrór) [inciter of strife]: An earth dvergar.

Thrudgelmir (Thrudgelmer, Þrúðgelmir, Thrúthgelmir) [mighty roarer]: The son with six heads born when Ymir's left foot began a son on his right foot. He was born in Muspelheimr. His son was Bergelmir. Another son was Bolthorn who was Mimir and Bestla's father. Thus he was Odin, Vili, and Ve's grandfather.

Thrudhamar (Thruðhamar, Þruðhamar, Thruthhamer): Another name for Mjolnir, Thor's hammer.

Thrudheimr (Þrúðheimr, Thrúðheimr, Thrudheim, Thrúðheim, Thrúthheim, Thrandheim, Thrudheimer) [land of might]: The name of Thor's estate in Asgardr. It was also known as Thrudvangar. The hall located there was named Bilskirnir.

Thrudr (Thrud, Thrúd, Thrûd, Thruðr, Thrûðr, Þrúðr, Þrûðr, Thrude, Thrudi, Thruth) [mighty]: A valkyrie. She was Thor's eldest daughter. Her mother was Sif. Her sister, Thor and Sif's other daughter, was Lora. Thrudr had been raped by the jotun Hrungr.

Thrudvangar (Thrúðvangar, Thrudvanga, Trudvang, Thrudvang, Þrúdvangr, Þrúðvangar, Þryðvangar, Thrudvanger) [paddocks of power, fields of might]: The name of Thor's estate in Asgardr. It was also known as Thrudheimr. The hall located there was named Bilskirnir.

Thrung: One of Freyr's attendants.

Thrym (Þrymr, Thrymr, Thrymer, Trym, Ryme) [noisy]: An hrymthursar living in Thrymheimr who had the power to cause snowstorms. He stole Mjolnir and offered it back to the Æsir in exchange for Freyja's hand in marriage. Thor and Loki journeyed to see him disguised as Freyja and a maidservant in order to regain Mjolnir. Once Thor had the hammer in his hands he threw off his disguise and slew Thrym, Thrym's sister, and the rest of the wedding party.

Thrymgjoll (Þrymgjoll): One of Solblindi's parents with Valgrindr.

Thrymheimr (Þrymheimr, Þryheimr, Þrymheim, Thrymheim, Thrymheimer, Trymheim) [land of noise]: The land in Jotunheimr where Thrym lived. Thjassi also lived in this land.

Thudr (Thuðr, Thuð, Þuð, Thud, Thuth) [thin one]: An ekename for Odin.

Thudr (Thuðr, Thuð, Þuð, Thud, Thuth) [thin one]: A dvergar.

Thundr (Þundr, Þun, Thund): An ekename for Odin.

Thund (Þundr, Þund, Thund): The river the Einherjar had to wade through on their way to Valhalla.

Thurse (Thursen, Þurs, Thurs) [thirst]: A name for the jotuns.

Thviti (Thvite, Þviti, Þvit) [thwacker]: The name of the boulder used to bind Fenriswulf.

Thyn [frothing]: A river flowing from Asgardr to Midgardr.

Tind: One of Arngrim and Eyfura's twelve berserker sons. His brothers were Hadding, Hervard, Hjorvard, Hrani, Angantyr, Bui, Brami, Barri, Reifnir, and Tyrfing. Related to Ottar the Simple.

Tjaldari [racer]: One of the horses in Asgardr.

Toflur (Tǫflur): The actual name of the game which resembled draughts. Its loss signaled the end of the Golden Age. One of the first incidents after the Rebirth was the discovery of the game by Thor's son, Modr.

Totrughypja (Tötrughypja) [clothed in rags]: A daughter of Thræl and Thir.

Trollweiber (Troll arvis): These were phantoms which journeyed to Midgardr on dark nights in order to scare the inhabitants. They rode wolves which had bridles made of snakes.

Tronubeina (Trönnbeina, Trönubeina) [cranelegs]: A daughter of Thræl and Thir.

Tun: A liquid measure referring to a barrel, such as in a tun of mead.

Tveggi: An ekename for Odin.

Tviblindi (Tvíblindi, Tvívlindi) [double-blind]: An ekename for Odin.

Tyr (Týr, Tǫr, Ty): One of the Æsir. He was known by the ekename hinn einhendi ass (one-handed god) due to the fact while Fenriswulf was being bound he bit off Tyr's hand which had been laid in his mouth as surety he would be set free. When he wasn't he swallowed Tyr's hand. Ever after the two were enemies. Tyr's foster-father was the jotun Hymir who was married to Griseldis, his Æsir mother. His real father was Odin. He and Thor journeyed to Hymir's hall in order to steal a kettle so Ægir would have a kettle large enough to brew enough mead so he could give the Æsir a great feast. Tyr and Garmr slew each other at Ragnarokr. He was the member of the Æsir called upon by wrestlers.

Tyrfing (Týrfing): One of Arngrim and Eyfura's twelve berserker sons. His brothers were Hadding, Hervard, Hjorvard, Hrani, Angantyr, Bui, Brami, Barri, Reifnir, Tind. Related to Ottar the Simple.

Udal: The land given to Jarl by Heimdallr.

Udr (Uðr, Uð) [frothing wave]: An ekename for Odin.

Uhland: Another name for Vanaheimr.

Ulf: Alf the Old's father. His father was Sæfari. Related to Ottar the Simple.

Ulfhednars (Ulfhednars) [wolf-skinned]: A name sometimes given to Berserks when they attacked during battle howling like wolves.

Ulfrun (Úlfrun, Ulfrinna) [she wolf]: One of Heimdallr's nine jotun mothers.

Ullin (Ullin): A member of the Æsir.

Ullr (Uller, Úller, Ull, Ulle, Oller, Ollerus, Schildas) [magnificent]: Thor's foster son. His natural parents were Sif and Aurvandil. His hall was Ydalir. He married Skadi after her marriage to Njordr broke up. When Odin was banished Ullr took over and ruled Asgardr for ten years. He took the name of Odin during his rule. But he was deposed by an evil sorcerer named Mithotyn. He was the god of skis and one of Baldr's friends. He could also use his bow as a ship if need be.

Ulvrung (Ulvrune): The name Odin used when he seduced the nine wavemaidens and begat Heimdallr.

Uni (Une): An elf.

Upheimr (Upheim, Uppheimr) [up land]: The name given to the heavens by the jotuns. Also known as Upphiminn.

Upphiminn [up heaven]: Same as Upheimr.

Uppr Dagr (Uppi dagadr) [dayed up]: This was the fate that befell dvergues and jotuns if they were hit by the rays of the sun. They were dayed up, which meant they were turned to stone. Dvergues could avoid this if they wore a red tarnkappe which made them invisible so the sun's rays could not see them and thus could not harm them.

Uppsah Spring: The norns went to this spring to fetch aurr to spread on Yggdrasyll in order to help stave off decay.

Uppsala (Uppsalir): The land in Midgardr where Freyr lived when he wasn't in Alfheimr. Also the name of a city in Sweden.

Urdarbrunnr Well (Urdarbrunnar Well, Urdarbrunnar Well, Urdarbrunnr Well, Udar-brunnr Well, Urdar-brudr Well, Urdarbrunn Well, Urdar Fountain, Urd-Fount, Urdr's Well, Well of Urdr, Well of Hudr) [Well of Urd, Well of Fate]: One of two wells nourishing Yggdrasyll (Hvergelmir Well and Mimirsbrunnr Well were the other two). It was next to Mimir's Hall. The Asgardr root of Yggdrasyll was there. Most of the Things held by the Æsir were held at this root. Hvergelmir and Mimirsbrunnr flowed into it making it very sacred. Anything dipped in it became white. Four harts browsed here eating the leaves from Yggdrasyll.

Urdr (Urð, Urd, Urðr, Urdar, Urdur, Urth, Urda, Hudr) [past]: One of the three Norns. The other two were her sisters Verdandi and Skuldr. They lived near Urdarbrunnr Well and wove a tapestry of destiny that foretold the fates of all things. They tended to the upkeep of Yggdrasyll.

Uri (Ure): An elf.

Utgardr (Útgarð, Utgard, Útgardar, Utgarda, Utgarth, Utgaard, Outgaard) [the outland]: Another name for Jotunheimr. It was a land of vast distances.

Utgardr-Loki (Utgarð-Loki, Utgard-Loke, Útgardr-Loki, Útgardarloki, Útgardur-Loki, Utgardaloki, Útgarda-Loki, Utgard's Loki, Utgardhaloki, Utgard-Loke, Utgarda-Loki, Utgarth-Loki, Utgaard-Loki) [outland Loki]: The ruler of Utgardr.

Vadgelmir (Vadgelmir): A river.

Vafthrudnir (Vafþrúdnir, Vafþrûdnir, Vafthrúdner, Vafthrúthnir, Valthrupnir, Vafthrudner, Vafþrúdnir, Vafthrüdnir, Vafthrûdnir, Valfthrudnir) [good at difficult riddles]: A jotun of great wisdom whom Odin in the guise Gangraaf visited in order to gain knowledge. Odin bested Vafthrudnir in a battle of wits and subsequently slew him and all his household.

Vafudr (Vafudr, Váfud, Vafuth, Vofuth) [wanderer, wayfarer]: An ekename for Odin.

Vagasker (Vágasker, Vágaskerand Singasteinn) [treasure stone]: The area where Loki hid as a seal after stealing the Brisingamen Necklace from Freyja for a second time. Singastein was a part of the area.

Vakr (Vaker, Vak) [wakeful, watchful]: An ekename for Odin.

Vakr (Vaker, Vak) [wakeful, watchful]: A horse ridden by Morginn.

Vala: A Volva, prophetess.

Valfreyja (Valfreya): The name Freyja used when she led the Valkyries.

Valaskjalf (Valaskjálf, Válaskjálf, Valaskjolf, Valaskialf, Valaskjalv) [shelf of the slain]: The name of Odin's main hall. It was a white hall roofed with silver. In the watchtower

there was a throne called Hlidskjalf where Odin could sit and see out over all the Worlds of the Tree. Frigg also had a throne there that allowed her to see out over all the Worlds of the Tree.

Valfadir (Valfödr, Valfedr, Valfadir, Valfodr, Valfader, Val-fader, Valfather) [father of the slain]: An ekename for Odin since the slain in Valhalla belonged to him.

Valgrindr Gate (Válgrindr, Válgrind, Vagrin, Vagrindr, Vagrind) [gate of the slain]: There were several gates containing the dead in various lands. Valgrindr Gate was a wholly-barred gate leading into Valhalla. It was built by the master mason and his horse Svadilfari when they were building Asgardr's walls. The Einherjar (newly called warriors to Valhalla) passed through this gate on their way to Valhalla. Two other gates were Nagrindr Gate and Helgrindr Gate.

Valgrindr: The name of one of Solblindi's parents. The other was Thrymgjoll.

Valhalla (Valhöll, Valhol, Valhǫll, Valhal, Valhall, Valholl, Walhalla) [hall of the slain]: The last hall built in Asgardr. It was located near Gladsheimr and was equal in size to Bilskirnir, Thor's 540 room hall. The roof slates were tiled with shields, while the walls were made of shafts of spears. Each door was wide enough to allow 800 warriors through at a time. An eagle hovered over the western door. There was a bear's head above the main gate. Yggdrasyll's branch with the Satin eagle on it hung over it. The pine tree Læradr grew in the center of the main hall. The hart Eikthrynir stood on the roof eating at Læradr. The Einherjar stayed in this hall waiting for the last great battle.

Vali (Váli, Áli, Vale, Ale, Ole): One of Loki and Sigyn's sons. Narfi was the other. Narfi was turned into a wolf and ate Vali. Then his intestines were turned into a magical chain used to bind Loki.

Vali (Vali, Áli, Vale, Ale, Ole): A dvergar.

Vali the Avenger (Váli the Avenger, Vale the Avenger, Áli the Avenger): Odin's last born son, and the last born of the Æsir. His mother was Rindr of Vestraslir in Midgardr. He vowed neither to comb his hair nor wash until he had avenged Baldr's death by slaying Hodr. He survived Ragnarokr. His horse was Hrafn.

Valkyrie (Vallkyr) [chooser of the slain]: Singular of Valkyries.

Valkyries (valkyrja, valkyrs, valkyrjur, valkyrior, valkyriar, valkyrier) [choosers of the slain]: The warrior maidens sent by Odin to influence battles. They also served mead in Valhalla. Some were Odin's daughters. One of Odin's ekenames is Herjan, so the valkyries were sometimes known as Herjan's Disir. All were virgins. Some of the valkyries were Gudr, Rota, Skuldr, Hrist, Mist, Skeggjold, Skogul, Hildr, Hjor, Hjorthrimul, Thrudr, Hlokk, Gollr, Herfjotur, Geironul, Randgridr, Rostgridr, Reginleif, Gondul, Gunnr, Geirskogul, Thrimul, Sangridr, and Svipul. They frequently flew to Midgardr as Swan Maidens wearing swan coats. If their swan cloaks were taken while they were bathing, then the holder of the coats could order the valkyries to do his or her bidding. They are also known as valmeyar.

Valland: A land where Harbardr fought.

Valmeyar (valmeyjar) [val maids, battle maids]: Another name for the Valkyries.

Valol (Valól) [field of battle]: The field of battle where the Valkyries dispensed victory and defeat.

Valr: A name for all the slain in battle.

Valsharmr (valsharm, valsharm): The name of Freyja's falcon-guise which Loki sometimes borrowed with or without her permission. Also known as falkeham and fiadrhamr.

Valtamr (Valtam) [one used to battle]: The fictitious name of Odin's father.

Van (Ván, Vón, Von) [hope]: One of two rivers flowing from Fenriswulf's bloody slaver after he was bound. The other river was Vil.

Van: A male member of the Vanir.

Vana: A female member of the Vanir.

Vanabrudr (Vanabrúdr) [bride of the Vanir]: An ekename for Freyja.

Vanadis (Vanadís, Vanadîs) [goddess of the Vanir]: A term used collectively to represent the female of the Vanir, although sometimes it was used to represent Freyja.

Vanagud (Vanaguð, Vanagod) [god of the Vanir]: An ekename for Freyr.

Vanaheimr (Vanaheim, Vana-heim, Vanaheimar, Vanaland): The land where the Vanir lived.

Vanargandr (Vánargandr, Vánagandr) [afraid of the wolf of the marsh]: The name of Freyja's wolf.

Vandals: A group of warriors who conquered many lands. They were favored by Odin in a battle against the Vinilers. Their leaders were Ambri and Assi.

Vanir (Vaner, Vanr, Van): The other set of gods. They were generally fertility gods rather than warrior gods. They were also known as the Vans. They used witchcraft and a magic called vigspa when they fought.

Vans (Wanes): The male of the Vanir.

Var (Vár, Var, Varr, Vara, Vor, Vór) [oath]: An attendant of Frigg's. The goddess to whom vows were consecrated, particularly betrothals and marriage vows. The oaths were called varars.

Var (Vár, Vår, Varr, Vara, Vor, Vór) [oath]: An elf.

Varar (Várar): The name given to the oaths sworn invoking Var's name.

Varns, Forest of: A forest on the western horizon. This was where King Billingr of the Varns lived. It was also known as the land of the Ruthenes (Ruthenia, Russia).

Vartari: The leather thong used by Brokkr to lace together Loki's lips after he won the wager of Loki's head which he couldn't collect.

Varulve: A term for wehrwolves.

Vasudr (Vásuth, Vasuð, Vásaðr) [wet and cold one]: An old god before the Æsir whose son was Vindsval, whose son in turn was Summer.

Ve (Vé, We) [holiness]: A son of Bor and Bestla. His brothers were Odin and Vili. The three were the first of the Æsir. he helped kill Ymir. He and his brother Vili deposed the evil sorcerer Mithotyn (who had deposed Ullr). They jointly ruled the Æsir for nine months during the last part of Odin's banishment.

Vebond (Vébǫnd): The holy ropes attached to poles marking off the circular boundary for a holmgang.

Vecka (Vecha, Vak): The form of a wise woman Odin assumed in order to win the love of the Princess Rindr in Ruthenia. In this guise she made love to Rindr and subsequently Vali the Avenger was conceived. This action brought disgrace to Odin and caused his banishment.

Vedrfolnir (Vedrfölnir, Vedfolnir, Vedfolner, Vedurfoggner, Vethrfolnir) [weathered one]: The name of the hawk sitting in Yggdrasyll. He was being watched by the eagle Edgar.

Vegdrasil: A dvergar.

Vegsvinn (Végsvínn, Vegsvín) [wayfaring]: A river flowing from Midgardr to Hel.

Vegtamr Valtamssonr (Vegtam Valtam's Son, Vegtam Valtamsson) [wanderer son of Valtam]: The name Odin used when he raised the Volva from the dead to gain knowledge about Ragnarokr.

Veidi ass (veiði áss) [god of the hunt]: An ekename for Ullr.

Veigr (Veig): An earth dvergar.

Veorr (Véorr, Veor, Véur, Véurr, Veur) [defender]: An ekename for Thor.

Veratyr (Veratýr) [god of men]: An ekename for Odin.

Verdandi (Verðándi, Verlandi, Verthandi, Verdande) [present]: A jotun. One of the norns. The other two were her sisters, Urdr and Skuldr. The three lived near Urdarbrunnr Well and wove a tapestry of destiny which foretold the destiny of all things. They also tended to the upkeep of Yggdrasyll.

Verland (Verlandi) [land of men]: A land where Thor's mother, Jordr (also known as Fjorgyn) lived.

Vestraslir (Vestrasalir) [the western hall]: The land where Rindr, Vali the Avenger's mother, lived with her father King Billingr. It was also the land of the Ruthenes (Ruthenia, Russia) and the land of the Varns.

Vestri (Vestre, Westri, Westre) [west]: The name of one of the four earth dvergues holding up Ymir's skull. The other three were Austri, Sudri, and Nodri.

Vidarr the Silent (Víðarr the Silent, Víðar the Silent, Vídar the Silent, Víthar, Vítharr): The son of Odin and Gridr who lived in the solitude of the Jarnvidr Forest. He was second to Thor in strength and avenged Odin's death at Ragnarokr by slaying Fenriswulf. He had a special boot which gave him protection when he stepped inside Fenriswulf's mouth and was able to snap the wolf's jaws apart. He survived Ragnarokr. He was also known as the hinn thogli ass (the silent god).

Vidblainn (Vídbláinn, Vidblain) [wide blue]: After Ragnarokr, this was a land to the south of Andlang. It was a happy land over Gimils Cave.

Vidfinnr (Viðfinnr, Víðfinn, Vidfin): A cruel jotun who forced his son and daughter, Hjiuki and Bil, to fetch water from a magical well for him.

Vidfonir (Víðófnir, Vedfolner) [tree snake]: The name of a golden cock perched in Yggdrasyll. It crowed at the last battle. It was cut in two by Loki at Ragnarokr with his magic sword Lævateinn, which was the only weapon that could destroy it.

Vidr (Víð, Víd, Vith) [broad]: One of the eleven rivers flowing from Elivagar.

Vidrir (Viðrir, Vithrir) [god of weather]: An ekename for Odin.

Vidris Grey (Viðris Grey) [Odin's bitch]: A colloquialism that represented wolves.

Vidurr (Viðurr, Viður, Vithur): An ekename for Odin.

Vif [wife]: A daughter of Karl the Yeoman and Snœr.

Vifill: He rode Stufr.

Vigdi (Vígði) [hallowed]: Another name for Mjolnir, Thor's hammer.

Vigg [carrier]: A horse in Asgardr.

Viggr (Víggr, Vigg, Vig, Veig): An earth dvergar.

Vigridr Plain (Vigrid Plain, Vígríðr Plain, Vígríth Plain, Vigrith Plain, Vigard Plain) [battle place]: The battlefield on the island of Oskopnir where the last great battle was fought during Ragnarokr. It was 100 rosts on either side.

Vigspa: The battle magic used by the Vanir to fight the Æsir during their war.

Vil (Víl) [despair]: One of two rivers flowing from Fenriswulf's bloody slaver after he was bound. The other was Van (hope).

Vili (Vili, Víle, Víli, Wile, Vili) [will]: The second son of Bor and Bestla. His brothers were Odin and Ve. They were the first of the Æsir. He helped to kill Ymir. He and his brother Ve deposed the evil sorcerer Mithotyn (who had deposed Ullr) and ruled the Æsir for nine months during the last part of Odin's banishment.

Vili (Víli): A rock dvergar.

Villi-eldr [blazing]: An ekename for Loki.

Vilmegir (Vílmegir, Velmegir): The servants who carried the mead (actually Heidrun's urine) to the dead in Niflhel.

Vimur (Vimer, Veimer): A river which Thor, Loki, and Thjalfi had to wade to reach Geirrodr's Garth. The three were almost drowned when Greip, Geirrodr's daughter relieved herself in the river forcing the river to flood. It was also known by the name Hemra.

Vina (Vína, Vín, Vino): A river which flowed from Asgardr to Midgardr.

Vindalfr (Vindálfr, Vindálf) [wind elf]: An earth dvergar.

Vindheimr (Vindheim) [wind home]: The place where many thought the old gods lived after Ragnarokr.

Vindler (Vindlér) [boarer]: An ekename for Heimdallr.

Vindljone (Vindlóne, Vindljóni) [wind bringer]: See Vindsvalr.

Vindsvalr (Vindsval, Vindsual) [wind-cool]: An old god before the Æsir. He was the son of Vasudr. His son was Summer, father of Winter. Also known as Vindljoni.

Vingnir (Vingner) [the winged]: A foster parent of Thor's.

Vingolf (Vingólf, Vinjolf, Vingolv) [hall of friends]: The hall built for the Asynjur.

Vingthor (Vingthór, Ving-Thor, Vingthôr, Vîngþôrr, Vingþórr) [winged Thor]: An ekename for Thor used to honor his foster father Vingnir.

Vinndalf (Vinndálf, Vindálf) [wind elf]: An earth dvergar.

Vinnilers (Winilers, Winnili): A group of warriors and farmers living on the island of Skadan on Midgardr. They were favored by Frigg in a battle against the Vandals. Their leaders were Ibor and Ajo.

Virfir (Virvir): A rock dvergar. One of Dvalin's Hosts. Lived in Juravale's Marsh.

Vit ok hrœring (vit ok hroering) [wit and movement]: The faculties of sense and understanding given to Askr and Embla by Vili.

Vitr (Vit, Vitur): An earth dvergar.

Vœttir (Voettir, Vættir, vettir): Wights or spirits.

Volsungr: Grandfather of Sigurdr Fafnirsbani. One of the Hraudungs. Related to Ottar the Simple.

Volva (Völva, Vǫlva, Vúlva, volve): The prophetess in Niflhel whom Odin, in the guise of Vegtamr Valtamssonr, sought out and raised from the dead in order to gain information concerning Ragnarokr. She had once been Angroboda. Her name is also used to represent seeresses in general.

Vonargander: An ekename for Fenriswulf derived from the rivers caused by the bloody slaver flowing out of his mouth.

Vond: A river flowing from Midgardr to Hel.

Vor (Vór, Vör) [beware]: An attendant of Frigg's. Nothing was hidden from her.

Well of Mimir: Another name for Mimirsbrunnr.

Well of Urdr: Another name for Urdarbrunnr Well.

Weregild: Payment, usually of gold, to expiate a crime, generally the killing of one of the other party's relative. Blood payment was when the atonement was with battle, a life for a life.

Wolf Joint: A name given to the wrist joint in remembrance of where Fenriswulf bit off Tyr's hand.

Worlds of the Tree: The nine words each of the nine roots of the Yggdrasyll go to. They are: Midgardr, Jotunheimr, Niflheimr, Muspelheimr, Vanaheimr, Alfheimr, Svartalfheimr, and Helheimr, and Asgardr.

Wyrd: One of the ancients. The mother of the three Norns, Skuldr, Verdandi, and Urdr.

Ydalir (Ýdalir, Ydaler, Ýdale, Ydal) [yew dales]: The name of Ullr's hall.

Yggr (Ygg) [terrible]: An ekename for Odin.

Yggdrasyll (Yggdrasill, Ygdrasil, Yggdrasil, Yggdrasyl, Ygdrassil, Ygdrasyl, Igdrasil) [horse of Yggr]: The world tree planted by Bor and Bestla during the flood and subsequently nourished by Ymir's blood. It was a mighty ash tree with nine roots leading to all the worlds. There were three main roots leading to Midgardr, Niflheimr, and Jotunheimr. Each of these had a well. The other roots lead to Muspelheimr, Asgardr, Vanaheimr, Alfheimr, Svartalfheimr, and Helheimr. The fruit from Yggdrasyll was good for women sick with child. Also called Mimameidr and Hoddmimir's Holt.

Ylfa: Plural of elves.

Ylfings: One of the warrior families mentioned by Hyndla as being related to Ottar the Simple.

Ylgr (Ylg) [broad]: One of the eleven rivers flowing from Elivagar.

Ymir (Ymer, Ymr): The jotun formed when the intense heat of Muspelheimr and extreme cold of Niflheimr met in Ginnungagap. He was known as Aurgelmir by the jotuns. He had several sons including Thrudgelmir, Bor and Bolthorn. After he was slain by Odin, Vili, and Ve, a great flood caused by his blood flowed throughout the nine Worlds of the Tree. His body was used to form Midgardr. His skull became the sky, his brains the clouds, and his blood and sweat became the rivers, lakes, and oceans. His bones became mountain crags, his toes, double teeth and splintered bones became the rocks and pebbles on Midgardr. His eyebrows were used to make grass and flowers, while his curly hair became the trees and plants. His eyelashes were used to form a hedge around Midgardr to protect it from evil beings who were constantly trying to enter. He was sometimes known as Brimir or Blainn. Also called Aurgelmir, Brimir, Fornjotr, Neri, Thirvald, Thrigeitr, and Alvald.

Yngvi: A dvergar. One of Dvalin's Hosts. Lived in Juravale's marsh.

Ysja [noisy, harridan]: A daughter of Thræl and Thir.

Norse
Genealogy

Norse
Genealogy

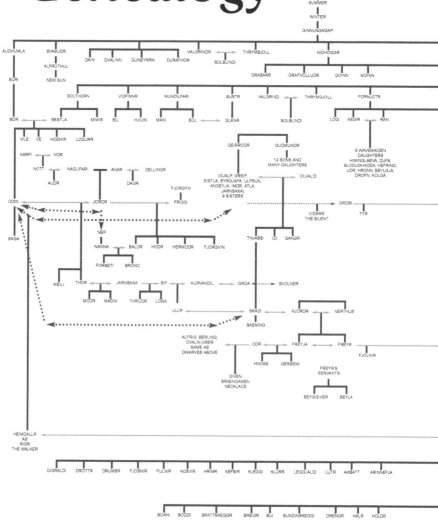

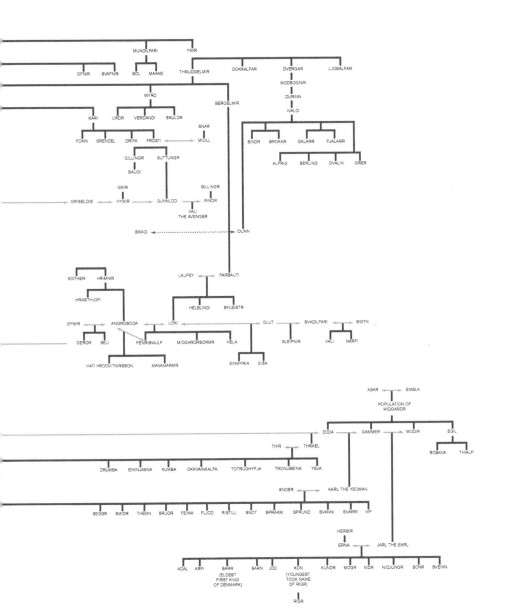

Books From
Hollow Earth Publishing

Hollow Earth Publishing will be publishing a series of books retelling all the Scandinavian Sagas in English. We are striving to make certain they are the best retellings available. We will also be reprinting out-of-print books dealing with Scandinavian Sagas as well as publishing books on other topics.

The Norse Myths *(by Heilan Yvette Grimes) is the most complete version of the Norse Myths in the English language. Includes a Glossary and Genealogy Chart.*

The Ring (The Legend of the Niebelungenlied: The Volsungr Saga and The Saga of Ragnar Lodbrokr) *(by Heilan Yvette Grimes) is the ring saga from the Norse perspective. It makes a lot more sense than the Germanic version, and is a lot gorier. Pay attention to whomever has the ring. Nothing good will come to that person. Includes a Glossary and Genealogy Chart.*

The Book of Twitter: How to Get 100,000+ Followers and what to Do With Them After You've Got Them *(by Heilan Yvette Grimes) is the best book available for how to use twitter. Detailed information on how to setup your twitter account, how and what to tweet, how to get followers, and how to manage your twitter account. thebookoftwitter.com*

H.– The Story of Heathcliff's Journey Back to Wuthering Heights *(by Lin Haire-Sargeant) is the story of Heathcliff's lost years after he runs away from Cathy and returns three years later a gentleman with money. What happened? Who was his mentor? Haire-Sargeant masterfully combines Wuthering Heights and Jane Eyre to tell Heathecliff's story..*

UPCOMING;

The Laxdaela Saga *(by Heilan Yvette Grimes) is the only medieval epic with a woman as the protagonist. Includes a Glossary and Genealogy Chart.*

The Viking Age, Vols. I and II *(by Paul b. Du Chaillu) is a complete redesign of the 1889 legendary work about the Vikings, their customs, clothing, housing, life, weapons, and legends. In short, everything you ever wanted to know about the Vikings. Originally 1160+ pages and 1366 illustrations. Because of printing costs, this book will only be available digitally. But it will be fully searchable.*

The Book of Runes *(by Heilan Yvette Grimes) is everything you need to know about runes including history, kinds of runes, their properties, and how to use them*

Hollow Earth Publishing
PO Box 51480
Boston, MA 02205-1480
hollowearthpublishing.com

Made in the USA
Columbia, SC
30 August 2023

22288429R00180